Algebra and Algebraic Thinking in School Mathematics

Algebra and Algebraic Thinking in School Mathematics

Seventieth Yearbook

Carole E. Greenes
Seventieth Yearbook Editor
Arizona State University
Mesa, Arizona

Rheta Rubenstein
General Yearbook Editor
University of Michigan—Dearborn
Dearborn, Michigan

 NATIONAL COUNCIL OF
TEACHERS OF MATHEMATICS

Copyright © 2008 by
THE NATIONAL COUNCIL OF TEACHERS OF MATHEMATICS, INC.
1906 Association Drive, Reston, VA 20191-1502
(703) 620-9840; (800) 235-7566; www.nctm.org
All rights reserved

Library of Congress Cataloging-in-Publication Data

The National Council of Teachers of Mathematics is a public voice
of mathematics education, providing vision, leadership, and professional development to support teachers in ensuring equitable
mathematics learning of the highest quality for all students.

Printed in the United States of America

Contents

Part 3: Studies on the Learning of Algebra

Part 4: Algebra in the Classroom

Part 5: Educating Teachers

        DEBORAH SCHIFTER
        Education Development Center, Newton, Massachusetts
        VIRGINIA BASTABLE
        Mount Holyoke College, South Hadley, Massachusetts
        SUSAN JO RUSSELL
        TERC, Cambridge, Massachusetts
        LISA SEYFERTH
        Horace Mann School, Newton, Massachusetts
        MARGARET RIDDLE
        Northampton Public Schools, Northampton, Massachusetts

        ESTHER MARIE HUNTZINGER BILLINGS
        Grand Valley State University, Allendale, Minnesota

        BETH HERBEL-EISENMANN
        Iowa State University, Ames, Iowa
        ELIZABETH D. PHILLIPS
        Michigan State University, East Lansing, Michigan

Preface

UNTIL relatively recently, the study of algebra was reserved for college-intending high school students. Other high school students were relegated to the "general math" track or to courses that provided a review of grades 4–8 arithmetic. Different political and educational professional groups have pointed out that this practice of "tracking" students at the high school level serves to exacerbate inequities between ethnic and socioeconomic groups. One proposal to reduce these inequities was to have all students study algebra. From this proposal was born the "algebra for all" movement. School districts nationwide began to require first-year algebra of all their students in either grade 8 or 9, and the completion of that course became a condition for high school graduation.

Shortly thereafter, articles began to appear in the popular press describing the poor performance of students in algebra. Several districts claimed that failure in first-year algebra was the major contributor to school dropout. What could be causing this failure?

Some mathematics educators suggested that students' difficulties with algebraic ideas could be attributed to a lack of preparation for the study of algebra. They claimed that the elementary school curriculum, with its emphasis on arithmetic, did not treat aspects of algebra that would better prepare students for the formal study of algebra.

Recognizing the importance of early exposure to fundamental ideas of algebra and the need for the development of those ideas to be well articulated across grade levels, the National Council of Teachers of Mathematics (NCTM) dedicated its 1988 Yearbook, *The Ideas of Algebra K–12,* to the teaching of algebra. A year later, NCTM published *Curriculum and Evaluation Standards for School Mathematics,* in which algebra was identified as one of the core content strands for exploration by students in grades K–12. In 2000, NCTM published *Principles and Standards for School Mathematics,* which reaffirmed the need for well-articulated instruction in algebra across grades beginning at the prekindergarten level. Accompanying each of the *Standards* documents were books (the Addenda series for the 1989 *Standards* and the Navigations series for the 2000 *Standards*) designed to illustrate how the goals cited in the *Standards* documents could be achieved in school mathematics programs.

Unfortunately, many attempts to prepare students better for algebra have not resulted in greater achievement in first-year algebra. Students in grades 8 and 9 are still struggling with important algebraic concepts and skills, and many are discontinuing their study of higher-level mathematics because of their lack of success in the course. At the elementary school level, teachers are not clear about what algebraic ideas they should explore with their students and what approaches and pedagogical methods they should employ. The need to attend to algebra in the elementary school curriculum is highlighted in the charge given to the National Mathematics Advisory Panel, appointed by the president of the United States in 2006. According to the document, the panel is to identify "the skills needed for students to learn algebra and to be ready for higher level mathematics" and to consider better ways of delivering instruction.

The Seventieth Yearbook is designed to bring us up to date on the status of algebra in our schools and, in particular, the history of changes in the algebra curriculum; the current situation in enrollment in, and success with, courses in algebra; the nature of algebra and algebraic thinking; research into the teaching and learning of algebra; classroom strategies for developing students' algebraic thinking abilities and their understanding of some of the big ideas of algebra; and methods for preparing or updating teachers to teach algebra. The Yearbook is separated into five parts.

Part 1 focuses on historical perspectives on algebra in the curriculum. Kilpatrick and Izsák trace the journey of algebra instruction from the years when it became a course option for students at the university level to its entrance into high school and then middle school mathematics programs. They describe changes in the algebra curriculum from a focus on equations to that of functions. Chazan considers the current status of algebra in our schools and, in particular, who studies algebra, when they study the subject, what they study, and how their learning is assessed.

Part 2 considers the nature of algebra and algebraic thinking. Arcavi leads the reader through a variety of tasks aimed at helping students see the purpose of algebra and of ways to use algebra to model, analyze, and "demystify" mathematical problems. Cuoco identifies "general purpose methods," or tools that students can use to investigate and gain deeper understanding of important algebraic ideas. Using vignettes illustrating difficulties students have with algebra, Saul advances the idea that algebra is not simply the study of variables and functions; rather, algebra is a tool that can be used to gain greater understanding of major mathematical ideas. Bezuszka and Kenney focus on recursive thinking as one aspect of algebraic thinking and on recursion as a core concept of algebra. They illustrate both topics with different types of problems. Banchoff considers the nature of algebraic thinking by demonstrating its connections with geometric thinking, and he stresses the value of using both types of reasoning to solve mathematical problems.

Part 3 addresses research on the learning of algebra and how topics from traditional mathematics programs can be modified or extended to develop students' algebraic thinking. Warren and Cooper describe tasks, problems, and sets of questions they used to help young children distinguish repeating from growing patterns, identify relationships between sets of data, and generalize relationships. Fujii and Stephens present vignettes that show that students in grades 2 through 8 naturally employ algebraic types of strategies to the solution of number sentences that contain variables. Baek describes elementary school students' multiplication techniques and points out how those techniques involve the application of algebraic general-izations. Moss, Beatty, Barkin, and Shillolo describe their study of the effects of online conferencing on fourth-grade students' abilities to solve complex function problems. Cai and Moyer present results of international studies that compare how educators in the United States, Singapore, and China approach and treat the development of algebraic thinking of elementary school students.

Part 4 focuses on classroom practices that have proved successful in developing students' algebraic reasoning abilities and their understanding of important ideas of algebra. Watanabe gives a Japanese perspective on the development of algebraic thinking in the elementary school—a perspective in which algebraic ideas are explored in conjunction with the study of addition, multiplication, and proportions. Ferrucci, Kaur, Carter, and Yeap offer a detailed description of the "model" method used in the Singapore mathematics program and the value of this type of representation of mathematical relationships in the identification of problem structures and the solution of algebra problems. To engage their middle school students in the study of variables, Gay and Jones use the context of an amusement park to help their students understand what variables represent, how they can be used to construct equations, and how they can be manipulated. Using variations of a toothpick problem, Tabach and Friedlander describe how such a context-based approach to algebra can facilitate the understanding of variables in expressions, the difference between changing and constant quantities, and the equivalence of algebraic expressions. Anderson describes a sequence of problems and activities she used with her middle school students to develop their understanding of linear relationships and, in particular, the equation $y = mx + b$. This part of the Yearbook concludes with Zbiek and Heid's examination of ways to use technology (computer algebra systems, dynamical geometry construction environments, and graphing calculators) to facilitate students' understanding of important concepts and functions in intermediate algebra.

Part 5 presents strategies employed for preparing and updating teachers to develop their students' algebraic thinking abilities and their knowledge of algebra. Schifter, Bastable, Russell, Seyferth, and Riddle use case studies of elementary school students in the process of developing their algebraic thinking abilities as the centerpiece of a professional development program for teachers. Recognizing the importance of having teachers grow in their own mathematical abilities prior to—or while—working with their students, Billings focuses on four pictorial growth pattern tasks that she uses with preservice and in-service teachers to develop their algebraic thinking talents. Herbel-Eisenmann and Phillips describe a professional development program in which teachers' pedagogical content knowledge of algebra is developed in concert with analyses of their students' work.

On behalf of the Seventieth Yearbook Editorial Panel, I thank the authors for their outstanding contributions, for their willingness to respond to all requests for additional information "ASAP," and for their dedication to mathematics education.

To my colleagues on the editorial panel, I thank you for the many hours you spent developing the call for manuscripts, reviewing articles, communicating with and assisting authors, and assisting me with final editing tasks. I have the greatest respect and awe for your comprehensive knowledge of mathematics education and of algebra and algebraic thinking in particular. The panel members are the following:

Bradford Findell, Ohio Department of Education, Columbus, Ohio

Carolyn Kieran, University of Quebec—Montreal, Montreal, Quebec

Janet Pittock, Scholastic, Inc., New York, New York

Steve Rosenberg, Boston University, Boston, Massachusetts

Deborah Upton, Stonehill College, Easton, Massachusetts

The work of the editorial panel was guided by our brilliant general yearbook editor, Rheta Rubenstein. Rheta has a unique ability to listen to six panel members talking at once, gleaning the essence of the conversation, and generating perfect representations of the principal ideas offered. Rheta, we all thank you.

Others who helped with the many communications with authors and read and transcribed my horrible handwriting, and to whom I am most grateful, are Patricia Bickford, Cristin Menna-LaPierre, Chris Urbine, and Beth Purdy. Finally, a grand thanks to Harry Tunis for his guidance and to Charles Clements and David Webb, members of the NCTM editorial staff, for their work in producing this Yearbook.

Carole E. Greenes
Seventieth Yearbook Editor

Part 1

Historical Perspectives on Algebra in the Curriculum

1

A History of Algebra in the School Curriculum

Jeremy Kilpatrick
Andrew Izsák

If there is a heaven for school subjects, algebra will never go there.
It is the one subject in the curriculum that has kept children from
finishing high school, from developing their special interests and
from enjoying much of their home study work. It has caused more
family rows, more tears, more heartaches, and more sleepless
nights than any other school subject.

—Anonymous editorial writer [ca. 1936]

IN THE United States and Canada before 1700, algebra was absent not only from the school curriculum but also from the curriculum of the early colleges and seminaries. That situation changed during the eighteenth and nineteenth centuries as colleges and universities across North America began to offer courses in algebra. In January 1751, when Benjamin Franklin's academy was established, the new master Theophilus Grew offered "Writing, Arithmetic, Merchants Accounts, Algebra, Astronomy, Navigation, and all other branches of Mathematics" (Overn 1937, p. 373), and "algebra to quadratics" continued to be part of the freshman curriculum after the academy became the University of Pennsylvania in 1779.

Algebra is first mentioned as being in the Harvard curriculum in 1786 but was probably taught there much earlier, perhaps as early as 1726 (Cajori 1890, p. 25). By 1742, Yale freshmen were studying algebra along with arithmetic. As of 1814, in what appears to have been the earliest collegiate mathematics course in Canada, students at King's College in Windsor, Nova Scotia, were being taught "Euclid and Wood's algebra" (Archibald and Charbonneau 1995, p. 16). College algebra was in those days what had been called since the time of Isaac Newton *specious arithmetic* or *universal arithmetic,* meaning that it expressed symbolically rules for operating with any species of quantity. Students learned to manipulate expressions and solve simple equations with numerical coefficients. Most rules were given without proof, factoring was omitted, and negative quantities were avoided as far as possible, being of somewhat questionable status.

By 1820, Harvard had decided to require algebra for admission, and Columbia, Yale, and Princeton followed suit in 1821, 1846, and 1848, respectively (Jones 1967, p. 50; Overn 1937, p. 374). Candidates for the 1846 freshman class at Yale, for example, were told that they would be examined in elementary algebra "preceding quadratic equations" (Diane E. Kaplan, personal communication, July 21, 2006). In Canada, McGill University had opened its doors officially in 1821, and as of 1857 and probably before, the matriculation examination included "Arithmetic; Algebra, to Quadratic Equations; Euclid's Elements, 3 books" (Carolyn Kieran, personal communication, June 26, 2006). When the Polytechnique Montréal opened in 1873 (as the École Polytechnique), some algebra was most certainly offered, but it is not clear what, if any, was required for entrance. The catalog for 1878–1879 says explicitly that algebra was taught, together with functions and an introduction to differential calculus, in the first two years of the three-year curriculum (Louis Charbonneau, personal communication, July 12, 2006).

Algebra Enters the School Curriculum

In 1827, by passing America's first high school law, Massachusetts made the teaching of algebra, geometry, and surveying mandatory in the high school of every town with 500 families or more. As that list of subjects suggests, algebra, as well as other branches of mathematics, "was originally introduced into secondary education in America for practical rather than disciplinary reasons and because of its applications to surveying and navigation rather than for the purpose of meeting a college entrance requirement" (Overn 1937, p. 374).

As the nineteenth century progressed, however, a course in algebra was increasingly required for college entrance, and algebra "was moved from the colleges to the secondary schools with little or no modification" (Osborne and Crosswhite 1970, p. 158). Thus algebra was introduced into the school curriculum for disparate purposes: as vocational preparation or as academic preparation. In subsequent decades, debate and even discord would arise over the appropriate emphasis of school algebra and to whom the subject should be taught.

Competing Conceptions of School Algebra

Generalized Arithmetic

For most of the nineteenth century, while mathematicians such as William Rowan Hamilton, George Boole, Arthur Cayley, and James Joseph Sylvester were developing the foundations of modern algebra, school algebra remained an extension and generalization of school arithmetic built largely by induction on a base of numerical quantities and operations on them. A survey of U.S. algebra textbooks published from 1820 to 1928 revealed that throughout that period, more than half of the exercises were given over to algebraic techniques (factoring, roots, powers, and fundamental operations), with the next greatest amount of attention given to equations and formulas (Chateauneuf 1929; see also Osborne and Crosswhite 1970, p. 159). Influenced by nineteenth-century faculty psychology (the mind is composed of separate faculties or powers) and the corresponding educational model of mental discipline (drill and repetition are the best ways to strengthen young minds and cultivate memory), textbook authors and teachers stepped up the complexity and difficulty of algebra exercises, particularly during the years from 1880 to 1910 (Overn 1937, p. 376). According to David Eugene Smith (1926), factoring in particular "began to occupy an undue amount of space in the closing quarter of the nineteenth century" (p. 10). Amy Olive Chateauneuf noted that in the 1890s attention to techniques for manipulating algebraic expressions reached a crescendo, occupying some 64 percent of all textbook exercises (1929, p. 151).

Writing in the First Yearbook of the National Council of Teachers of Mathematics (NCTM), Smith (1926, p. 3) described the elementary algebra of 1900 as consisting of

> a large amount of abstract manipulation of polynomials, including long problems in the multiplication and division of integral and fractional expressions, with extended work in the finding of roots, in factoring, in lowest common multiple, and in highest common factor, and with equally useless manipulations of complex fractions and radicals. Simultaneous linear equations extended to four and more unknowns, and simultaneous quadratics of the trick variety were in evidence.

He went on to characterize the teaching of algebra in 1900:

> The subject was usually taught as if it were a purely mathematical discipline, unrelated to life except as life might enjoy the meaningless puzzle. Valuable as the teacher might feel it to be, the majority of pupils looked upon it as a fairly interesting way of getting nowhere. (P. 20)

By the end of the nineteenth century, the practical value of studying algebra, if it had ever been prominent, appears to have faded.

Functional Thinking

Meanwhile, the decade from 1880 to 1890 had seen many schools in Europe begin to make the function concept the core of secondary school mathematics (Nordgaard 1928, p. 70), using it to streamline the curriculum, unify the branches of mathematics, correlate mathematics "with science, introduce students to mathematical theory, and provide more applications." As a result, calculus became the obvious extension and culmination of the study of functions, their graphs, and the properties of curves. In 1902, France became "the first country in the world to include work in the calculus as a regular and required part of the curriculum in her secondary schools" (p. 77). In 1904, Felix Klein proposed that "the function idea graphically represented should form the central notion of mathematical teachings, and, as a natural consequence, the elements of the calculus should be included in the curriculum of *all* 9-class [high] schools" (quoted by Nordgaard, p. 81). The following year, at a conference in Merano, Italy, the reforms proposed by Klein were adopted by the German Society of Natural Scientists. It was at that meeting that the expression *funktionales Denken* (functional thinking) was coined.

Klein's endorsement of the function concept influenced secondary school mathematics around the world, but in the United States and Canada it was apparently very much a minor influence. Chateauneuf's (1929) survey of U.S. elementary algebra textbooks showed that exercises on graphs—the main place that functions appeared—averaged less than a tenth of 1 percent during the nineteenth century and had not reached 5 percent by 1928. Rather than taking function as a unifying concept, the members of the Conference on Mathematics of the Committee of Ten (National Educational Association 1894, pp. 105–6) had proposed that algebra be treated as generalized arithmetic in the middle grades to provide inductive preparation for its formal introduction in ninth grade. The committee members endorsed the equation, and not the function, as deserving "especial emphasis" (p. 112)—a view that prevailed throughout the first decades of the twentieth century. William Betz (1926) noted that "after much controversy, a new and greatly reduced algebra program is taking form" (p. 163) in the junior high school. He claimed that there was considerable uncertainty as to how much attention should be given to traditional word problems, and there was a continuing debate over the function concept. In his view, instead of reorganizing algebra around the function concept, textbook authors had retained all the old material and simply tried "to glue on a few patches of functional work. It is this *double* burden, and *not* the function idea as such, which is causing many secondary teachers to view the new program as a sort of bête noire" (p. 163).

School Algebra under Fire

The decades from 1890 to 1940 saw an enormous growth in U.S. high school enrollments, from less than 7 percent of the fourteen- to seventeen-year-olds attending school in 1890 to more than 73 percent by 1940 (James and Tyack 1983). Enrollment growth in Canada during the same period was apparently second only to that of the United States (Goldin 2001; *Encyclopedia of Canada* 1948). During that period, enrollments in algebra first grew but then began to shrink, at least in the United States (see Jones and Coxford 1970, p. 54, for enrollment data from 1890 to 1955). In 1890, more than 45 percent of U.S. high school students were taking algebra, and that number increased to almost 57 percent by 1910. Algebra was fast becoming a major source of failure in school, however, and enrollments began to decline as it was increasingly made an elective rather than a required subject. Enrollments in algebra decreased steadily after 1910, falling to around 30 percent by 1940 and below 25 percent by the 1950s. In contrast, more recent enrollment numbers are much higher. The National Assessment of Educational Progress, for example, revealed that in 1999 more than 90 percent of seventeen-year-olds had taken at least one course in algebra (Campbell, Hombo, and Mazzeo 2000, p. 63). In 2004, 29 percent of thirteen-year-olds were taking algebra, primarily in eighth grade, and the percentage of seventeen-year-olds whose highest mathematics course was second-year algebra had increased from 37 percent in 1978 to 53 percent in 2004 (Perie, Moran, and Lutkus 2005, pp. 56, 58).

Herbert Kliebard and Barry Franklin (2003) noted that the declines in enrollment in high school mathematics in the first half of the twentieth century were part of a general movement in which the U.S. school curriculum was revised to reflect the ideal of social efficiency: the doctrine that "the job of the schools first and foremost was to train children and youth for their predicted adult roles" (p. 405; for a fuller treatment of the effects of social efficiency arguments on school mathematics, see Stanic 1986). Edward Lee Thorndike (1923) and his students examined how algebra tasks were rated in importance by college teachers of science and the way in which topics in algebra were used in high school textbooks and *Encyclopedia Britannica* articles. They concluded, "Algebra is a useful subject, but its utility varies enormously" (p. 89). In particular, teachers should pay more attention to reading and using algebraic symbolism, formulas, and graphs and give less attention to teaching students such skills as solving quadratic equations or working with sequences or the binomial theorem. Arguments grew that algebra was of little value to the average student. Critics like David Sneddon claimed that "algebra taught in American high schools is a nonfunctional and therefore nearly valueless subject for 90 per cent of all boys and 99 per cent of all girls" (quoted by Reeve 1936, p. 1).

Describing the "progress in algebra" in the first quarter of the twentieth century, David Eugene Smith (1926) acknowledged that the purpose of teaching algebra "a quarter of a century ago seems to have been to make mathematicians; the purpose today is to make well-informed American citizens" (p. 20). That purpose, he said, "consists in giving to everyone a general idea of the meaning of algebra, together with a few definite and useful applications which everyone is likely to meet" (p. 21).

School Algebra in the New Math Era

The new math era, which began in the mid 1950s and ended in the mid 1970s, witnessed a sea change in school algebra—from generalized arithmetic to systemic structure and proof. A main impetus for this change was to prepare students deemed "college capable" for the study of advanced mathematics. The change had been anticipated by such mathematicians as Eric Temple Bell (1936), who argued that algebra provided a less complicated structure than geometry and ought to be presented to students in its abstraction, a hypothetico-deductive system open to multiple interpretations. He demonstrated how the field postulates could be used to convey algebraic ideas, an approach that was pursued in textbooks published during the new math era. For example, the authors of the School Mathematics Study Group's *First Course in Algebra* chose to introduce the properties of arithmetic operations and then to state and prove theorems based on those operations, beginning with a theorem on the uniqueness of the additive inverse (Pollak 1965). Another example is presented by the *Algebra I* book from the so-called Ball State project (Brumfiel, Eicholz, and Shanks 1961), which after introducing four postulates, proves that if $x + a = a + b$, then $x = b$. This axiomatic approach had been encouraged by Saunders Mac Lane (1957), who wrote enthusiastically, "The proofs of algebraic theorems are neater and easier than those of geometry! Traditionally, high school geometry is said to be the subject where logic can best be learned. Algebra would be a better place!" (p. 100).

As it turned out, students had trouble seeing the logic behind the algebraic theorems, and teachers struggled to convince them that the proofs were necessary and important. René Thom (1973) summarized one view of the problem when he observed that meaning is more important than rigor in mathematics and that although algebra has an extremely rich syntax, "the 'meaning' of an algebraic symbol is established with difficulty or is non-existent" (p. 207). He noted "the heuristic poverty of algebra, where each new difficulty presents itself like a wall which necessitates entirely new methods if it is to be surmounted" (p. 208). For Thom, axiomatics should appear at the end of algebra instruction, not the beginning.

Four points (2 through 5) of the College Entrance Examination Board's (1959) nine-point program came to characterize the approach to elementary algebra undertaken during the new math era (p. 33):

2. Understanding of the nature and role of deductive reasoning—in algebra, as well as in geometry

3. Appreciation of mathematical structures ("patterns")—for example, properties of natural, rational, real, and complex numbers

4. Judicious use of unifying ideas—sets, variables, functions, and relations

5. Treatment of inequalities along with equations

As part of this approach, various terms were replaced or redefined. Much of the new language helped unravel some of the mysteries of elementary algebra, which had never been clear about distinctions among such terms as *literal numbers, unknowns, variables,* and *constants.* The terminology of *literal number* and *literal equation* was dropped; equations and inequalities became open sentences; a variable—no longer defined as "a quantity that varies"—was said to be a symbol to be replaced by names of set elements, usually numbers; and a function was defined as a set of ordered number pairs having certain properties.

The effort to modify the algebra curriculum during the new math era had some lasting effects. For example, inequalities are still included with the study of equations, loci are commonly defined as sets of points rather than as moving points, and trigonometry continues to be introduced by means of real-valued periodic functions. Because the mathematicians directing the reform believed that what was good mathematics for "college capable" students was also good for students who are less able, two-year courses were constructed that would treat the same topics as the one-year course (Begle 1969). Unfortunately, however, many two-year courses in introductory algebra tended to treat the content in a reductionistic fashion, employing numerous repetitive exercises and giving little attention to reasoning or complex problem solving. Nonetheless, as the new math era faded into the back-to-basics movement of the 1970s, with algebra instruction returning to an emphasis on manipulating symbols and solving simple equations, the idea remained alive that a larger percentage of high school students might profit from the study of introductory algebra if the course were extended over more than a year.

School Algebra in the Era of Standards

Algebra remained a prominent source of failure in high school during the 1970s and 1980s (Moses and Cobb 2001), and so when NCTM (1989, 2000) began its *Standards*-based reform efforts, school algebra came under heavy scrutiny once again. In recent years mathematics educators have pursued a set of interconnected changes with respect to algebra that are at least as complex and that have as far-reaching implications as those the reform has pursued with respect to any other branch of school mathematics. We consider next these changes with respect to several of the Standards that NCTM has put forth.

Approaches to Algebra

In the late 1970s and 1980s, research on students' understanding of algebraic manipulations and of the function concept (e.g., Kieran 1992; Leinhardt, Zaslazsky, and Stein 1990) helped mathematics educators clarify why so few students were learning algebra well. Some difficulties, such as students' tendency to interpret the equal sign as a command to compute an answer, suggested that aspects of arithmetic instruction were contributing to their difficulties with algebra. Others, such as students' difficulties in correctly identifying particular examples of relations as functions, suggested that a revision of the algebra curriculum would be required if students were to understand ideas of function. The late and abrupt introduction of algebra in isolation from other branches of mathematics and from applications to other disciplines apparently contributed to students' difficulties. In response, NCTM (1989) created a Patterns and Relationships Standard for kindergarten through fourth grade, a Patterns and Functions Standard and an Algebra Standard for fifth through eighth grade, and Algebra and Functions Standards for ninth through twelfth grade. NCTM's (2000) subsequent decision to establish a Content Standard for algebra from prekindergarten through twelfth grade, though it presented some problems of interpretation at the earlier grades, was generally welcomed by mathematics educators.

Meanwhile, researchers and curriculum developers began examining approaches that would allow students to connect algebra more clearly to their previous study of mathematics and to other domains. These approaches, some of which had been considered in earlier eras, included algebra as (*a*) generalized arithmetic, (*b*) a problem-solving tool, (*c*) the study of functions, and (*d*) modeling (e.g., Bednarz, Kieran, and Lee 1996). For several reasons, a number of curriculum development efforts focused on algebra as it might arise from attention to functions of quantities embedded in problem situations. One reason was a desire to move away from the manipulation of symbols in expressions and equations and toward an approach that students would find more motivating. A second reason was the perception that a focus on functions of quantities would allow learners to use their understanding of problem situations to develop conceptual understanding. Mathematics educators saw a shift in emphasis from equation solving to the study of functions as a shift from memorizing procedural rules toward making sense of problem situations. Using problems about varying quantities as an entry point to the study of functions, rather than the set-theoretic definition, allowed recent reform-oriented curricula (e.g., Star, Herbel-Eisenmann, and Smith 2000; van Reeuwijk and Wijers 1997) to introduce the study of functions in the middle grades. (See Daniel Chazan, this volume, for further discussion of equation- and functions-based approaches in recent U.S. curricula.)

A third factor stimulating a functions-based approach to algebra was the availability of increasingly powerful and affordable desktop and handheld computers that made possible new activities, particularly ones that made use of multiple connected representations, including graphs (see Romberg, Fennema, and Carpenter 1993, especially chapters 2–4). Before computers were widely available, graphs were time-consuming to create and awkward to manipulate. A typical task was to produce a graph by substituting values into an algebraic expression and plotting the resulting ordered pairs. New software linked graphs to other representations of functions and to problem situations in a variety of ways. For example, students could manipulate any one of three representations (an algebraic, tabular, or graphic representation), and the computer would update the other two (e.g., Moschkovich, Schoenfeld, and Arcavi 1993). Or students could examine connections between graphs and problem situations. For instance, computers attached to sensors could graph distance, speed, temperature, or other physical quantities with respect to time (Mokros and Tinker 1987). Such activities allowed students to manipulate the problem situation and see the resulting changes in graphs and to examine functions that could not be read-ily expressed in closed algebraic form. New software also made possible activities in which computers executed symbolic manipulations, allowing students to devote more attention to problem-solving strategies and investigating conjectures (Star, Herbel-Eisenmann, and Smith 2000).

Attention to Students' Thinking

Efforts to promote standards in school mathematics are causing teachers and researchers to look beyond how students perform symbol manipulations and the errors they make to how they think about algebraic concepts. Over the last half-century, mathematics educators have made progress not only in conceiving new instructional approaches that make use of increasingly available technology but also in understanding how students think about algebra. In much of the research in the 1970s and 1980s, researchers examined students' construction, manipulation, and interpretation of algebraic and graphic representations and catalogued their errors, which researchers often characterized as bugs or misconceptions (e.g., Kieran 1992; Leinhardt, Zaslazsky, and Stein 1990). A subsequent generation of research exam-ined more closely students' reasoning with representations, and several general findings emerged. One was that students often attend to representational features that teachers and researchers might not notice. For instance, although anyone expe-rienced with linear functions focuses on the slope and y-intercept when connecting $y = mx + b$ to its graph, learners do not necessarily appreciate the asymmetric role that the intercepts play. They may see the x-intercept as salient and try to include it in the algebraic representation along with the y-intercept (e.g., Moschkovich 1998; Schoenfeld, Smith, and Arcavi 1993). A second finding concerned the process by which students make connections between representations and problem situations. Simply telling students about correspondences between features of a representa-tion—such as m and b in $y = mx + b$—and a problem situation is typically insuf-ficient. Novices coordinate representations and problem situations by refining their understanding of both (e.g., Izsák 2004; Meira 1995). Such results reveal more subtlety and nuance in students' reasoning with representations than previous re-search on functions has found. The research has made clear that teaching and learn-ing with multiple representations linked to one another and to problem situations is necessarily very complex.

Algebra for All

From the outset, the NCTM (1989, 2000) *Standards* efforts stressed the need to make school mathematics—and algebra in particular—available to all students. Two arguments have led mathematics educators to consider how to teach ideas re-lated to algebra to a much broader range of students. The first argument has to do with economic opportunity and equal citizenship. Algebra is often referred to as a gatekeeper to a college education and the careers such education affords. NCTM

(2000) articulated an Equity Principle asserting the importance of high expectations and strong support for all students and explicitly stated that all students should learn algebra. Arguing that mathematical literacy is the civil rights issue of our time, Robert Moses and Charles Cobb, Jr., (2001) liken the introduction of computers controlled by symbolic representations to the introduction of the mechanical cotton picker: Just as the latter changed labor demands in agriculture during the 1940s and 1950s, the computer is currently changing labor demands in industry. Daniel Chazan (2000) and Robert Moses (Moses and Cobb 2001) have designed approaches to algebra intended to engage middle and high school students' interest and to make the content more accessible. Both approaches are based on problems drawn from students' lives.

The second argument has to do with reconceptualizing elementary school mathematics in ways that better prepare students for the formal study of algebra. A fundamental question is the extent to which the study of arithmetic can provide an adequate foundation for the subsequent study of algebra. Algebra has often been interpreted as *generalized arithmetic,* but that term has taken on at least two meanings. One meaning arises from the perspective that algebra involves problems in which some numbers in arithmetic computations are replaced by symbols. That perspective can amplify discontinuities between students' experiences in solving problems with arithmetic and with algebra. Explaining such discontinuities, Carolyn Kieran (1992) argued that algebra is difficult for students because the representations are abstract and because the required operations, especially those relating quantities in word-problem situations, conflict with operations students have learned to use through years of modeling with arithmetic: Students need to subtract where once they added, and to divide where once they multiplied.

A contrasting meaning for generalized arithmetic emphasizes opportunities for students to engage in generalizing activities while they are studying arithmetic. Romulo Lins and James Kaput (2004) offered a definition that encompasses such activity as well as more conventional equation solving: *Algebraic thinking* involves (*a*) deliberate generalization and expression of generality, and (*b*) reasoning based on semantically and syntactically guided actions on the forms of syntactically structured generalizations. This definition suggests how instruction related to algebra might be integrated across the grades. Examples of deliberate generalization that appear to be accessible to elementary school students include perceiving and expressing patterns and deducing some general properties of numbers, such as $a - a = 0$ for all whole numbers. These different meanings for generalized arithmetic imply rather different approaches to arithmetic instruction and deserve further deliberation and investigation.

Further work in the early learning of algebra is investigating alternatives to approaches based on generalizing experiences with whole numbers and counting. Barbara Dougherty (2004) reports on the Measure Up project, which is examining early elementary school students' capacities to compare lengths, areas, and volumes qualitatively. First graders introduce and use letters to express such comparisons. For instance, if $A = B$, then $B = A$, $A + C = B + C$, and $A - C = B - C$. A central question is how well such experiences prepare students for subsequent equation solving using formal algebra.

Issues in School Algebra

We close with three issues that are underrepresented in current research on the teaching and learning of algebra and that need to be addressed by teachers and researchers.

Tensions for Teachers

As noted by Kieran (1992) and Helen Doerr (2004), researchers have paid little attention to teachers' knowledge and practices with respect to the teaching of algebra. The few studies that have examined prospective and practicing teachers' subject matter and pedagogical content knowledge have emphasized their conceptions and misconceptions about the function concept. Doerr concluded that existing research suggests that teachers' understanding of functions is more procedural than conceptual and is not well connected. Other research has focused on teachers' use of arithmetic and algebraic strategies when solving equations and on their predictions about students' performance on equation-solving tasks presented in symbolic and word problem formats (Nathan and Koedinger 2000a, 2000b). Results indicate that teachers think of algebra primarily as a set of procedures for solving equations and are not well prepared to take other approaches to algebra, including those that make extensive use of technology. This finding implies, in turn, that teacher education at all grade levels is critical if approaches intended to make the subject accessible to a broader range of students are to move from research sites into classrooms across the United States and Canada.

Fractions as Foundations

Research that examines arithmetic foundations for algebra still focuses to a large extent on interpretations of the equal sign and whole-number arithmetic. Little attention has been given to the role that reasoning about fractional quantities can play in learning to reason with algebraic expressions. Yet fractions play a central role in algebraic reasoning. Hung-Hsi Wu (2001) argues that the most useful form of prealgebra is the development of computational fluency and the thorough study of fractions and fraction arithmetic. He contends that students who are not comfortable computing with numbers will be less disposed to manipulate symbols, that the explanation of fraction computation procedures provides a natural entrée into symbol use, that solving equations requires working with fractions, and that understanding fractions is prerequisite to understanding slopes of linear functions.

To Wu's arguments, we add three more: (1) Understanding the representation of fractions on the number line is necessary if learners are to understand graphs in the Cartesian plane, including interpolation between given points; (2) the study of fractions and the study of algebra address some of the same big ideas, as, for example, to add fractions or to add algebraic terms one has to ensure that all addends are expressed in the same units; and (3) fraction and whole-number arithmetic provide opportunities for learners to develop multiplicative structures and an understanding of the distributive property, both of which are central to working with algebraic expressions and equations.

Symbol Manipulation

Amid all the attention given recently to functions-based approaches to algebra, the role that algebraic manipulation can play in the learning of algebra has been downplayed, at least in the United States. The introduction of handheld calculators capable of symbolic manipulation has led to debates about which, if any, symbolic manipulation capacities are still important for students to develop. In other countries, there has been a growing recognition that through symbolic manipulation students can develop a deeper understanding of the mathematical objects with which they work (e.g., Artigue 2002; Kieran 2004).

Concluding Observation

To the casual observer, algebra might appear to be a stalwart of the school curriculum, and in many respects, it is. But as this brief history makes clear, school algebra has varied in the content taught, the purposes for which it has been included, and the students to whom it has been offered. If anything has been constant, school algebra has too often been seen as a source of difficulty and failure—a gauntlet to be run rather than territory to be claimed. At one time in the United States, algebra became no more than an elective, but that seems unlikely to happen again. Whether algebra will remain a separate course or courses, however, is unclear. In Europe and Asia, algebra is often integrated into a comprehensive curriculum that includes geometry and other branches of mathematics. Recent trends in North America suggest that algebra will increasingly be integrated into learners' experiences earlier and more fully. If the goal of making algebra comprehensible, useful, and a pleasure to learn is to be met, teachers, researchers, and curriculum developers will have to continue working together to develop approaches to teaching ideas related to equations and functions, approaches that may differ markedly from their own experiences when they learned the subject.

References

Archibald, Thomas, and Louis Charbonneau. "Mathematics in Canada before 1945: A Preliminary Survey." In *Mathematics in Canada—Les mathématiques au Canada,* edited by Peter Fillmore, pp. 1–43, Vol. 1, Canadian Mathematical Society—Société mathématique du Canada, 1945–1995. Ottawa, Ont.: Canadian Mathematical Society, 1995.

Artigue, Michèle. "Learning Mathematics in a CAS Environment: The Genesis of a Reflection about Instrumentation and the Dialectics between Technical and Conceptual Work." *International Journal of Computers for Mathematical Learning* 7 (October 2002): 245–74.

Bednarz, Nadine, Carolyn Kieran, and Lesley Lee, eds. *Approaches to Algebra: Perspectives for Research and Teaching.* Dordrecht, Netherlands: Kluwer Academic Publishers, 1996.

Begle, Edward G. "The Role of Research in the Improvement of Mathematics Education." *Educational Studies in Mathematics* 2 (December 1969): 232–44.

Bell, Eric Temple. "The Meaning of Mathematics." In *The Place of Mathematics in Modern Education,* Eleventh Yearbook of the National Council of Teachers of Mathematics, edited by William David Reeve, pp. 136–58. New York: Bureau of Publications, Teachers College, Columbia University, 1936.

Betz, William. "The Development of Mathematics in the Junior High School." In *A General Survey of Progress in the Last Twenty-five Years,* First Yearbook of the National Council of Teachers of Mathematics, edited by Raleigh Schorling, pp. 141–65. New York: Bureau of Publications, Teachers College, Columbia University, 1926.

Brumfiel, Charles F., Robert E. Eicholz, and Merrill E. Shanks. *Algebra I.* Reading, Mass.: Addison-Wesley Publishing Co., 1961.

Cajori, Florian. *The Teaching and History of Mathematics in the United States.* Bureau of Education Circular of Information No. 3. Washington, D.C.: U.S. Government Printing Office, 1890.

Campbell, Jay R., Catherine R. Hombo, and John Mazzeo. *NAEP 1999 Trends in Academic Progress: Three Decades of Student Performance.* NCES 2000-469. Washington, D.C.: National Center for Education Statistics, 2000.

Chateauneuf, Amy Olive. "Changes in the Content of Elementary Algebra since the Beginning of the High School Movement as Revealed by the Textbooks of the Period." Ph.D. dissertation, University of Pennsylvania, 1929.

Chazan, Daniel. *Beyond Formulas in Mathematics and Teaching: Dynamics of the High School Algebra Classroom.* New York: Teachers College Press, 2000.

College Entrance Examination Board, Commission on Mathematics. *Program for College Preparatory Mathematics.* New York: College Entrance Examination Board, 1959.

Doerr, Helen. "Teachers' Knowledge and the Teaching of Algebra." In *The Future of the Teaching and Learning of Algebra: The 12th ICMI Study,* edited by Kaye Stacey, Helen Chick, and Margaret Kendal, pp. 267–90. Boston: Kluwer Academic Publishers, 2004.

Dougherty, Barbara. "Using the Toolkit: An Elaborated Davydov Approach." In *The Future of the Teaching and Learning of Algebra: The 12th ICMI Study,* edited by Kaye Stacey, Helen Chick, and Margaret Kendal, pp. 87–92. Boston: Kluwer Academic Publishers, 2004.

Encyclopedia of Canada, s.v. "High Schools in Canada." Toronto: University Associates of Canada, 1948. www2.marianopolis.edu/quebechistory/encyclopedia/HighSchooleducationinCanada.htm (accessed August 1, 2006).

Goldin, Claudia. "The Human Capital Century and American Leadership: Virtues of the Past." *Journal of Economic History* 61 (April 2001): 263–91.

Izsák, Andrew. "Students' Coordination of Knowledge When Learning to Model Physical Situations." *Cognition and Instruction* 22, no. 1 (2004): 81–128.

James, Thomas, and David Tyack. "Learning from Past Efforts to Reform the High School." *Phi Delta Kappan* 64 (February 1983): 400–406.

Jones, Phillip S. "The History of Mathematical Education." *American Mathematical Monthly,* 74 (January 1967): 38–55.

Jones, Phillip S., and Arthur F. Coxford, Jr. "Mathematics in the Evolving Schools." In *A History of Mathematics Education in the United States and Canada,* Thirty-second Yearbook of the National Council of Teachers of Mathematics (NCTM), edited by Phillip S. Jones and Arthur F. Coxford, Jr., pp. 11–89. Washington, D.C.: NCTM, 1970.

Kieran, Carolyn. "The Learning and Teaching of School Algebra." In *Handbook of Research on Mathematics Teaching and Learning,* edited by Douglas A. Grouws, pp. 390–419. New York: Macmillan Publishing Co., 1992.

———. "The Core of Algebra: Reflections on Its Main Activities." In *The Future of the Teaching and Learning of Algebra: The 12th ICMI Study,* edited by Kaye Stacey, Helen Chick, and Margaret Kendal, pp. 21–33. Boston: Kluwer Academic Publishers, 2004.

Kliebard, Herbert M., and Barry M. Franklin. "The Ascendance of Practical and Vocational Mathematics, 1893–1945: Academic Mathematics under Siege." In *A History of School Mathematics,* edited by George M. A. Stanic and Jeremy Kilpatrick, pp. 399–440. Reston, Va.: National Council of Teachers of Mathematics, 2003.

Leinhardt, Gaea, Orit Zaslazsky, and Mary Kay Stein. "Functions, Graphs, and Graphing: Tasks, Learning, and Teaching." *Review of Educational Research* 60 (Spring 1990): 1–64.

Lins, Romulo, and James Kaput. "The Early Development of Algebraic Reasoning: The Current State of the Field." In *The Future of the Teaching and Learning of Algebra: The 12th ICMI Study,* edited by Kaye Stacey, Helen Chick, and Margaret Kendal, pp. 47–70. Boston: Kluwer Academic Publishers, 2004.

Mac Lane, Saunders. "Algebra." In *Insights into Modern Mathematics,* Twenty-third Yearbook of the National Council of Teachers of Mathematics (NCTM), edited by F. Lynwood Wren, pp. 100–144. Washington, D.C.: NCTM, 1957.

Meira, Luciano. "The Microevolution of Mathematical Representations in Children's Activities." *Cognition and Instruction* 13, no. 2 (1995): 269–313.

Mokros, Janice R., and Robert F. Tinker. "The Impact of Microcomputer-Based Labs on Children's Ability to Interpret Graphs." *Journal of Research in Science Teaching* 24, no. 4 (1987): 369–83.

Moschkovich, Judit. "Resources for Refining Mathematical Conceptions: Case Studies in Learning about Linear Functions." *Journal of the Learning Sciences* 7, no. 2 (1998): 209–37.

Moschkovich, Judit, Alan H. Schoenfeld, and Abraham Arcavi. "Aspects of Understanding: On Multiple Perspectives and Representations of Linear Relations and Connections among Them." In *Integrating Research on the Graphical Representation of Functions,* edited by Thomas A. Romberg, Elizabeth Fennema, and Thomas Carpenter, pp. 69–100. Hillsdale, N.J.: Lawrence Erlbaum Associates, 1993.

Moses, Robert P., and Charles E. Cobb,, Jr. *Radical Equations: Math Literacy and Civil Rights.* Boston: Beacon Press, 2001.

Nathan, Mitchell, and Kenneth Koedinger. "An Investigation of Teachers' Beliefs of Students' Algebra Development." *Cognition and Instruction* 18, no. 2 (2000a): 209–37.

———. "Teachers' and Researchers' Beliefs about the Development of Algebraic Reasoning." *Journal for Research in Mathematics Education* 31 (March 2000b): 168–90.

National Council of Teachers of Mathematics (NCTM). *Curriculum and Evaluation Standards for School Mathematics.* Reston, Va.: NCTM, 1989.

———. *Principles and Standards for School Mathematics.* Reston, Va.: NCTM, 2000.

National Educational Association. *Report of the Committee of Ten on Secondary School Studies with the Reports of the Conferences Arranged by the Committee.* New York: American Book Co., 1894.

Nordgaard, Martin A. "Introductory Calculus as a High School Subject." In *Selected Topics in the Teaching of Mathematics,* Third Yearbook of the National Council of Teachers of Mathematics, edited by John R. Clark and William D. Reeve, pp. 65–101. New York: Bureau of Publications, Teachers College, Columbia University, 1928.

Osborne, Alan R., and F. Joe Crosswhite. "Forces and Issues Related to Curriculum and Instruction, 7–12." In *A History of Mathematics Education in the United States and Canada,* Thirty-second Yearbook of the National Council of Teachers of Mathematics, edited by Phillip S. Jones and Arthur F. Coxford, pp. 155–298). Washington, D.C.: National Council of Teachers of Mathematics, 1970.

Overn, Orlando E. A. "Changes in Curriculum in Elementary Algebra since 1900 as Reflected in the Requirements and Examinations of the College Entrance Examination Board." *Journal of Experimental Education* 5 (June 1937): 373–468.

Perie, Marianne, Rebecca Moran, and Anthony D. Lutkus. *NAEP 2004 Trends in Academic Progress: Three Decades of Student Performance in Reading and Mathematics.* NCES 2005–464. Washington, D.C.: U.S. Government Printing Office, 2005.

Pollak, Henry O. "Historical and Critical Remarks on SMSG's First Course in Algebra." In *Philosophies and Procedures of SMSG Writing Teams,* pp. 11–22. Stanford, Calif.: School Mathematics Study Group, 1965.

Reeve, William David. "Attacks on Mathematics and How to Meet Them." In *The Place of Mathematics in Modern Education,* Eleventh Yearbook of the National Council of Teachers of Mathematics, edited by William David Reeve, pp. 1–21. New York: Bureau of Publications, Teachers College, Columbia University, 1936.

Romberg, Thomas A., Elizabeth Fennema, and Thomas Carpenter, eds. *Integrating Research on the Graphical Representation of Functions.* Hillsdale, N.J.: Lawrence Erlbaum Associates, 1993.

Schoenfeld, Alan H., John P. Smith III, and Abraham Arcavi. "Learning: The Microgenetic Analysis of One Student's Evolving Understanding of a Complex Subject Matter Domain." In *Advances in Instructional Psychology,* edited by Robert Glaser, Vol. 4, pp. 55–175. Hillsdale, N.J.: Lawrence Erlbaum Associates, 1993.

Smith, David Eugene. "A General Survey of the Progress of Mathematics in Our High Schools in the Last Twenty-five Years." In *A General Survey of Progress in the Last Twenty-five Years,* First Yearbook of the National Council of Teachers of Mathematics, edited by Raleigh Schorling, pp. 1–31. New York: Bureau of Publications, Teachers College, Columbia University, 1926.

Stanic, George M. A. "The Growing Crisis in Mathematics Education in the Early Twentieth Century." *Journal for Research in Mathematics Education* 17 (May 1986): 190–205.

Star, Jon R., Beth A. Herbel-Eisenmann, and John P. Smith III. "Algebraic Concepts: What's Really New in New Curricula?" *Mathematics Teaching in the Middle School* 5 (March 2000): 446–51.

Thom, René. "Modern Mathematics: Does It Exist?" In *Developments in Mathematical Education: Proceedings of the Second International Congress on Mathematical Education,* edited by A. G. Howson, pp. 194–209. Cambridge: Cambridge University Press, 1973.

Thorndike, Edward L., Margaret V. Cobb, Jacob S. Orleans, Percival M. Symonds, Elva Wald, and Ella Woodyard. *The Psychology of Algebra.* New York: Macmillan Co., 1923.

van Reeuwijk, Martin, and Monica Wijers. "Students' Construction of Formulas in Context." *Mathematics Teaching in the Middle School* 2 (February 1997): 230–36.

Wu, Hung-Hsi. "How to Prepare Students for Algebra." *American Educator* 25 (Summer 2001): 10–17.

2

The Shifting Landscape of School Algebra in the United States

Daniel Chazan

ALTHOUGH many critics suggest that the U.S. school system does not change, school algebra is shifting and changing before our eyes. These changes are of different kinds and reflect the complexity of the educational system in our society. These changes, filtered through the institutional pressures associated with compulsory schooling, come from competing sources: the vision articulated by the National Council of Teachers of Mathematics (NCTM) (2000), and the broader movement—also known by the name *standards*—to hold schools accountable for having students meet world-class academic standards relevant for both college and the world of work. This article begins with a description of structural changes in the role of algebra in the U.S. educational system—changes that are shifting the teaching responsibilities of secondary school mathematics teachers. At the same time, and perhaps partially in response to the structural changes to the role of algebra in U.S. schools, there are curricular changes. The article closes by identifying three sets of challenges and opportunities posed by these changes for mathematics educators.

Structural Changes Relevant to School Algebra

This section does not consider curricular issues in school algebra. Rather, it focuses on changes regarding which students study school algebra, when they study algebra, how their learning is assessed, the stakes of these assessments, and the rationales for these changes.

Who Studies School Algebra and Why?

In the not-too-distant past, say, twenty years ago, algebra was seen as abstract mathematics suitable only for students who were developmentally ready and college intending. Proportionally, African American, Hispanic, and white working-class students were underrepresented in courses in algebra (Gamoran 1987). As a result, such students and their teachers are also disproportionately the object of current policies.

Of course, twenty years ago, students had to study mathematics in high school; depending on their district and state, two, three, or, in very rare circumstances, one or four years of mathematics were required as part of a coursework load that would lead to high school graduation (Hawkins, Stancavage, and Dossey 1998, p. 48). However, the content of these years of study was left unspecified. As a consequence, a sizable percentage of students graduated from what some scholars called "the shopping mall high school" (Powell, Farrar, and Cohen 1985) with nonacademic training in mathematics, and with no study of algebra or geometry. The National Assessment of Educational Progress (NAEP) tracks course taking. On the 1990 NAEP, 17 percent of the surveyed twelfth-grade students indicated that their terminal mathematics course was prealgebra or arithmetic (Mitchell et al. 1999, p. 225).

The mathematics required of high school students is changing. Increasingly, over the last decade calls have suggested that all students study algebra before they graduate high school (College Board 2000). States are considering policies like those advocated by Achieve's American Diploma Project (ADP) (2004), which are meant to enforce such a course of action and ensure that students study more than first-year algebra. At the end of 2006, eight states had diploma requirements that met Achieve's standards; seven others raised their graduation requirements in the preceding year, but not to the level Achieve suggests; and twelve more were planning to raise graduation requirements. (This information was downloaded from www.achieve.org/node/332#states on November 28, 2006). These calls and policies are not just abstractions; they are changing what happens to children in school. For example, in a comparison of "highest math course taken," as reported by students on NAEP in 1990 and 1996, the percent of twelfth-grade students reporting that they have never taken a course in algebra or above dropped from 17 percent to 8 percent (Mitchell et al. 1999, p. 225); from 1978 to 1999, the percent dropped from 20 percent to 7 percent (Campbell, Hombo, and Mazzeo 2000, p. 63). On a national scale, these percentages represent large numbers of students.

Why Insist That All Students Study What Used to Be Considered Mathematics for Those Intending to Go to College?

The rationale is often couched in two sets of terms, the competitiveness of the United States in the global economy on the one hand, and the access of minority students to high-wage career opportunities on the other hand (ADP 2004; College Board 2000; Moses and Cobb 2002; RAND Mathematics Study Panel 2003). Research has examined much narrower outcomes. When Gamoran and Hannigan (2000) studied the benefits of college-preparatory mathematics, they found that enrolling in algebra, as opposed to a general math course, would lead to improved academic outcomes. (In this study, achievement in mathematics was assessed by the National Educational Longitudinal Study multiple-choice mathematics examination.) However, the researchers were careful to note that their results do not indicate what would happen if all students were required to study algebra (p. 241).

Side effects of policies that result in students' enrolling in an algebra class instead of a different mathematics course, including decreased arithmetic skill or an increase in the number of dropouts, have not been studied extensively. (See Carnoy and Loeb 2003 for an inconclusive attempt to examine changes to dropout levels as standards were raised.)

Yet, critics of such recommendations are on difficult rhetorical terrain. To suggest that not all students need to study algebra seems to be tantamount to suggesting that one does not see all students as capable thinkers or that one is willing to curtail the economic prospects of some members of our society. (See Noddings 1993 for an explication of the challenge of opposing such recommendations.)

When Do Students Study Algebra?

In an article in the *Mathematics Teacher,* Usiskin (1987) suggested that under certain conditions, algebra could and should be an eighth-grade course in the United States. But the very suggestion makes it clear that at that time, algebra was primarily a high school mathematics topic, or, more accurately, a pair of high school mathematics courses.

This also is changing. Now, in line with *Principles and Standards for School Mathematics* (NCTM 2000), algebraic thinking is being infused into arithmetic work at the elementary school level (for a report on the progress of such efforts, see Schliemann, Carraher, and Brizuela 2007). Middle-grade mathematics textbooks often include strands of work that is algebraic or preparatory for algebra. At the high school level, renewed interest has arisen in "integrated" courses. Although in most high schools, the "layer cake" with two algebra courses persists, National Science Foundation (NSF)–funded high school mathematics curricula, like the Interactive Mathematics Project (Fendel et al. 1997) and Core-Plus Mathematics (Coxford et al. 2003), take an integrated approach and offer algebra as a strand of study rather than as a pair of courses.

In line with Usiskin's (1987) call for offering algebra earlier in students' education and with international comparative studies that show that algebra is studied earlier in several countries (Martin et al. 2000), many districts in the United States require students who aspire to attend college to enroll in first-year algebra in grade 8, or even earlier. According to 1978 NAEP data, 16 percent of eighth-grade students were enrolled in courses in algebra; in 1999, the percent had increased to 22 percent (Campbell, Hombo, and Mazzeo 2000, p. 62).

How Is the Learning of Algebra Assessed, and What Are the Stakes of These Assessments?

Here, again, we see changes. In the past, for students who studied high school algebra, assessment was primarily the business of the classroom teacher or the school. The SATs or ACTs, as a hurdle to attaining college admission at particular universities, did not assess algebra directly but rather mathematics more broadly.

At present, in response to the legislation H.R. 1 of 2001, known colloquially as No Child Left Behind (NCLB), all students are expected not only to study algebra but also to demonstrate that during their years in high school, they have learned mathematics well enough to meet benchmarks on state examinations. Students also have to pass examinations developed by their teachers or their districts. In some states, such as Maryland and Texas, to graduate from high school or be awarded a state-certified diploma, students have to pass a state-developed end-of-course test. As states become more familiar with NCLB, the degree of difficulty of the tests is being clarified. It will be illuminating to track how data and political pressures influence the level of difficulty on these tests. Although most of these tests focus on introductory algebra, Achieve is working with a consortium of nine states to explore an exit exam for second-year algebra or its equivalent.

To reiterate, in the past it was possible to graduate from high school without having studied and passed a course that included the study of algebra. Now, in most states, students must not only take an algebra course or two in order to graduate but also pass an examination that tests whether they are able to meet state algebra-specific benchmarks.

The previous discussion focused only on structural changes relevant to the teaching and learning of school algebra. Changes to secondary school mathematics teachers' instructional responsibilities are addressed in the next section.

Changes to Secondary School Mathematics Teachers' Teaching Responsibilities

Taken together, the structural changes to school algebra represent substantial change—change that constitutes a large challenge to mathematics teachers. In the past, first-year algebra was a course in which students often were not successful. Although passing and failing rates are typically difficult to find, Gamoran and Hannigan (2000) note that even the most successful districts participating in the College Board's Equity 2000 program for six years had more than 25 percent of their students failing algebra. As the changes described above are carried out broadly in the United States, mathematics teachers are responsible for helping *all* their students be successful in their study of algebra or risk the severe economic consequences of not having a high school diploma. (In order to understand these consequences, scholars, like Entwisle, Alexander, and Olson [2004], investigate differences between the opportunities of those who drop out temporarily versus permanently.) From the point of view of the mathematics teacher, this is a major and demanding responsibility that has been mandated without a plan for how this new mandate can be achieved. It appears that teachers are being told to insist that their students jump higher, with the notion that students will comply and will then be successful.

The changes described, both in who studies algebra and when they study this content, have many implications for the teaching loads of middle or high school mathematics teachers. As more students take algebra before ninth grade, more middle school teachers with elementary school (K–8) certification are being asked to teach algebra, a domain of mathematics they were not prepared to teach. In systems that track by age, where higher-achieving students start algebra earlier than their peers, elementary-certified teachers teach algebra to those students who are the highest of achievers.

Whereas in middle schools the structural changes described earlier affect what mathematics is taught, at the high school level there are changes both in how many students are taught and what they are taught. NAEP trends suggest that more high school students are taking higher-level mathematics courses than in the past (Hawkins, Stancavage, and Dossey 1998). There are fewer general mathematics courses and more AP Statistics and Calculus courses to teach. At the same time, transcript studies indicate that more students are studying more mathematics. For example, the study by Perkins and colleagues (2004) indicates that from 1990 to 2000, the mean number of mathematics course credits jumped from 3.2 to 3.7 (pp. 2–4). Thus, high school mathematics departments are growing to accommodate the greater percentage of students studying mathematics. A particular challenge is for high school mathematics teachers to help students who have typically had difficulty to be more successful with more-advanced content than they might have been if they had been students a decade earlier. High school teachers, who may have chosen to teach high school for its disciplinary focus, may not be adequately prepared for this challenge.

At the same time, mathematics teachers may have less autonomy in meeting ambitious goals. The use of high-stakes state examinations on algebra content introduces new challenges for schools and districts. Districts and schools have to contend with the possibility that students will take and pass an algebra course but will not pass a state examination mandated for graduation. In large school districts, the pressure to help students succeed on the state's end-of-course examinations can lead to nine-week benchmark tests scored throughout the district to assess students' progress toward meeting the state assessment goals. Such assessments may lead teachers to face stark dilemmas about whether to stay with the pacing chart and the district examination schedule or fall behind in order to address difficulties students have with content previously taught.

There is a tremendous irony to the fact that these changes are being proposed during a time when the U.S. Department of Education seeks randomized controlled trials to justify even small-scale educational innovations. (See the Institute of Education Sciences [2003] *Effective Mathematics Education Research Grants, Request for Applications.*) Where are the randomized trials that show a positive impact for shifting graduation requirements to meet more demanding targets? Where is the evidence to show that such changes won't have unanticipated and unintended consequences, like a greater lack of arithmetic skill on important segments of the school population that will now devote more time to the study of algebra or increases in school dropout rates?

Changes to What School Algebra Is

So far, structural changes relevant to the teaching and learning of school algebra and changes to teachers' teaching responsibilities have been described. Changes to the algebra curriculum itself have not been discussed. Yet, there are substantial changes to the curriculum, perhaps linked to the structural changes described earlier.

This section will focus on shifts in the mathematical perspective on school algebra. Although these shifts may seem less dramatic than the policies described in earlier sections, these shifts are substantial. Perhaps they are what Kilpatrick and Izsák (this volume) describe as the earlier change from algebra as generalized arithmetic to algebra as structure (the story of algebra that highlights the relationship between factoring whole numbers and factoring polynomials over the complex numbers, which is familiar and comfortable to mathematicians like Wu [2001]). In time, these shifts may be as consequential for students as the policy changes described earlier.

Since reasoning with representations (Kilpatrick and Izsák, this volume) has become focal in discussions of school algebra (if not yet necessarily in classrooms) and since teachers struggle to help a wider range of students succeed in algebra, the curriculum's perspective on the x's and y's of school algebra has begun to shift subtly. (For another attempt to capture this shift, see Chazan and Yerushalmy 2003.) To appreciate this shift, it is useful to consider one mathematician's perspective on the real numbers. Weyl (2002, p. 453) writes:

> The system of real numbers is like a Janus head with two oppositely directed faces. In one respect it is the domain of + and • and their inverses, and in another it is a continuous manifold, and the two are continuously related. One is the algebraic and the other is the topological face of numbers.

This Janus-faced aspect of numbers has a particular implication for the conceptualization of the variables used in school algebra to write polynomials over the real numbers. While describing the algebraic properties of polynomials (think abstract algebra!), Weyl implicitly contrasts these algebraic properties with topological ones (think real analysis!) (pp. 455–56):

> The idea that the argument x is a variable that traverses continuously its values is foreign to algebra; it is just an indeterminate, an empty symbol that binds the co-efficients of the polynomial into a uniform expression that makes it easier to remember the rules for addition and multiplication. 0 is the polynomial all of whose coefficients are 0 (not the polynomial that takes on the value 0 for all values of the variable x).

To bring Weyl's comment back to school algebra, when a polynomial function is graphed or a table of values is created for an expression, it is the topological, not the algebraic, face of polynomials that is being presented to students. By way of contrast, when one argues that the equation $x - 2 = 0$ has only one solution because of the uniqueness of the additive inverse, the algebraic face is forward.

These two faces can be used to describe how curricula present what an equation is and what representations students can use when working with equations. Of course, curricula intend to teach understandings of equations that will allow students to move fluidly among different notions of what an equation is (see Sfard and Linchevski 1994 for an example of the fluidity required of students). No one view of equations in one variable listed below will identify how a particular curriculum teaches students. But the four possibilities listed below in italics will help concretize what Kilpatrick and Izsák call "reasoning with representations" (related to the topological) and differentiate it from "algebra as structure" (related to the algebraic).

For example, an algebra curriculum might conceptualize the equation in one variable $3x + 2 = 7$ as (1) *a representation of a set;* the solution set to this equation is $\{5/3\}$. In such a curriculum, when an equation in one variable is being solved, the question being asked of students is, "What are the elements of the set of numbers that can be used as replacements for x to make the conditional statement a true statement?" One might then represent this solution set on a number line and conceptualize the equation as another representation of this same set. The focus when solving equations in one variable is on the operations that can be carried out on both sides to arrive at the solution set; the values that can be substituted but that are not members of the solution set are not of interest.

The previous way of thinking seems quite consonant with the algebraic face of polynomials (and with algebra textbooks from the 1970s, like that of Dolciani and Wooton [1970]). There is a range of ways of conceptualizing equations that moves further and further into the realm of the topological and that incorporates other sorts of representations. In contrast to the previous view, an algebra curriculum can conceptualize this same equation, $3x + 2 = 7$, as (2) *a template for producing sentences about numbers*—sentences that can be true or false depending on the values used to replace x in this template. Students are then asked to identify replacements of x for which this statement is numerically true and replacements of x for which this statement is numerically false. Students might make a table to keep track of the values of x that make the statement true (although this way of thinking is not often explicitly made part of the school curriculum). Such a representation moves us closer to the topological view if the table traverses the values of x in numerical order.

Although these two ways of thinking about $3x + 2 = 7$ are relatively close to each other and have appeared in textbooks for many years, there are ways of conceptualizing equations in one variable that explicitly involve functions and that move the curriculum further in the direction of the topological. In the early twentieth century, although there were advocates for such functions-based perspectives (Hamley 1934; Fehr 1951), these views have become more common in textbooks only in recent years.

Students might be taught to view $3x + 2$ as the defining expression for a function. The curriculum might then conceptualize an equation like $3x + 2 = 7$ as (3) *a question about the inputs of a function,* as asking for what input(s) will this function produce the output 7? Of course, such a question is limited to equations where one expression is a number. In regard to representations, it might lead to the creation of a table that lists input values in numerical order with their associated outputs. Implicitly using arguments about the continuity of the input and output variables, students can seek to solve the equation by identifying inputs that generate outputs above and below 7. This is quite different from what used to be called a "guess and check" method. Using the table and reasoning by continuity, one can choose the next guess in principled ways; one pays attention to a range of substitutions for x, not just to the solution set.

Alternatively, a curriculum can teach students to think of $3x + 2 = 7$ as something like a system of equations in two variables—what Core-Plus Mathematics (Coxford et al. 2003) refers to as a system of functions—(4) *a comparison of two functions of one variable* where $3x + 2$ is being compared with the constant function $g(x) = 7$. Although this way of thinking might seem counterintuitive when one of the functions is a constant function, it is more plausible for equations like $3x + 2 = 7x$, where neither of the functions is a constant function. This perspective does not have the limitation of the previous possibility. (Functions-based algebra curricula differ in whether they insist on equations as always representing a comparison of two functions or whether some should be conceptualized as representing a question about a single function; see Yerushalmy and Chazan [in press].) In addition to the use of tables of values, such a comparison might use the topological face of polynomials to suggest the graphing of these two functions as continuous functions in a Cartesian planar coordinate system, as is often done now with graphing calculators.

In outlining these different views of equations, we may seem to have left behind the structural changes to school algebra, but the point is to highlight another way that school algebra is changing. With the shift in the conceptualization of algebra, tables of values and graphs on the Cartesian plane are now a larger part of the subject.

As can be seen from the previous discussion, who studies algebra, when they study algebra, the assessment of algebra learning, and the nature of school algebra are all changing. The algebra landscape is indeed shifting!

Opportunities and Challenges

What are mathematics educators to make of all these changes? David Cohen, a long-time observer of issues of educational policy and practice in the United States, has for much of his career pointed out the interdependency of policy and practice. He and his colleagues write (Cohen, Moffitt, and Goldin 2007, p. 522):

> The policymakers who define problems and devise remedies are rarely the ultimate problem solvers. They depend on the very people and organizations that have or are the problem to solve it. At the same time, those that have or are the problem depend on policymakers or others for some of the resources—ideas, incentives, money, and more—that may enable a solution.

Thus, changes of the kinds discussed so far are both challenges and opportunities at the same time. What are those opportunities and challenges?

1. Raising Standards, but Meeting Them as Well!

As mathematics teachers, we often bemoan that it is acceptable in our society to say that one is poor at math, but it is not acceptable to say that one cannot read effectively. A simplistic characterization of differences in societal attitudes toward mathematics education has parents in the United States telling their children that mathematics is a matter of ability, not effort, whereas in other countries, effort is emphasized. Some important institutions in our society are now seeking to change the message. According to Achieve (ADP 2004) and many of our state legislatures, everyone can do algebra, and to graduate from high school, all students are expected to study content that includes the equivalent of two courses in algebra. This expectation rules out the possibility that algebra requires some ability given only to some and not to others. This view is consonant with the Equity Principle as articulated in NCTM's *Principles and Standards for School Mathematics* (2000).

Yet, these expectations also pose a serious challenge to mathematics educators. How can we work to ensure that all students can indeed meet these higher standards and that the raising of standards does not mean a corresponding increase in the numbers of those in our society who do not complete high school?

A part of this challenge is systemic: How can we put in place a system for continual examination of our expectations over time? How will that system work toward long-term goals by setting reasonable short-term goals? Is there a way to ensure that one cohort of students does not bear the complete brunt of our desire to raise standards? Is there a way to create a system that monitors how well we are meeting our expectations for students and continually adjusts our expectations for our students both to meet the long-term desires of our society and to provide data about our track record and capacity to meet the standards we are setting?

Another aspect of this challenge has its feet in the classroom. It is crucial to gain some understanding of why students struggle with algebra and of how to help them succeed. For example, how can we help students whose arithmetic skills are poor find success with more advanced mathematics? As increasing numbers of students study algebra in earlier grades, teachers of algebra will need to find strategies to work with students in ways that allow an assessment of individual strengths and weaknesses and attention to the particular skills individual students may not have acquired earlier in their mathematical careers.

Likewise, we need to have better ideas about how to help students connect mathematics with the lives they are leading, no matter who they are and what they are intending to do. We have to help them find ways to connect what they value in themselves and their communities with what we aim to teach them. If we are able to develop responses to such challenges, we also will need to develop mechanisms for this knowledge to be shared widely and made a part of the induction of all teachers new to the profession.

2. Preparation for College and the World of Work

The American Diploma Project (2004) suggests that the same mathematics is useful preparation both for postsecondary education and for the world of work; students who intend to attend college and students who are headed to the workforce will both benefit from studying what educators used to conceptualize as mathematics for the college-intending. This may be viewed as an opportunity to unify and streamline curricular offerings.

At the same time, there are important challenges. Algebra 1, for example, historically has focused on manipulations of linear and quadratic equations in one and two variables. At the turn of the twentieth century, these skills were deemed important prerequisite skills for future mathematical study in college (Stanic 1987). Do we really believe this is the mathematics that is important for all students in the United States to master in the early twenty-first century, both students who are college intending and those who are not? When students know that handheld devices can solve the problems they are being asked to learn to solve, do we want to continue to devote big chunks of time to have students learn to solve such problems by hand? Will this really teach them what they need to know both for the world of work and for their postsecondary education?

Earlier, I alluded to the rhetorical challenges faced by mathematics teachers who do not think that mathematics is the key to addressing societal inequities and who are skeptical about the utility of requiring any particular body of knowledge of all students in a society. There are rhetorical challenges as well for those who are willing to require the same knowledge of all students but who do not see the content of first-year algebra, for example, as the appropriate material. If we, as mathematics teachers, do not agree that algebraic manipulation is the skill that all students need (e.g., in the vein of Kaput 1995; Schwartz 1999) but would instead point to other mathematics as important, then we have to articulate why we do not believe the mathematics conjured up by the name Algebra 1 or Algebra 2 is what all students should study. We have to describe the mathematics that we think is more important, and we must address concerns about changing the curriculum. If mathematics educators wish to change the mathematics of what used to be the college-intending high school mathematics curriculum, of concern is whether this change meets societal demands for increasing mathematics requirements for all students.

Gaining acceptance for changes to the curriculum that is increasingly being required of all students involves engagement with the diverse audiences that seek a mathematically literate cohort of high school graduates. These include politicians, the business community, and those involved in preparing undergraduates in scientific and technological fields, as well as some mathematicians who have often been vocal in their opposition to curricular change. Such engagement will challenge us as mathematics teachers to explain why we value the processes of problem solving, reasoning and proof, communication, connections, and representation enough to highlight them in *Principles and Standards for School Mathematics* (NCTM 2000). Explaining why we value the Process Standards requires communicating effectively what it means for students to solve problems with multiple representations and understanding whether such sense-making practices are important and valuable to stakeholders in the mathematics education process. To illustrate the value of such sense-making practices, we need to pursue ways of engaging stakeholders so that they will come face to face with the strengths of students who do poorly on standardized tests and the weaknesses of those who do well. One particular strategy for bringing stakeholders face to face with our reasons for valuing sense making is to invite the business community and local mathematicians into our schools to help score performance examinations in mathematics (for a description of this work in one high school, see Lehman 1999). Such a strategy involves stakeholders in the messy task of judging students' attempts to use mathematics sensibly.

3. Describing Our Expectations

One important component of the NCTM vision for mathematics education at the high school level is the integrated study of mathematics as strands to replace the traditional and prevalent model of a layer cake of courses. When the National Science Foundation funded the initial round of curriculum projects in the 1990s, none of the high school curricula followed a layer-cake model. By contrast, the American

Diploma Project (ADP 2004) uses the course titles in the layer-cake model to convey expectations for graduation.

One important virtue of Achieve's choice to formulate requirements by making reference to course names is that people who have experienced such a course think they know what is then being required of students (ADP 2004). Again, there is an opportunity here. Achieve has identified a way of communicating with the public about raising expectations for mathematics learning in the United States. Any alternative description of course content requires the development of modes of description of the mathematical focus of children's study that can be used effectively with the public.

To meet this challenge, NCTM needs to consider whether in this climate it should continue to push a vision of the high school mathematics curriculum as integrated, and if it continues to do so, how to articulate to the general public the importance or value of this vision to such an organization. Alternatively, with NCTM's vision, is it possible to leave the layer cake as it is and have Algebra 1, for example, survive as a course name, even if approaches to algebra change?

Conclusion

The three challenges or opportunities described above confront us at a time when society demands immediate results. Achieve would like all students to graduate from high school having completed the content of Algebra 1, Geometry, and Algebra 2 (ADP 2004). Whether mathematics educators are willing to join in articulating such a goal or not, an ongoing challenge will be to show that, although we argue about setting goals that can be realistically achieved in a reasonable time frame, we do wish to see our students' achievement enhanced and will do all that we can to facilitate their success with mathematics.

Regardless of what happens with the curriculum, mathematics teachers have faced and will face important challenges as the point people in the policy changes— the people in direct contact with students and their parents. Mathematics teachers are at a locus of cultural conflict between those who insist on raising standards and those, not usually active participants in the policy debates, who do not understand why what was good enough for them is not deemed sufficient for their children. Mathematics teachers are the faces that students and the community see as they are required to study particular content and to learn it well enough to pass tests designed by the states. We need tools and arguments that will help us explain to our students and to their families why our society is requiring this mathematics of them.

REFERENCES

American Diploma Project (ADP). *Ready or Not: Creating a High School Diploma That Counts.* Washington, D.C.: ADP, 2004. (downloadable from www.achieve.org/)

Campbell, Jay, Catherine Hombo, and John Mazzeo. *NAEP 1999 Trends in Academic Progress: Three Decades of Student Performance.* NCES 2000-469. Washington, D.C.: U.S. Department of Education, Office of Educational Research and Improvement, National Center for Education Statistics, Educational Resources Information Center, 2000.

Carnoy, Martin, and Susanna Loeb. "Does External Accountability Affect Student Outcomes?" *Educational Evaluation and Policy Analysis* 24, no. 4 (2003): 305–31.

Chazan, Daniel, and Michal Yerushalmy. "On Appreciating the Cognitive Complexity of School Algebra: Research on Algebra Learning and Directions of Curricular Change." In *A Research Companion to "Principles and Standards for School Mathematics,"* edited by Jeremy Kilpatrick, W. Gary Martin, and Deborah Schifter, pp. 123–35. Reston, Va.: National Council of Teachers of Mathematics, 2003.

Cohen, David, Susan Moffitt, and Simona Goldin. "Policy and Practice: The Dilemma of Implementation." *American Journal of Education* 113, no. 4 (2007): 515–48.

College Board. *Equity 2000: A Systemic Education Reform Model.* Washington, D.C.: College Board, 2000.

Coxford, Arthur, James Fey, Christian Hirsch, Harold Schoen, Gail Burrill, Eric Hart, with MaryJo Messenger, Elizabeth Ritsema, and R. Walker. *Contemporary Mathematics in Context: A Unified Approach* (Courses 1–3). Columbus, Ohio: Glencoe/McGraw-Hill, 2003.

Dolciani, Mary, and William Wooton. *Modern Algebra, Book One: Structure and Method.* Boston: Houghton Mifflin, 1970.

Entwisle, Doris, Karl Alexander, and Linda Olson. "Temporary as Compared to Permanent High School Dropout." *Social Forces* 82, no. 3 (2004): 1181–1205.

Fehr, Howard. *Secondary Mathematics: A Functional Approach for Teachers.* Boston: D. C. Heath & Co., 1951.

Fendel, Daniel, Diane Resek, Lynn Alper, and Sherry Fraser. *Interactive Mathematics Program* (Years 1–4). Berkeley, Calif.: Key Curriculum Press, 1997.

Gamoran, Adam. "The Stratification of High School Learning Opportunities." *Sociology of Education* 60, no. 3 (1987): 135–55.

Gamoran, Adam, and Eileen Hannigan. "Algebra for Everyone? Benefits of College-Preparatory Mathematics for Students with Diverse Abilities in Early Secondary School." *Educational Evaluation and Policy Analysis* 22, no. 3 (2000): 241–54.

Hamley, Herbert R. *Relational and Functional Thinking in Mathematics.* Ninth Yearbook of the National Council of Teachers of Mathematics. New York: Bureau of Publications, Teachers College, Columbia University, 1934.

Hawkins, Evelyn, Frances Stancavage, and John Dossey. *School Policies and Practices Affecting Instruction in Mathematics: Findings from the National Assessment of Educational Progress.* NCES 98-495. Washington, D.C.: U.S. Department of Education, Office of Educational Research and Improvement, 1998.

Institute of Education Sciences. *Effective Mathematics Education Research Grants, Request for Applications.* NCER 03-05. Washington, D.C.: Institute of Education Sciences, 2003. Available at www.ed.gov/offices/IES/funding.html, 2003, January 15.

Kaput, James. "Long-Term Algebra Reform: Democratizing Access to Big Ideas." In *The Algebra Initiative Colloquium,* Vol. 1, edited by Carole Lacampagne, William Blair, and James Kaput, pp. 33–49. Washington, D.C.: U.S. Department of Education, 1995.

Lehman, Michael. "Group Performance Assessments." In *Bringing the NCTM Standards to Life: Exemplary Practices from High School,* edited by Yvelyne German-McCarthy, pp. 157–73. Larchmont, N.Y.: Eye on Education, 1999.

Martin, Michael, Ina Mullin, Eugenio Gonzalez, Kelvin Gregory, Teresa Smith, Steven Chrostowski, Robert Garden, and Mary O'Connor. *TIMSS 1999 International Mathematics Report: Findings from IEA's Repeat of the Third International Mathematics and Science Study at the Eighth Grade.* Chestnut Hill, Mass.: International Study Center, Lynch School of Education, Boston College, 2000.

Mitchell, Julia, Evelyn Hawkins, Pamela Jakwerth, Frances Stancavage, and John Dossey. *Student Work and Teacher Practices in Mathematics.* NCES 1999-453. Washington, D.C.: U.S. Department of Education, Office of Educational Research and Improvement, 1999.

Moses, Robert, and Charles Cobb, Jr. *Radical Equations: Civil Rights from Mississippi to the Algebra Project.* Boston: Beacon Press, 2002.

National Council of Teachers of Mathematics (NCTM). *Principles and Standards for School Mathematics.* Reston, Va.: NCTM, 2000.

Noddings, Nel. "Politicizing the Mathematics Classroom." In *Math Worlds: Philosophical and Social Studies of Mathematics and Mathematics Education,* edited by Sal Restivo, Jean P. Van Bendegem, and Roland Fischer, pp. 150–61. Albany, N.Y.: State University of New York Press, 1993.

Perkins, Robert, Brian Kleiner, Stephen Roey, and Janis Brown. *The High School Transcript Study: A Decade of Change in Curricula and Achievement, 1990–2000.* NCES 2004-455. Washington, D.C.: National Center for Education Statistics, 2004.

Powell, Arthur, Eleanor Farrar, and David Cohen. *The Shopping Mall High School: Winners and Losers in the Educational Marketplace.* Boston: Houghton Mifflin, 1985.

RAND Mathematics Study Panel. *Mathematical Proficiency for All Students: Toward a Strategic Research and Development Program in Mathematics Education.* Santa Monica, Calif.: RAND Corp., 2003. www.rand.org/publications/MR/MR1643

Schliemann, Analucia D., David W. Carraher, and Barbara M. Brizuela. *Bringing Out the Algebraic Character of Arithmetic: From Children's Ideas to Classroom Practice.* Mahwah, N.J.: Lawrence Erlbaum Associates, 2007.

Schwartz, Judah. "Can Technology Help Us Make the Mathematics Curriculum Intellectually Stimulating and Socially Responsible?" *International Journal of Computers for Mathematical Learning* 4, no. 2 (1999): 99–119.

Sfard, Anna, and Liora Linchevski. "The Gains and the Pitfalls of Reification—the Case of Algebra." *Educational Studies in Mathematics* 26, no. 2 (1994): 191–228.

Stanic, George. "Mathematics Education in the United States at the Beginning of the Twentieth Century." In *The Formation of School Subjects: The Struggle for Creating an American Institution,* edited by Thomas Popkewitz, pp. 145–75. New York: Falmer Press, 1987.

Usiskin, Zalman. "Why Elementary Algebra Can, Should, and Must Be an Eighth-Grade Course for Average Students." *Mathematics Teacher* 80 (September 1987): 428–38.

Weyl, Hermann. "Topology and Abstract Algebra as Two Roads of Mathematical Comprehension." Reprinted in *Mathematical Evolutions,* edited by Abe Shenitzer and John Stillwell, pp. 149–62. Washington, D.C.: Mathematical Association of America, 2002.

Wu, Hung-Hsi. "How to Prepare Students for Algebra." *American Educator* 25, no. 2 (2001): 10–17.

Yerushalmy, Michal, and Daniel Chazan. "Technology and Curriculum Design: The Ordering of Discontinuities in School Algebra." In *Second Handbook of International Research in Mathematics Education,* edited by Lyn D. English. Boca Raton, Fla.: Taylor & Francis Group, in press.

Part 2

The Nature of Algebra and Algebraic Thinking

3

Algebra: Purpose and Empowerment

Abraham Arcavi

Augustus De Morgan told the following story (1915, p. 339).

> Diderot paid a visit to Russia at the invitation of Catherine the Second. At that time he was an atheist, or at least talked atheism.... His lively sallies on this subject much amused the Empress, and all the younger part of her Court. But some of the older courtiers suggested that it was hardly prudent to allow such unreserved exhibitions. The Empress thought so too, but did not like to muzzle her guest by an express prohibition: so a plot was contrived. The scorner was informed that an eminent mathematician had an algebraic proof of the existence of God, which he would communicate before the whole Court, if agreeable. Diderot gladly consented. The mathematician ... was Eüler. He came to Diderot, with the gravest air, and in a tone of perfect conviction said, "*Monsieur,* $\frac{a + b^n}{n} = x,$ *donc Dieu existe; répondez!*" ("Monsieur, $(a + b^n)/n = x$, whence God exists; answer that!"). Diderot, to whom algebra was Hebrew, ... and whom we may suppose to have expected some verbal argument of alleged algebraical closeness, was disconcerted; while peals of laughter sounded on all sides. Next day he asked permission to return to France, which was granted.

THE story portrays algebra as a pungent source of power "to mystify and intimidate, rather than to enlighten" (Koblitz 1984, p. 254). Mathematics in general, and algebra in particular, can be used to intimidate in many ways. For example, by means of an unintelligible concatenation of symbols some arguments can be wrapped with respectability and paralyze an interlocutor by means of "convincing" and hard to refute "evidence" (for more examples, see Koblitz 1984). Thus, a knowledge of mathematics, and particularly a knowledge of algebra, is crucial for, among other things, the inspection, understanding, and development of a critical appraisal of the large amount of information and arguments with which we are confronted at all times.

An algebraically literate student would have, for example, defied the symbolic authoritarianism in the story above by questioning Eüler about his relationship between the formula and the gist of his argument. A central aspect of algebraic literacy seems to be the ability to question any use, misuse, or abuse of algebraic expressions that makes unwarranted conclusions.

Is algebra education advancing this literacy goal? Maybe, but not as keenly as it should. How could this goal be advanced? Project 2061 (American Association for the Advancement of Science [AAAS] n.d.) provides an indirect answer to this question by choosing "Identifying a sense of purpose" as the first category of analysis in their algebra textbook evaluation published in 2000. Do textbooks convey a purpose for what they are supposed to teach? Do students obtain from their textbooks (or their teachers) a sense of why and how the algebra knowledge they learn can serve them? The evaluation study performed by Project 2061 analyzed thirteen popular algebra textbooks in the United States. The chart "Summary of Instructional Analysis Ratings of Algebra Textbooks" reports that out of the twelve programs evaluated on "conveying unit purpose," three did poorly, four did fairly, three were satisfactory, two were good, and none was excellent. If algebra is not taught as a purposeful activity, it will hardly be perceived as such, and if it lacks purpose, we may find ourselves in agreement with the assertion that "most math textbooks from algebra on *disempower* kids" (Moses and Cobb 2001, p. 99, emphasis added). Learning materials should gain their strength from "their power to empower" (ibid.), and we would like to link such strength to purposefulness.

Tasks that are purposeful can be characterized as having "a meaningful outcome for the learner, in terms of an actual or virtual product, the solution of an engaging problem, or an argument or justification for a point of view" (Ainley, Bills, and Wilson 2005, p. 194).

In this paper, I present ideas and examples of tasks and activities related to the teaching of algebra that were designed having purposefulness in mind. I claim that advancing the goal of purposefulness has the potential to direct the teaching of algebra toward student empowerment. The empowerment I propose to advance should aim at nurturing the students' feelings that they have power, not over others (as illustrated in the opening story above), but over problematic situations or dilemmas. Such empowerment refers to the sense of ownership of what one does, which is not dictated by external sources of authority (e.g., teachers, textbooks) but rather by one's decision when and how it makes sense to use certain knowledge. Thus, in our situation, empowerment refers to the sense of independence over our own algebraic knowledge and when to apply it in order to solve a problem, to gain new insights, to discard fake arguments, to detect fallacies, to experience a sense of "victory" over an intellectual obstacle, to carry out informed decisions, and also to create (even small pieces of) mathematics. These goals can be achieved by imbuing the teaching with problem situations that can exemplify the power and purpose of algebra and that are not always very common in most textbooks. The examples that follow are aimed as a contribution in these directions.

Magic with Numbers

A material that begins with abstractions or phenomena outside students' range of perception, understanding, or knowledge does not adequately meet the criterion [of purposefulness]. However, a material that starts with an unfamiliar but highly interesting phenomenon that is likely to motivate students may meet the criterion. (AAAS, Project 2061 n.d.).

Magic usually arouses admiration and also curiosity about how a "trick" was performed. Apparently, it is a universal human need to try to understand how something unlikely to happen can be made to occur. The teaching of algebra can and should build on this human characteristic that can be harnessed to the design of activities with which to start a lesson or a unit.

Consider the following "magician trick" (Arcavi 2002), which can be tried with people of all ages, especially with ten-to-twelve-year-old students. Ask students in the class to input a three-digit number of their choice into their calculators. Then ask them to input the same three-digit number immediately to the right of the first, in order to obtain a six-digit number of the form $xyzxyz$. Concentrate as if you are invoking supernatural powers and say, "Now, divide your six-digit number by … (simulating concentration) 91." Call their attention to the fact that the quotient obtained by all of them is a whole number. Then request students to divide their results by 11. At this stage most will be manifestly surprised to see appearing, on the display of their calculators, their originally chosen three-digit numbers. To strengthen the sense of surprise (and at the same time start preparing for the collaborative discussion toward uncovering the "magic"), remind students that although you did not know any of the numbers chosen, you brought back *all* their six-digit numbers to the originally chosen three-digit numbers by two consecutive divisions, using the same divisors for all of them. The next step is to repeat the process, but now ask for consecutive divisions by 13 and 77, and finally a next round with divisions by 7 and 143. The repetition has a twofold intention: (1) to reinforce the sense of surprise (the same "trick" can be performed in at least three different ways), and (2) to furnish more information on which students can start an inquiry with the purpose of uncovering by themselves the source of the magic. Power, in this situation, would mean enabling them to "expose" the magician and demystify what seems supernatural by properly applying some important pieces of mathematical knowledge.

The length of the collective inquiry process of a class, and the excitement therein, is certainly a function of the mathematical sophistication of the students. Usually the steps followed would consist of first realizing that the two consecutive divisions can be performed as one, if one multiplies the two successive divisors, and to discover that in the three cases (91×11, 13×77, 7×143) the division performed was the same (by 1001). Then the attention turns to the original three-digit number and the six-digit number created from it. Some students realize that $xyzxyz$ is precisely

1001 times the number xyz. Thus, the whole trick was to multiply a given three-digit number by 1001 and then divide the result by 1001. By doing so, obviously one returns to the original number. In the process, students are led to realize that forming the six-digit number was a multiplication in disguise and that dividing by the three possible pairs of decompositions was the inverse operation, also in (another) disguise.

Purposefulness, in this instance, is related to the power to uncover a "trick," to understand how and why it works, and to think about the possibility of designing similar ones (would this work with 101? 10,001? other numbers?). Such power is related to the experience of applying one's mathematical knowledge in an inquiry, which is a very different activity from solving a sequence of traditional textbook exercises. In the process there are many important mathematical properties that one has to notice and handle creatively:

- First, the division $(N : a) : b$ is equivalent to $N : (a \times b)$.

- Second, there are three different decompositions of 1001 into a product of two integers (which are in fact the three possible combinations of its only three prime factors, 7, 11, and 13).

- Third, a six-digit number of the form $xyzxyz$ is 1001 times xyz. The operation of multiplication by 1001 and its product can be noticed at once through the very form of the six-digit number $xyzxyz$ by reading it out loud and as an instance of the distributive law and its relationship, in this example, with our decimal notation system.

Why is this task related to algebra even if it does not involve explicit symbolic manipulation? I propose that this prealgebra task has a lot to do with algebra, or at least with conveying the sense of algebraic activity, since it goes beyond one specific calculation. One can discuss with students the fact that whereas each of them chose a different number, all ended up experiencing the same phenomenon: a property of a class of numbers. One can also notice the general property of dividing by a and then by b as being equivalent to dividing by $a \times b$. One can discuss obvious properties (multiplying and dividing by the same number as inverse operations). One can also notice that trivial properties can be disguised, waiting for us to uncover and understand them. All the examples above are illustrations of algebraic principles and how one may use them to understand and gain power over some situations.

The Tiered Structure

The following task is an adaptation from Rachlin, Matsumoto, and Wada (1992, p. 209): "Fill in the white cells in figure 3.1 in such a way that each number is the sum of the two numbers immediately above it."

Most students, even those who have some proficiency with algebra and alge-

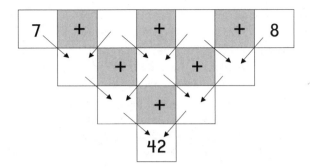

Fig. 3.1. The tiered structure

braic techniques, approach this task numerically. Some choose two numbers and place them in the first row, then add them and see what happens. It is quite rare that a first guess will lead to a correct solution, namely, to fill all the cells such that the last sum becomes 42. Consider, for example, a first trial with 3 and 5. In this instance, the numbers in the cells in the second row will be (from left to right) 10, 8, and 13. The two numbers in the third row will be 18 and 21, which add to 39 and not 42, as required. Close, but not a solution. If approached reflectively, such a first guess can serve as the basis for an informed trial and error. For example, if the first numbers are slightly increased to, say, 4 and 6, it may work—but it does not, since the final sum becomes 45. More attempts could end up with 4 and 5, which solve the problem. Other students approach the tiered figure bottom up, namely, trying different decompositions of 42 into two addends, and seeing whether they can arrive at the upper row reaching the given numbers, 7 and 8.

Experience shows that very rarely do students and also mathematically literate adults spontaneously approach the problem algebraically. As reported in Arcavi (1994), the invocation of symbols as a powerful tool to make sense of situations like those above does not seem to be immediate, even after having ample experience with algebra. Whereas symbolic manipulations are extensively exercised, the use of symbols as a means to uncover the structure or the properties of a certain array of numbers is not at our students' fingertips. Such uses of symbols, if frequently exercised, can furnish a strong sense of purpose and illustrate the power they offer us in illuminating the "inner fabric" of a situation. In our example, all we need to do is introduce x and y respectively in the empty cells of the upper row and proceed with the calculation. The cells in the second row will be $7 + x$, $x + y$, and $y + 8$. The cells in the next row will be $7 + 2x + y$ and $x + 2y + 8$. Thus, $7 + 2x + y + x + 2y + 8$ should be 42. Or, $3(x + y) = 42 - 8 - 7$, and $x + y = 9$. The symbols show us elegantly, concisely, and unequivocally the condition for this problem to have a solution, and that there are infinitely many solutions if we allow the cells to be filled not only with natural numbers.

This task shows a purpose of algebra because symbols and symbolic rules are the basis for solving the problem concisely in a few steps. Furthermore, we propose to discuss with students some issues related to the very use of symbols, which become intellectually empowering in a genuine and deep way, beyond the realization that symbols should be applied. How can this be done? The very act of using x and y to fill the first cells should be regarded, not only as a mere use of a letter instead of an unknown number but also in the spirit of the powerful problem-solving heuristic of "working backwards": "What are we required to do? Let us visualize the final situation we aim at as clearly as possible" (Polya 1971, p. 227). Filling the cells with x and y is like imagining the problem solved, except that one does not know which numbers solve it; thus one uses unknowns.

Assuming the problem solved allows us, through the symbols, to explore *the characteristics* of such a solution, even if one does not know it. The characteristics are thus displayed in implicit, "unfinished," intermediate operations (e.g., $7 + x$, $y + x$), which will finally allow us to find the solution. In the process, we discuss with students the nature of the symbolic representation, for example, that we may not know right away the addends of the final sum $[3(x + y) + 15]$ that yields 42, but we know some properties: the sum is formed by three times the sum of the numbers we chose for the cells plus the sum of the two given extremes.

This analysis not only calls attention to the symbolic process itself but also synthesizes in a compact way what the process does: whereas the 7 and the 8 contribute to the 42 just once, the unknown numbers chosen to fill the empty cells in the first row accumulate three times before reaching the 42. Why is this so? Each time we descend one of the three rows, the chosen numbers are added once, whereas the given numbers are not. Thus by reading aloud the meaning of the relationship found (the sum of the two chosen cells should be one-third the difference between the final number, 42, and the sum of the initial numbers, $7 + 8$), one can also understand the why of the structure of the result and even generalize for any initial and final numbers (other than 7, 8, and 42). The symbols allow us to discern what we did numerically in our first trials without being aware of it. Thus, the algebraic symbols did more than compactly yield the solution, they led us to see its structure and its raison d'être.

In summary, I claim that the task above offers opportunities for sharing the purpose of symbols (to solve a task and to uncover its hidden structure) and also for experiencing how symbols in a compact way allow us to handle and carry on both the meaning of the activity itself (placing unknowns and running with them) and the makeup of its solution (the sum of the two chosen numbers is 9).

Finger Arithmetic

Several elementary computation methods have been developed throughout history, some of which may still be in use in some parts of the world. The following is an interesting method for multiplying two numbers between 5 and 10 (Smith 1958,

p. 201): "For example, to multiply 7 by 8, raise two fingers on one hand and three on the other, since $5 + 2 = 7$ and $5 + 3 = 8$. Then add the numbers denoted by the raised fingers, $2 + 3 = 5$, and multiply those denoted by the others, $3 \times 2 = 6$, and the former result is the tens, 50, and the latter is the units, the product being 56." Figure 3.2 illustrates the representation of the multiplication 7×8.

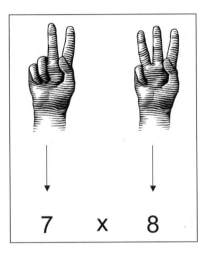

Fig. 3.2. Representation of 7 × 10

The fingers raised in each hand represent each of the factors (2 represents 7, 3 represents 8). As stated, the total number of raised fingers (5) indicates the tens digit of the result, and the product of the bent fingers forms the units digit (6). Very young students may be happy to learn this rule. Teaching mnemonics, rules that are easy to remember and fun to apply and other kinds of tricks, are willingly accepted by students, since they may be perceived as "productive." However, this is not the kind of empowerment that has deep and long-lasting educational significance.

I propose to use this finger multiplication task in order to illustrate a kind of purposeful use of algebra with potential to empower students in the following sense. Once the students become acquainted and proficient with this finger calculation strategy, the questions to discuss are (1) "Why does this method work?" and (2) "Can I invent other methods of this type?" Here, algebra is not used to find a solution. Rather, it is a justification tool on the basis of which one may design a new mathematical rule that can serve us well. "Discussions regarding justification allow students to (a) observe how a rule applies across various cases, (b) construct generalizations to related situations, and (c) reflect on their own reasoning regarding the viability of their rules" (Lannin, Barker, and Townsend 2006, p. 441).

In order to create a justification, one needs to model the situation, and a first step toward modeling is to choose the variables. For example, we can choose x and

y to represent the number of raised fingers. In this instance, we are performing the multiplication $(5 + x)(5 + y)$. The calculation strategy stipulates that the result should be $10(x + y) + (5 - x)(5 - y)$. To justify would mean to find a way to establish that the two expressions, $(5 + x)(5 + y)$ representing the original calculation to be performed and $10(x + y) + (5 - x)(5 - y)$ representing the calculation strategy of this method, are indeed equivalent. Algebra provides the syntactic rules to show this equivalence. Thus these rules have a clear and established purpose: how to reach one expression from another in order to justify a calculation strategy.

The justification produced above depends on the particular way we model the situation. It is very important to share with students that another general and legitimate justification may be obtained if we decide to model the situation differently. It is *our* decision how to model, and sometimes this freedom of choice may result in less or more straightforward work, or in less or more transparency of the result, depending on personal experiences and preferences. For example, if instead of choosing the variables to represent the *raised* fingers, we choose the variables to represent the *bent* fingers. Then the symbolic representation of the numbers we are multiplying becomes $(10 - x)(10 - y)$, and the calculation strategy is now represented by $10(5 - x + 5 - y) + xy$. As before, justifying means showing that these two expressions are equivalent. The situation can also be represented by choosing x and y as the numbers to be multiplied, in which case the raised fingers are represented by $x - 5$ and $y - 5$ respectively, the bent fingers by $10 - x$ and $10 - y$, and what remains to be shown is that xy and $10(x - 5 + y - 5) + (10 - x)(10 - y)$ are equivalent. As indicated, throughout this activity the syntactic rules had a clear purpose; they were used to show that two expressions are equivalent and that this equivalence is in fact the justification of the given calculation strategy.

Justifying is, in itself, a powerful mathematical activity, but it can also serve as the springboard for creating our own rules and seeing if, when, and how they work. For example, we can use the five fingers of each hand to represent numbers between 10 and 15. Can we devise a rule for multiplying any two such numbers? We might first look at a possible special case. For example, let us consider 14×12. On one hand we raise two fingers to represent 12, and on the other hand we raise four fingers to represent 14. Now we need to create a rule that allows us to "read" from the configuration (6 fingers raised and 4 fingers bent) the result of the multiplication, namely, 168. Which combination of the number of raised and bent fingers would work in this example? The task may require some time. Students may not find a rule very easily, or they may find some rules that work for special cases only. But after more trials, some students may arrive at a correct rule to read the result from the finger configuration: 100 should be presupposed (the product of any two numbers between 10 and 15 is always greater than 100), the addition of the raised fingers yields the tens (as before), but the units of the result is the product of the same numbers indicated by the raised fingers (not the bent ones), in other words, $100 + 60$ (6 raised fingers altogether) + 8 (2 × 4—the product of the raised fingers). As before, we can justify the strategy choosing variables in several ways. Students may approach the activity differently, by beginning with the symbolic representation $(10 + x)(10 + y)$, in which x and y represent the raised fingers, expanding it to obtain $100 + 10x + 10y + xy$, and reading the finger calculation strategy directly from this symbolic form.

In summary, these tasks may empower students to justify using syntactic rules, but they may also empower students through experiencing the creation of rules "of their own" and their justifications.

Improving Examination Grades

As reported elsewhere (Arcavi 2002), some mathematical situations may have to do with students' lives and experiences, in or out of school, which are not necessarily classroom tasks or homework assignments. Such mathematically rich and genuinely relevant situations should be appropriated and explored in the mathematics class, since they may constitute good examples of purposeful content. The following situation was inspired by a real event of that kind. Imagine, for example, that the majority of the students in a class failed an examination (in any subject) and that the teacher, instead of repeating the exam, decides to apply a "correction factor." Assume that the grading scale is 0 to 100, with 100 being the maximum grade, and that the teacher established $f(x) = 10\sqrt{x}$ as the correction factor (which seems to be common among many teachers) where x is the original grade and $f(x)$ is the improved one. Thus, for example, if a student were originally entitled to 64, the improved grade using this factor would be $10\sqrt{64}$, or 80. This "real life" situation opens up several important questions for students: Will this correction factor improve the grades of all students? Will some students gain more than others, and if so, is the correction "fair"—namely, *who* gains more? Is this a correction factor you would choose, or can you think of another preferable one? Answering these relevant questions necessitates algebra, in the broadest sense of the term, namely, using symbols, the concept of function and its graphical representations, and solving inequalities.

In order to gain an intuitive feeling for how this correction factor works, we can begin its exploration by trying different grades. In general, one can see that the new grades are greater, except for the two extreme cases of 0 and 100. However, how can we be sure that this is indeed true? Is it possible that for some grades the correction factor results in a lower grade? Can we have a general confirmation that our correction factor increases all grades in the range 0–100? Interestingly, some students suggest that this is true because the function $(f(x) = 10\sqrt{x})$ is increasing. This is an interesting confusion triggered by the use of language, particularly, the verb *increase*. How can one dispel this confusion? We can begin by posing counterexamples: $f(x) = x^2/100$ is an increasing function. However, with this correction factor, grades in the 0–100 range decrease. Another even more straightforward example would be $f(x) = 0.5x$. Analyzing the counterexamples leads to revisiting the definition of an increasing function, $x_2 > x_1 \Rightarrow f(x_2) > f(x_1)$, and to noticing that this definition does not say anything about either $f(x_2) > x_2$ or $f(x_2) < x_2$. Thus, what kind of comparison do we need to perform in order to answer our question? We need to compare the value of the dependent variable against the value of the independent variable. Or, in terms of the problem situation, we need to compare the corrected grade with the uncorrected one. We may write the function for the uncorrected grade, which is the "simplest" of all the functions, the identity $g(x) = x$, and then compare $f(x)$ and $g(x)$. This straightforward step may not be easy for students for two reasons. First, it is inspired by the goal of having two functions to compare that require knowledge of the tools to do such a comparison and is highly dependent on the curriculum trajectory from which they come. Second, $g(x) = x$ may be symbolically the simplest function, but it is not necessarily conceptually easy, especially when it comes to modeling a situation, here the uncorrected factor. Once this stage is overcome, one can draw the juxtaposed graphs of the uncorrected and the corrected grades (as shown in fig. 3.3).

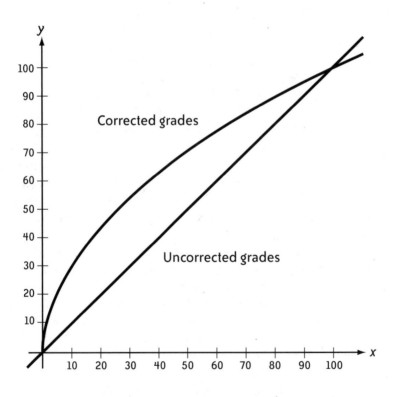

Fig. 3.3. Graphs of $f(x) = 10\sqrt{x}$ and $f(x) = x$

The graphs show that in the 0–100 range, the corrected grade is always "above" the uncorrected one (the identity function). They also show more than that. For example, if for any reason the examination had a bonus question, which could have led to grades above 100, this correction factor will decrease those original grades that were above 100. The graphs also show that the increase is different for different grades and that the lower and middle grades benefit more. In order to inspect this issue further, one can, for example, explore the difference function $h(x) = 10\sqrt{x} - x$.

Some students may approach this problem only symbolically by posing the inequality $10\sqrt{x} < x$. If they are familiar with this type of inequality, they can solve and find that the corrected grade is lower than the uncorrected only outside the 0–100 range. However, unlike the graphical representation, this solution does not yield much information about the differences between the two grades. Such an explicit comparison of solutions emerging from two different representations helps students to learn about the distinct characteristics—advantages and disadvantages—of the mathematical tools (e.g., representations) at their disposal.

The symbolic nature of this correction factor is interesting to explore further. If examined closely, one realizes that the corrected grade $10\sqrt{x}$ is the geometric mean between the uncorrected grade and 100. Since the mean of two numbers is always between them, in the 0–100 range the correction will always increase the original grade. Knowing that the geometric mean is always less than the arithmetic mean can also lead us to establish the nature of the correction: it will increase the original grade but will never reach half the difference between the original grade and 100 (the arithmetic mean). This would inspire the creation of another, more generous correction factor: the arithmetic mean between the uncorrected grade and 100. The exploration of this new factor and its reduced symbolic expression, $t(x) = 0.5x + 50$, yields interesting insights, can generate lively discussions, and can inspire students to design and then create and explore yet other correction factors of their own. They could also explore, for example, who would prefer which factor and why.

This example shows how a situation that arose from outside the mathematics teaching context can be harnessed to illustrate how an algebraic model, through its symbolic and graphical representations, can help us understand a real-life situation, answer relevant questions, make decisions, and propose new approaches (e.g., new correction factors).

Epilogue

The four examples described above illustrate a spectrum of tasks and problems aimed at sharing with students the purpose of learning algebra, its potential, and the possibility to harness its power to our own advantage. The spectrum represents different algebraic themes, such as the following:

- *Generalizing without symbols*: informal prealgebra, in which properties of numbers and operations are generalized through a large number of examples

- *Solving equations and making sense of their solutions*: variables or unknowns are used to derive expressions (equations) that express relationships that solve a problem

- *Exercising algebraic rules*: syntactic rules are applied, reflected on, and related to justification and proof

- *Building models and learning from them*: symbolic and graphic models are used in order to better understand a real-life situation

In the examples presented, we also showed how certain types of tasks and problems may encourage students to create their own significant pieces of mathematics (e.g., to invent a new magician's trick, to propose a new strategy for finger calculation, to design a new correction factor tailored to what one would like) and to test and explore those creations. This kind of creativity is seldom experienced in algebra classrooms and can have an impact on students' sense of purpose, ownership, and intimacy with what they learn and produce.

There are studies focusing on the learning processes of algebra beginners working on specific tasks designed to experience the need for algebra (e.g., Arcavi 1995) and how such a need results in meaningful engagement with the content. More work in these directions is needed in order both to enhance existing curricula and to guide the development of new ones, explicitly and coherently sharing with students the purposes and nature of algebra. This is important for *all* students, and certainly for those alienated by algebra who usually perceive it as an esoteric endeavor far removed from common sense, let alone from their daily lives. It is important also for those who manage to "survive" algebra but come out of their instruction with a bitter taste. And it is important for those who succeed at mathematics and make it the career of their choice. They may find out later in their professional life that instruction at school failed to share with them the essence of the trade and that they had to struggle to develop it by themselves. As an example, consider a mathematician's acknowledgment of his annoyance when he explicitly realized that, for example, problem-solving strategies "had not been mentioned [by formal instruction] at any time during my academic career" (Schoenfeld 1985, p. xi).

And this brings us back to Augustus De Morgan. It is precisely on the value of mathematics education for all that he so vehemently asserted: "It is admitted by all that a finished or even a competent reasoner is not the work of nature alone: the experience of every day makes it evident that education develops faculties which would otherwise never have manifested their existence. It is, therefore, as necessary *to learn to reason* before we can expect to be able to reason, as it is to learn to swim or fence, in order to attain either of those arts" (De Morgan 1898, p.7).

REFERENCES

Ainley, Janet, Liz Bills, and Kirsty Wilson. "Designing Spreadsheet-Based Tasks for Purposeful Algebra." *International Journal of Computers for Mathematical Learning* 10 (December 2005): 191–215.

American Association for the Advancement of Science. *Project 2061.* www.project2061. org/.

Arcavi, Abraham. "Symbol Sense: Informal Sense Making in Formal Mathematics." *For the Learning of Mathematics* 14 (November 1994): 24–35.

———. "Teaching and Learning Algebra: Past, Present and Future." *Journal of Mathematical Behavior* 14 (March 1995): 145–62.

———. "The Everyday and the Academic in Mathematics." In *Everyday and Academic Mathematics in the Classroom,* Monograph No. 11 of the *Journal for Research in Mathematics Education,* edited by Mary E. Brenner and Judit N. Moschkovich, pp. 12–29. Reston, Va.: National Council of Teachers of Mathematics, 2002.

De Morgan, Augustus. *Study and Difficulties of Mathematics.* Chicago: Open Court Publishing Co., 1898.

———. *A Budget of Paradoxes.* 2nd ed., edited by David Eugene Smith. London: Open Court Publishing Co., 1915.

Koblitz, Neal. "Mathematics as Propaganda." In *Mathematics: People, Problems, Results,* edited by Douglas M. Campbell and John C. Higgins, vol. 3, pp. 248–54. Belmont, Calif.: Wadsworth International, 1984.

Lannin, John, David Barker, and Brian Townsend. "Why, Why Should I Justify?" *Mathematics Teaching in the Middle School* 11 (May 2006): 438–43.

Moses, Robert P., and Charles E. Cobb, Jr. *Radical Equations: Math Literacy and Civil Rights.* Boston: Beacon Press, 2001.

Polya, George. *How to Solve It.* Princeton, N.J.: Princeton University Press, 1971.

Rachlin, Sidney L., Annette N. Matsumoto, and Li Ann T. Wada. *Algebra I: A Process Approach.* Honolulu: University of Hawaii, 1992.

Schoenfeld, Alan H. *Mathematical Problem Solving.* Orlando, Fla.: Academic Press, 1985.

Smith, David Eugene. *History of Mathematics.* Vol. 2, *Special Topics of Elementary Mathematics.* Reprint. New York: Dover Publications, 1958.

4

Introducing Extensible Tools in High School Algebra

Al Cuoco

ELEMENTARY algebra, developed either in a formal first-year algebra course or in a program that develops several mathematical strands at once, is where students are introduced to topics that will dominate high school mathematics. It is also the locus for formalizing previous experiences and for developing tools that allow one to solve equations, calculate with algebraic expressions, graph equations, and model situations with mathematical functions. The methods beginners learn and the habits they develop should serve them well as they progress into more advanced corners of a discipline. The tools learned in elementary courses should be extensible, so that they can be refined to handle the subtleties and technicalities that arise later. These claims are based on the stance that a mathematical discipline like algebra, more than its collection of results, *is* the collage of methods and habits of mind used by its practitioners (see Cuoco, Goldenberg, and Mark 1996; Cuoco 1998; and Cuoco 2005a for more about habits of mind in mathematics). If we grant this premise, it follows that students in elementary algebra should learn to solve the problems, do the calculations, and build the whole edifice of topics they will master, using algebraic tools and habits of mind that fit into the larger landscape of algebra as it has evolved into a modern scientific discipline (Bashmakova and Rudakov 1995; Kleiner 2005). All too often, this is not what happens. When I taught algebra, popular texts, curricula, and the traditions that live in the folklore of algebra teaching were full of ad hoc methods and techniques that might work locally but had little or no application after the article at hand was finished. Veteran algebra teachers will recognize—

- the "box" method for setting up word problems that works only for problems designed to yield to it;

This article is dedicated to the memory of Jim Kaput, 1942–2005.

- the "$y = mx + b$," "point-slope," and other rote methods for graphing (or finding equations) that work only for lines;
- the factoring and expanding methods, like FOIL, that work only for quadratic polynomials.

These and many other methods have no counterpart in mathematics outside of secondary school. Furthermore, they are extremely inefficient. Students need to *unlearn* them when they have to solve problems that don't fit the constraints of the methods.

The purpose of this paper is to describe some general-purpose tools and approaches that can be introduced in elementary algebra and that can be extended as students gain mathematical sophistication. These tools are based on an analysis of the habits of mind used by algebraists, on the classroom experiences of many middle and high school teachers, and on some epistemological theories about how algebraic ideas develop. They are being implemented by my colleagues and me as part of a four-year high school curriculum (Education Development Center, forthcoming.)

By *tools*, I mean methods for carrying out many of the basic tasks in elementary algebra—things like solving equations and transforming polynomials. The tools I describe are *general-purpose* ones. By this, I mean that the tools

- *have staying power*—they can be used well beyond the topics in elementary algebra;
- *are extensible*—they can be modified to handle a wide array of mathematical situations;
- *are ubiquitous in the discipline*—they are "tools of the trade" for mathematicians and mathematics professionals; and
- *are embedded in the culture of mathematics*—they seem obvious and often go unnoticed.

In fact, as the paper develops, I'll justify a stronger claim. Methods like the ones presented here not only are effective for helping students solve problems in elementary and, eventually, more advanced algebra but also dovetail with the style of work used by algebraists and others who use algebra in their work. This style of work centers on several uses of abstraction as applied to numerical and algebraic calculations:

- to find and exploit regularity in calculations in order to construct generic algorithms;
- to associate an algebraic equation with a geometric object (and vice versa);
- to group pieces of an expression, thinking of them as single "chunks," in order to reduce a calculation to one already understood.

Modeling Situations with Equations

The difficulties that high school students have with algebra word problems are legendary, and the quintessential word problem ("Mary is 10 years older than her brother was 5 years ago...") is the butt of many cartoons and jokes. Teachers have devoted a great deal of effort to exposing the roots of the difficulties people have with such problems. Two very common perceptions are that students have difficulty with word problems because

- they have a general difficulty reading, and
- they are not familiar with the contexts described in the problems.

But an analysis by some middle and high school teachers in Woburn, Massachusetts, showed that there's got to be more to it (Cuoco 1993). They observed that the following problem causes no difficulty with prealgebra students who understand the connections among rate, time, and distance.

> Mary drives from Boston to Washington, a trip of 500 miles. If she travels at an average rate of 60 mph on the way down and 50 mph on the way back, how many hours does her trip take?

But the next problem is baffling to many of the same students a year later in algebra class.

> Mary drives from Boston to Washington, and she travels at an average rate of 60 mph on the way down and 50 mph on the way back. If the total trip takes $18\frac{2}{3}$ hours, how far is Boston from Washington?

This analysis led to an effective method, one that we call Guess-Check-Generalize, for solving these kinds of problems. Essentially, it exploits students' abilities to solve the prealgebra problem to help them construct "the equation" whose solution settles the algebra problem. Here's how it works for the second problem above. The first step is to guess at an answer; suppose Boston is 500 miles from Washington. The purpose of the guess is *not* to stumble onto a right answer. Rather, it is to focus on the steps one takes to check the guess (in spite of our proclamations that the point is not to get the right answer by guessing, many students are at first reluctant to take a guess, fearing they'll be incorrect). So, if the guess is 500 miles, then Mary takes $\frac{500}{60} = 8\frac{1}{3}$ hours to drive down and $\frac{500}{50} = 10$ hours to get home. The total trip is $18\frac{1}{3}$ hours, so 500 is not the right answer, but we have begun to construct an algorithm for checking *any* guess. We ask students to be explicit about what they did to check the guess. If they are not sure, they take another guess, and another, and another, until they are able to articulate something like "You take the guess, divide it by 60, then divide it by 50, add your answers and see if you get $18\frac{2}{3}$." The generic "guess checker" is then

$$\frac{\text{guess}}{60} + \frac{\text{guess}}{50} = 18\frac{2}{3}.$$

This gives them the equation that models the problem:

$$\frac{x}{60} + \frac{x}{50} = 18\frac{2}{3}.$$

From here, many students have no trouble finding the solution.

This method was hatched by a group of middle and high school teachers, inspired by their classroom experiences and by two other sources:

> Education researchers have built on the work of Piaget, creating an epistemological theory of encapsulation that describes how learners use abstraction to reify isolated actions (calculations, in our example) into coherent processes (here, algorithms) (Breidenbach et al. 1992; Sfard 1991; Sfard and Linchevski 1994).

> Many highly theoretical investigations in algebra begin with a careful analysis of patterns that emerge from repeated calculations, leading to functions defined by algorithms. For example, the classical theory of equations that leads to Galois's theory is concerned with developing algorithms that can be applied to polynomial equations in order to find their roots, and the inspiration for these algorithms comes from abstracting off the general principles (like the connection between roots and coefficients) involved in solving specific equations.

The Guess-Check-Generalize tool captures a very common habit that is useful throughout algebra: carry out several concrete examples of a process that you don't quite "have in your head" in order to find regularity and to build a generic algorithm that describes every instance of the calculation. It is also extensible. The encapsulation spiral is infinite in both directions so that the algorithms can eventually be encapsulated into objects in their own right and passed off to "higher order" operators like function composition, the derivative, and the difference operator (Cuoco 1995).

Graphing Equations

Many years ago, I was working with a group of high school seniors as they graphed conics. They seemed to be on top of the ideas. I would give them equations, and they would produce nearly perfect graphs. I'd give them conics, and they could find the equations and put them in normal form. So, if given $9x^2 - 36x + 4y^2 + 24y + 36 = 0$, the students could transform this into

$$\frac{(x-2)^2}{4} + \frac{(y+3)^2}{9} = 1$$

and produce a picture-perfect ellipse. It seemed to me that all was well. But as I walked around the room, I asked what I thought was a simple question: I gave students the coordinates of a point that looked like it might be on the ellipse, like (3, 5.6), and asked if it really *was* on the graph. Student after student had no idea how to tell. These young people—and, it turns out, many others—did not understand the fact that one can test a point to see if it is on the graph of an equation by seeing if its coordinates satisfy the equation. Equations are, for these students, a kind of code from which one can read off information that allows one to produce a graph. One approach to this phenomenon is to provide students with opportunities to connect equations and graphs without elaborate formalisms, using the idea that the equation of a graph is the *point tester* for the graph in the sense that it tells us whether or not a point is on the graph by checking some numerical fact about its coordinates. For example, suppose we want the equation of the horizontal line that passes through (5,1). Students typically have no trouble drawing the line, and when given several points, they usually have no trouble explaining why each is on or off the line. To see if a point is on the line, check to see if its y-coordinate is 1. So, the point-tester is $y = 1$, and the equation is $y = 1$.

Another example: What's the equation of the line whose graph bisects quadrants 1 and 3? The check is to see if a point is on the line and that its coordinates are the same. The equation is thus $y = x$. These are simple examples, but they reinforce the meaning of the correspondence between equations and their graphs. And the point-tester idea works well for more complex equations and their graphs. It is a general-purpose tool that can be used throughout mathematics. In first-year algebra, the point-tester idea helps students find equations for lines. The method involves a somewhat unorthodox approach to slope. "The slope of a line" approach to graphing linear equations places some undue cognitive demands on students. Students are asked to think about a number (slope) that is an invariant of an infinite geometric object (the line). This is difficult for at least two reasons:

1. The invariant is not part of the geometric object itself. Rather, it is a numerical quantity derived from the geometry of the line (indeed, the slope of a line is an example of the *derivative*, which students will study in calculus).

2. It is derived by means of a calculation that seems at first glance to depend on a *choice* of two points on the line.

Another approach starts with the more concrete idea of "slope between two points" (we use the notation $m(A, B)$ for the slope between A and B) as a number that can be calculated directly from coordinates. This approach to equations for lines synthesizes this perspective on slope with the point-tester and the Guess-Check-Generalize ideas. Students make an explicit assumption (which can be supported by experimentation and proved in a geometry course when they study similar triangles):

> **Assumption:** Three points A, B, and C lie on the same line if and only if $m(A, B) = m(B, C)$.

Suppose you are given two points, say, $A = (3, -1)$ and $B = (5, 3)$. What is the equation of the line that contains A and B? Students develop the habit of checking several points to see if they are on the line, *keeping track of their steps* (the encapsulation theme again). At first, they are given some points to check, say, $X = (7, 6)$, $P = (1, -5)$, and $Q = (9.5, 10.5)$. In each instance, they check the slope between the point to be tested and, say, B, and they see if it is equal to $m(A, B)$ (that is, 2). The generic check is that the slope from (x, y) to $(5, 3)$ should equal 2, so the point-tester is

$$\frac{y - 3}{x - 5} = 2.$$

This equation (some care has to be taken with the fact that x can't be 5 on the left-hand side of this equation) is then simplified and transformed into a linear equation in x and y. *After* this foundation is solid, students can develop robust fluency in sketching lines from their equations and finding equations for given lines.

The point-tester method will serve students well as they progress through high school and beyond. They can use it to analyze conics (the original context in which I noticed the obstacle) and more general curves defined by algebraic equations in two variables. Indeed, when this correspondence between curves and equations (by means of coordinates of points) is established, one can make sense of ideas from algebraic geometry and number theory. For example, finding primitive Pythagorean triples is equivalent to finding rational points on the graph of $x^2 + y^2 = 1$ (Cuoco 2005b). A method (general-purpose in its own right) for finding such points is to take a line with rational slope through a rational point on the graph, say, $(0, -1)$, and to find its other intersection point with the circle. The reasoning that this second intersection point must have rational coordinates—and that all rational points on the circle are obtained in this way—is classical algebraic thinking that makes basic use of the point-tester and encapsulation habits. For example, here is a problem (with answers attached) from a later course in advanced algebra from the CME Project (Education Development Center, forthcoming):

Here's the unit circle and a line that passes through $(0, -1)$. (See fig. 4.1.)

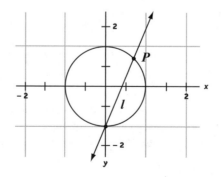

Figure 4.1

Find the coordinates of P if the slope of l is

1. 1   ans: $(1, 0)$

2. 2   ans: $\left(\dfrac{4}{5}, \dfrac{3}{5}\right)$

3. $\dfrac{3}{2}$ ans: $\left(\dfrac{12}{13}, \dfrac{5}{3}\right)$

4. 4   ans: $\left(\dfrac{8}{17}, \dfrac{15}{17}\right)$

5. $\dfrac{6}{5}$ ans: $\left(\dfrac{60}{61}, \dfrac{11}{61}\right)$

6. $\dfrac{r}{s}$ ans: $\left(\dfrac{2rs}{r^2 + s^2}, \dfrac{r^2 - s^2}{r^2 + s^2}\right)$

The ideas here extend to some basic notions used in the analysis of elliptic curves (see Koblitz 1993 for more on this). Applications of these ideas to optimization problems are described by Suzuki (2005).

Factoring Polynomials

It's likely that factoring quadratic polynomials is the target of more special-purpose techniques than any other topic in elementary algebra. Some years ago when national reports and organizations (National Council of Teachers of Mathematics [NCTM] 1989, 2000; U.S. Department of Education 1995) called for reduced attention to these techniques, many teachers welcomed the idea, knowing that the time spent on mastering this or that quadratic factoring method had little payoff later on. This doesn't mean that *factoring* should receive reduced emphasis. Indeed, polynomial algebra sits at the historical core of algebra, and it plays a central role in current research. Even in elementary algebra, factoring can have applications in the context of solving equations, so that students begin to develop the correspondence between roots of a polynomial equation and linear factors of the polynomial, a correspondence that holds over any algebraic system in which the product of nonzero elements is nonzero. Some factoring methods that can be introduced in elementary algebra *are* extensible, preview important ideas, and give students a chance to develop the habits of reasoning about calculations in algebraic structures and transforming a calculation in an invertible way to one that is easier to carry out. Factoring a quadratic polynomial $x^2 + bx + c$ (with leading coefficient 1) amounts to finding numbers α and β such that $\alpha + \beta = b$ and $\alpha\beta = c$. This "sum-product" approach is important for at least three reasons:

- Algebra teachers (in the field tests of the CME Project [Education Development Center, forthcoming], for example) report that students understand the method and can get up to speed with it in one or two class periods. The method can be used later to derive the quadratic formula, and it helps students interpret the *form* of the expressions that result from applying the quadratic formula to the general equation $ax^2 + bx + c = 0$, whose roots are then

$$\gamma = \frac{-b + \sqrt{b^2 - 4ac}}{2a} \text{ or } \delta = \frac{-b - \sqrt{b^2 - 4ac}}{2a}.$$

- This method previews a much more general correspondence between the coefficients of a polynomial equation and the symmetric functions of its roots, a correspondence that finds utility in all parts of algebra and its applications (see Barbeau 1989; Cuoco 2005b; Graham, Knuth, and Patashnik 1989; and Wilf 1994 for some of these applications).

Many students who can factor monic (leading coefficient of 1) quadratics by the sum-product approach often have much more difficulty when the leading coefficient is not 1. One approach here is to use the correspondence between roots and factors and to employ the quadratic formula. That is, to factor a quadratic polynomial, set it equal to 0, use the quadratic formula to find the roots, and then reconstruct the factors from the roots. This method is certainly efficient, but it involves a fair amount of computational overhead. It also depends on the existence of a formula for solving the equation—something that doesn't exist for degrees higher than 4 and something that is not usually developed in elementary algebra until near the end of the course. Here again, there are general-purpose methods that live on beyond their utility for developing this particular skill. One such method starts with the observation that $4x^2 + 36x + 45$ can more easily be factored if one "chunks" the terms and writes it as $(2x)^2 + 18(2x) + 45$. One can think of this as a "quadratic in $2x$," thinking of $2x$ as the variable. One can even replace $2x$ by some symbol, say, z, and write the quadratic as $z^2 + 18z + 45$, which factors by the sum-product method: $(z + 15)(z + 3)$. Replacing z by $2x$ gives the factorization of the original quadratic.

The coefficients in our example were especially suited for this technique. What if we are faced with something like $6x^2 + 11x - 10$? One can reason like this:

1. Multiply the polynomial by 6 to make the leading coefficient a perfect square, remembering that we have to divide by 6 at some point to get back to where we started: $6(6x^2 + 11x - 10) = 36x^2 + 11 \cdot 6x - 60$.

2. This is a quadratic in $6x$; let $z = 6x$, so the right-hand side becomes monic: $z^2 + 11z - 60$.

3. This factors by the sum-product method: $(z + 15)(z - 4)$

4. But $z = 6x$, so we have $(6x + 15)(6x - 4)$

5. Factor out common factors: 3 from the first binomial and 2 from the second, producing $6(2x + 5)(3x - 2)$.

6. Dividing by 6 gives the factorization of the original polynomial.

We call this the *scaling method* for factoring nonmonic polynomials. It has the benefit of reducing a complicated problem to one that is simpler to solve. It is also a general-purpose tool that can be applied to scale a polynomial of any degree so that the transformed polynomial has leading coefficient of 1. For cubics, one scales by the *square* of the leading coefficient. In general, if

$$f(x) = a_n x^n + a_{n-1} x^{n-1} + \dots + a_1 x + a_0,$$

then

$$a_n x^{n-1} f(x) = (a_n x)^n + a_{n-1}(a_n x)^{n-1} + \dots + a_n x^{n-2} a_1 (a_n x) + a_n x^{n-1} a_0.$$

Letting $z = a_n x$, we have a monic polynomial in z.

The scaling method is just one tool in an extensive toolbox—the theory of *transformations of equations*—that can be used to turn polynomial equations into certain canonical forms that might be easier to solve. The theory contains methods for removing terms of an equation by linear substitutions (a generalization of "completing the square") as well as tools for finding equations whose roots are reciprocals, negatives, or even powers of the roots of a given equation (Cuoco 1999). All this leads directly to ideas studied in undergraduate algebra courses, to classical results like Cardano's formula for the solution of cubic equations, to Galois's theory, and to more modern areas such as computational algebra (the mathematics behind computer algebra systems) and algebraic number theory.

Designing Extensible Tools

How does one design or identify general-purpose and *extensible* tools like the ones described in this article? How can such tools find their way into the mainstream of middle and high school classrooms? These difficult and perceptive questions were suggested by the editorial panel of this yearbook. One way to think about them gets right to the heart of the culture of teaching mathematics at all levels. The design of extensible tools that can be used in secondary school mathematics but that have the staying power necessary for applications throughout mathematics is an ideal project for collaborative groups of secondary school teachers, mathematics educators, and professional mathematicians. The expertise and experience needed to understand the subtleties of the secondary school curriculum (including the places where many students stumble), to know the way ideas in this curriculum connect to core mathematical themes in more advanced mathematics, and to recognize the kinds of tools one can introduce early and polish over the years is dispersed over the whole mathematical community. The culture of teaching in the United States and in many other countries, however, works against such collaborations. I conjecture that the mutual isolation among mathematicians, teachers, and education researchers is one of the root causes for the emergence of ad hoc methods like the ones described in the introduction to this article. Here are four examples of collaborations that show what is possible when different parts of the mathematical community work together:

The Park City Mathematics Institute (PCMI) (www.admin.ias.edu/ma/) has been in existence since 1991. PCMI is one of the most prominent examples in the United States of a program that brings together many parts of the mathematics community. Mathematicians, graduate students, undergraduates, undergraduate faculty, education researchers, and secondary school teachers spend three weeks together each summer around a focused mathematical theme. A central component of the Secondary School Teachers Program—and one that routinely gets extremely positive reviews—is a two-hour mathematics class each morning that is developed by a team of mathematicians, educators, and practicing teachers. One example of how ideas percolate from such a collaboration occurred when a mathematician participant at PCMI became intrigued with the innovative ways in which the two instructors (both secondary school teachers) were using interactive geometry environments. Together, the mathematician and the teachers devised some sketches that extended the ideas in the morning course from Euclidean to hyperbolic geometry.

Focus on Mathematics (www.focusonmath.org) is an NSF-supported partnership of teachers, mathematicians, and educators in the Boston area. Centered at Boston University, one component of the partnership is a collection of about twenty study groups of teachers and mathematicians that meet regularly after school in the partnership districts to work on mathematical problems. These collaborations have resulted in joint presentations at national meetings of the NCTM, the Mathematical Association of America, and the American Mathematical Society; articles published in NCTM journals (Sinwell 2004; Olsen 2006); and the introduction of general-purpose tools into the high school programs in the partnership—tools from differential calculus, from generating functions and formal algebra, and from linear algebra. In addition to the study groups, the partnership sponsors other collaborations. One that is especially germane to this discussion is a committee formed of mathematicians, educators, and teachers, charged with the task of analyzing the difficulties students have across the partnership with ideas surrounding the notion of linearity. The committee produced an analysis that is a synthesis of mathematics, pedagogy, and research, and its next task is to develop curricular interventions—tools for understanding and using linearity—based on its findings.

The **Regional Institute for Research in Education (IRRE)** in Venice (www.irre.veneto.it/), funded by the Italian Ministry of Education, has been active for more than twenty years and is dedicated to the improvement of all aspects of precollege education—all grades and all disciplines—through research in education and special in-service initiatives. In mathematics, IRRE profits from a long-standing collaboration with the mathematics department at the University of Padova. Each year, a group of fifteen to twenty expert and devoted high school teachers are selected by IRRE and invited to meet monthly at the university to discuss mathematical topics relating to the precollege curriculum. The community sponsors one-day conferences on school mathematics (the 2006 meeting was attended by

400 high school teachers), and it produces monographs and books, with articles jointly authored by teachers and university faculty. A recent volume (Millevoi, Motteran, and Scimemi 2006) takes up the question of *approximation* across the grades and contains articles that develop many methods and approaches that can be started early and carried through the grades.

The **Institute for Mathematics and Education at the University of Arizona** (ime.math.arizona.edu) builds collaborations among mathematicians, educators, and teachers aimed at making concrete improvements in mathematics education. Its current projects include (1) increasing the capacity of universities to furnish content-based professional development for teachers, (2) offering policy seminars for mathematical scientists and business people interested in making contributions in mathematics education, and (3) collaborating on the analysis of curriculum materials.

These are just some examples of the kinds of collaboration that can help introduce and sustain general-purpose tools in secondary school mathematics.

Conclusion

Most of the tools presented in this article were conceived by collaborations such as the ones described in the previous section. They are examples of approaches to topics in elementary algebra that can be developed through general-purpose methods that have applications throughout mathematics. The use of approaches like these is an effective way to bring coherence to precollege mathematics, to place the topics we teach in the larger mathematical landscape, to prepare students for the more formal aspects of mathematics that have evolved over the centuries, and to help students see one of the most wonderful features of our discipline: that starting with a very few simple and extensible ideas, one can produce intricate and highly textured results and theories of great beauty and enormous utility.

REFERENCES

Barbeau, Ed. *Polynomials.* New York: Springer Verlag, 1989.

Bashmakova, Izabella G., and Alexei N. Rudakov. "The Evolution of Algebra 1800–1870." *American Mathematical Monthly* 102 (March 1995): 266–70.

Breidenbach, Daniel, Ed Dubinsky, Julie Hawks, and Devilyna Nichols. "Development of the Process Conception of Function." *Educational Studies in Mathematics* 23 (June 1992): 247–85.

Cuoco, Al. "Action to Process: Constructing Functions from Algebra Word Problems." *Intelligent Tutoring Media* 4 (March/April 1993): 117–27.

———. "Computational Media to Support the Learning and Use of Functions." In *Computers and Exploratory Learning,* edited by Andrea diSessa and others, pp. 79–108. New York: Springer Verlag, 1995.

————. "Mathematics as a Way of Thinking about Things." In *High School Mathematics at Work: Essays and Examples for the Education of All Students,* edited by Mathematical Sciences Education Board, National Research Council, pp. 102–6. Washington, D.C.: National Academy Press, 1998.

————. "Raising the Roots." *Mathematics Magazine* 72 (December 1999): 377–83.

————. "Advanced Algebra in High School: Beyond Representation." In *Developing Students' Algebraic Reasoning Abilities,* edited by Carole Greenes and Carol Findell, pp. 46–60. Boston and Denver, Colo.: Houghton Mifflin and National Council of Supervisors of Mathematics, 2005a.

————. *Mathematical Connections: A Companion for Teachers and Others.* Washington, D.C.: Mathematical Association of America, 2005b.

Cuoco, Al, Paul Goldenberg, and June Mark. "Habits of Mind: An Organizing Principle for Mathematics Curriculum Development." *Journal of Mathematical Behavior* 15 (December 1996): 375–402.

Education Development Center (EDC). *The CME Project.* A Comprehensive High School Program Funded by NSF Grant ESI 02 42476. Upper Saddle River, N.J.: Pearson Education, forthcoming.

Graham, Ronald, Donald Knuth, and Oren Patashnik. *Concrete Mathematics.* Reading, Mass.: Addison-Wesley Publishing Co., 1989.

Kleiner, Israel. "The Roots of Commutative Algebra in Algebraic Number Theory." *Mathematics Magazine* 68 (February 2005): 3–14.

Koblitz, Neal. *Introduction to Elliptic Curves and Modular Forms.* New York: Springer Verlag, 1993.

Millevoi, Tomaso, Margherita Motteran, and Benedetto Scimemi. *L'Approssimazione nella Didattica della Matematica.* Milan: Ghisetti e Corvi, 2006.

National Council of Teachers of Mathematics (NCTM). *Curriculum and Evaluation Standards for School Mathematics.* Reston, Va.: NCTM, 1989.

————. *Principles and Standards for School Mathematics.* Reston, Va.: NCTM, 2000.

Olsen, Allen. "Delving Deeper: Divisibility Tests." *Mathematics Teacher* 100 (August 2006): 46–52.

Sfard, Anna. "On the Dual Nature of Mathematical Conceptions: Reflections on Processes and Objects as Different Sides of the Same Coin." *Educational Studies in Mathematics* 22 (February 1991): 1–36.

Sfard, Anna, and Liora Linchevski. "The Gains and the Pitfalls of Reification—the Case of Algebra." *Educational Studies in Mathematics* 26 (March 1994): 191–228.

Sinwell, Benjamin. "The Chebyshev Polynomials: Patterns and Derivation." *Mathematics Teacher* 98 (August 2004): 20–25.

Suzuki, Jeff. "The Lost Calculus (1637–1670): Tangency and Optimization without Limits." *Mathematics Magazine* 78 (December 2005): 339–53.

U.S. Department of Education. *The Algebra Initiative Colloquium.* Washington, D.C.: U.S. Department of Education, 1995.

Wilf, Herbert S. *Generatingfunctionology.* 2nd ed. Boston: Academic Press, 1994.

5

Algebra: The Mathematics and the Pedagogy

Mark Saul

W HY IS algebra so difficult to learn? What is it about the subject that students find challenging? These are questions that face novice teachers of mathematics almost as soon as they arrive in the classroom. As teachers accrue experience in their practice, new questions emerge. What are the rough patches in a course on algebra? What makes these particular parts of the subject difficult? What might help students over these spots? Answers to these questions can focus teachers' inquiry in support of their students.

What Is Difficult about Algebra?

This paper concerns one way to analyze some of the difficulties in algebra stemming from the content itself. The work described is a result of collaborative discussion among teachers, researchers in mathematics education, and mathematicians. One of the themes of this paper is the power brought to problems of education when these three points of view—those of teachers, researchers, and mathematicians—are combined.

With respect to mathematical content, we can distinguish three ways of looking at the phenomenon of algebra: as a generalization of arithmetic, as the study of binary operations, and as the study of the field of rational expressions and related fields. The analysis is of the content, but the utility of this way to describe the content arises from the classroom. Examining the content in this way can explain some difficulties students have with algebra and help us resolve them. The last part of the paper describes some examples of this possibility.

It gives me pleasure to acknowledge the contributions, direct or indirect, to this article made by the following people: Richard Askey, Hyman Bass, Daniel Biss, Thomas Carpenter, Albert Cuoco, Ed Dubinsky, Carolyn Kieran, Ralph Raimi, Yoram Sagher, and Chi Han Sah.

The motivation for the discussion is a set of vignettes that lead to general observations about the nature of algebra and why it is difficult. Of course, the novice teacher may not easily be able to distinguish, in the living classroom, the patterns brought out here. Work in a real classroom does not organize itself so neatly.

Just as we cannot reconstruct a solid object simply from our knowledge of one of its projections, any analysis of teaching and learning from a single point of view cannot capture all the subtleties of the situation. In this article, three milestones in the learning of algebra are described. These occur in almost every classroom, but they are not always consciously noted. For a related view of this field, see Sfard (1995), who distinguishes three slightly different milestones. Sfard's discussion uses a historical background to present insights into learning. Although the following discussion draws on the history of the subject as part of the exposition, the focus is not Sfard's. Here a mathematical background is used to offer insights into teaching. For more on the field, see Kieran (in press).

What Algebra Is Not

Andrei is an average student beginning the seventh grade. He can solve simple linear equations, such as $2x - 3 = 17$. He does this by replacing the variable with values until he finds one that works. He knows that 4 is too small because $2 \times 4 - 3$ is only 5, and he needs 17. He knows that 30 is too big because $2 \times 30 - 3 = 57$, and he needs only 17. (I'm exaggerating: Andrei can typically get much closer with his guesses.) Giving x larger or smaller values as needed, Andrei quickly comes to a solution. He can recognize when he has arrived at a solution. But Andrei cannot solve the equation $2.3x - 3.02 = 17.83$ in the same way. He cannot even solve $3x - 3 = 17$ in the same way. However, given a number, he can tell whether or not it is a solution to either of these equations.

There are students like Andrei in many grades. He might be a ninth- or tenth-grade student who "got by" in first-year algebra but doesn't understand what he's studied. So now he is struggling in a more advanced course. Many remedial students, some much older than Andrei, have just the same difficulties.

Andrei's confusion tells us much about what algebra is not. Algebra is not the study of variables. Andrei knows how to use the variable x. He knows that the statement $2x - 3 = 11$ is true when $x = 7$ and false when $x = 5$. We can be sure that he knows this because he can use arithmetic to generate the statements that result from x taking on specific values.

Indeed, we use variables very often in the early grades in posing problems that are completely arithmetic rather than algebraic. The second-grade teacher who asks, "*What* + 7 = 12?" is using the word *what* as a variable. Students often work these problems by substituting for *what* in the same way that Andrei substitutes for *x*. And just as Andrei would not substitute *elephant* for *x,* younger students would not make an inappropriate substitution for *what.*

Algebra is also not the study of functions. Andrei has good intuitive ideas about the function $f(x) = 2x - 3$. He knows that $f(x)$ increases as x increases and that if x takes a value between 10 and 20, $f(x)$ will take a value between 17 and 37. These are all properties, essentially analytic properties, of a function, not of an equation.

It is important to see that the function concept is pedagogically and mathematically separate and distinct from the learning of algebra. We use algebra to represent functions. But we also use geometry when we draw graphs. And we use natural language. We even have functions such as random variables, whose values cannot be easily recorded algebraically.

Algebra does help us describe and investigate a wide range of functions, including analytic properties of these functions. But the acquisition of the function concept is not the same thing as an understanding of algebra. Rather, the algebraic study of functions gives the student practice in applying algebraic skills and makes those skills more vivid. In just the same way, computing discrete probabilities makes fractions more vivid, but the central notion of a fraction is not directly related to notions of probability.

Andrei has a good beginner's intuition about variables and functions but has not reached the heart of algebra. Andrei's understanding of functions, such as $f(x) = 2x - 3$, is more closely related to analysis than to algebra.

A First Milestone:
Algebra as "The General Arithmetic"

Bob is a successful eighth-grade algebra student. He has no trouble factoring the difference of two squares and can work the following exercises routinely:

$$4a^2 - 1 = (2a + 1)(2a - 1)$$
$$9 - b^4 = (3 + b^2)(3 - b^2)$$
$$n^4 - 16 = (n^2 + 4)(n^2 - 4) = (n^2 + 4)(n + 2)(n - 2)$$

With some hints, he can even factor $(g - h)$ as

$$(\sqrt{g} + \sqrt{h})(\sqrt{g} - \sqrt{h}).$$

But if asked to factor 4899, he does not notice that this number is $70^2 - 1$ and cannot use this to perform the factorization, even when his teacher shows him that $4899 = 4900 - 1$. Instead, Bob notices that the given number is a multiple of 3 but not of 5. He then tests 7, 11, and so on, to identify the prime factors of 4899.

The phrase quoted in the title of this section is taken from Isaac Newton, who began a treatise on (elementary) algebra with just this title. Here are his words (Whiteside 1972, p. 539):

> Common arithmetic and algebra rest on the same computational foundations and are directed to the same end. But whereas arithmetic treats questions in a definite, particular way, algebra does so in an indefinite universal manner, with the result that almost all pronouncements which are made in this style of computation—and its conclusions especially—may be called theorems. However, algebra most excels, in contrast with arithmetic, where questions are solved merely by progressing from the given quantities to those sought, in that for the most part it regresses from the sought quantities, treated as given, to those given, as though they were the ones sought, so as at length and in any manner to attain some conclusion— that is, equation—from which it is permissible to derive the quantities sought. In this fashion the most difficult problems are accomplished, ones whose solution it would be useless to seek of arithmetic alone. Yet arithmetic is so instrumental to algebra in all its operations that they seem jointly to constitute but a unique, complete computing science, and for that reason I shall explain both together.

Sir Isaac's words offer several insights. Perhaps the easiest to see is his first message that algebra generalizes arithmetic by making arithmetic statements into formal theorems. It is essentially this point that Bob missed. In fact it is probably not Bob's fault, but rather the fault of our teaching. Early and "easy" algebra is unmistakably about arithmetic. The equations that Andrei struggles with are perceived by him as statements about particular numbers, not generalizations of sets of statements about numbers. Perhaps this happened to Bob. He cannot see the factorization of $4899 = 70^2 - 1$ as a special case of the factorization of $x^2 - 1$. It may be that we rush students into algebraic "exercises," transforming algebraic expressions without regard to what the variables represent.

This lack of regard is not always a bad thing, and at a certain stage and for some students, it is essential. But at the stage at which Bob finds himself, it is important that he continue to think of the variables of algebra as representing numbers and the statements of algebra as generalizations of the statements of arithmetic. Unfortunately, sometimes our teaching techniques work against this. An understanding of Bob's level of mathematical sophistication and what he needs to move to the next step can help prevent this pedagogical error.

A Second Milestone: Algebra as the Study of Binary Relations on Sets

Cathy, in the eighth grade, solves equations in ways Andrei cannot. She sees the following equations as the same type:

$$2x + 3 = 10$$
$$3x - 1 = 10$$
$$4.2x + 4.5 = 6.7$$
$$\frac{3x}{4} + \frac{1}{2} = \frac{5}{6}$$
$$12 = 2x - 3$$

Cathy can subtract 3 from both sides of an equation and divide both sides by $\frac{3}{4}$, but she cannot use these techniques to solve an equation such as $3x - 2 = 5x + 18$. Nor can she "plug in numbers" for this equation, because there is no "target" number to look for.

Newton's description of algebra as proceeding "backward" from arithmetic is exactly what Cathy has understood. It is the concept that Andrei, who continues to see simple equations from an arithmetic point of view, is missing.

Cathy is also missing something. But what? This is a difficult pedagogical question. The appearance of the unknown on both sides of an equation is a step that some students find difficult to understand. Students are rarely successful in using trial-and-error to solve this sort of equation. Rather, they must, at some point, transform the equation by getting the unknowns all on the same side. In so doing, they are adding to their understanding of the meaning of equality. As Carpenter, Franke, and Levi (2003) found, younger children see the symbol for equality as something like a "return" button on a calculator. It is a cue to perform some algorithm implementing the indicated operation. Younger students have trouble interpreting a question such as, $7 + 5 = what? + 4$. For them, the equal sign is in the "wrong place." They can solve the problem in several ways. Sometimes they think, "Four is one less than 5, so the number for *what* has to be one more than seven." They can perform the addition on the left, transforming the equation into $12 = what? + 4$. Or they can subtract 4 from both sides, obtaining $7 + 1 = what$.

Students of arithmetic rarely follow the last procedure because it requires a new step in understanding the symbol for equality. This step involves the relationship between statements of equality and the arithmetic operations. That is, a statement of equality remains true if we add or subtract the same quantity to both sides. Students must stop thinking about the equality of two numbers and instead think more directly about the equality of two expressions. Because they can replace an arithmetic expression with a single number, students rarely come to this concept of equality before encountering algebraic expressions.

Analyzing the equality of algebraic expressions requires that students turn their attention to the operations indicated in those expressions. Although Cathy has not taken this step completely, she has progressed in this direction. She does not concentrate on the particular numbers that appear in the equations. What allows her to generalize across the equations is her understanding that it is not the particular numbers but the operations being performed on the numbers that are important. This interpretation of Newton's observations leads to a more modern concept of algebra: the study of binary operations on sets. That is, we can think of algebra as "generalizing" arithmetic in more than one way. The simplest way is the one that Newton points out: algebraic identities are generalizations of arithmetic statements. The identity $(x + y)^2 = x^2 + y^2 + 2xy$ is true because the arithmetic statement resulting from substituting values for x and y is always true.

But there is another level of generalization inherent in algebra. Newton's algebra came to him from the East, from Hindu and Islamic mathematicians, through the mathematicians of Renaissance Italy and the work of François Viète (see, for example, Boyer 1985). This work focused on the solution in radicals of several kinds of polynomial equations. It was incomplete in Newton's day; no one knew how to solve the general quintic equation using radicals. The full "solution" to this problem by Galois, Abel, and others had to wait until the early nineteenth century.

This full solution involved the development of yet another concept of how algebra generalizes arithmetic. When investigating the relationship between the roots and the coefficients of a polynomial equation, we need to look at operations other than the arithmetic operations, defined on sets other than the rational, real, or complex numbers. In particular, the notion of a permutation and the composition of permutations assumed a prominence unrecognized in Newton's time.

In this process, the "laws" of algebra—associativity, distributivity, and so on—became objects of interest in their own right rather than statements describing how rational numbers combine. These laws now defined the structures induced by new operations on new sets of objects. Slowly, the study of algebra grew away from the study of the field of real numbers to more general structures (fields, rings, and groups) built out of binary operations on sets. This view of algebra can be seen as another way in which algebra generalizes the arithmetic of the rational numbers.

In the classroom, this change in emphasis, from numbers to operations, can be encouraged in several ways. The metaphor of equality as a "balance" is often useful, but there are students for whom it does not make sense.

An odd by-product of the use of technology can help students like Andrei (in our first vignette) make this transition. When a calculator is used, the actual algorithm being applied to two numbers is invisible to the student. We can exploit this observation to turn the student's attention away from the algorithm, which replaces a pair of numbers with a single number, and toward the operation implemented by the algorithm. For instance, in working with Andrei, I permitted him to use a calculator for equations such as $2.81x + 1.34 = 7.36$, but I insisted that he tell me what he was going to do with the calculator before he could touch it. This seemed to have the effect of getting him to concentrate on the operations he was performing and the order in which they were performed. It also moved Andrei toward Cathy's realization that equations with the same form can be solved in the same way.

Another way to help Andrei make the transition to thinking about operations is to describe the process orally. For example, to solve an equation like $2x + 3 = 11$, I might tell Andrei a story like the following. "Once there was a number x. It got multiplied by 2. Then 3 got added. The result was 11. What was the original number?" With some support, Andrei could answer this by working "backward." "The result was 11 after adding 3, so it must have been 8 before this. The product of the number and 2 was 8, so the original number is 4."

One can read this "story," and Andrei's solution, as building toward the concept of an inverse function. But since these particular functions are so close to the operations of multiplication and addition, this technique also serves to turn Andrei's attention to the operations he is performing and away from the particular numbers he performs them "on."

A Third Milestone: Algebra for Algebra's Sake

Dina is an average student in first-year algebra, the type whose education is the bread-and-butter of the algebra teacher. She has mastered the factoring of trinomials and is studying the "special case" of the difference of two squares. She knows well the identity $x^2 - y^2 = (x + y)(x - y)$ and has multiplied this out and done the corresponding factorization countless times, but she is struggling with factoring expressions such as, $4a^2 - 9b^2$, $25c^2 - 1$ (although she recognizes 1 as a perfect square), and $4 - d^2$.

She has still more trouble with $\frac{e^2}{4} - 9f^2$ because she is not used to treating fractions as perfect squares.

Elizaveta can do all the problems that are difficult for Dina, but when given the expression $(e + f)^2 - 4$ to factor, she is puzzled. Elizaveta is not sure what factoring this expression might mean. And she is surprised that

$$(\sqrt{g} + \sqrt{h})(\sqrt{g} - \sqrt{h}) = g - h.$$

So, of course, she wouldn't think of factoring $g - h$ in this way.

Froim is doing well in intermediate algebra. He knows, of course, how to factor $A^2 - B^2$, but when he studies trigonometric identities, he has difficulty with $\cos^2 x - \sin^2 x$. In one of the review books, Froim's teacher finds parallel exercises in factoring algebraic and trigonometric expressions. Froim works through these, learning to exploit the parallel.

Gabe is on the school math team. He knows that $x + \dfrac{1}{x}$ is a function that achieves its minimum (on the positive reals) when $x = 1$. He knows this, not from calculus, but from the arithmetic and geometric mean inequality:

$$\frac{A + B}{2} \geq \sqrt{AB},$$

for positive numbers A, B, with equality when A = B. Letting $A = x$, $B = \dfrac{1}{x}$, we get $x + \dfrac{1}{x} \geq 2$, with equality occurring when $x = \dfrac{1}{x} = 1$. Here are some functions that Gabe has to think about. Each concerns a function of a positive real number x, and Gabe must minimize each function:

$$\frac{x+1}{x-2} + \frac{x-2}{x+1}$$

$$\tan x + \cot x$$

$$\log_a x + \log_x a$$

Sitting next to Gabe on the math team is Harriet, who knows that $x^3 + y^3 = (x + y)(x^2 - xy + y^2)$ but is struggling to factor $x^6 + y^6$.

So far we have looked at two major steps in students' acquisition of an understanding of algebra: a first step in which algebra is seen as a generalization of arithmetic, and a second step in which algebra is viewed as the study of binary operations.

Many students never get beyond this step, and in fact an understanding of algebra as a study of binary operations on sets of objects takes students very far. They can harness algebra to the study of arithmetic and use algebra to think more generally about types of arithmetic statements. They have access to the structures of algebra, based on general properties of binary operations. The students described above, from Dina through Gabe, are beginning to take a third step in their understanding of algebra.

This third step brings us directly to modern conceptions of algebra—mathematicians working in contemporary algebra study structures (such as groups, rings, and fields) and not just operations. Often, students (and teachers) are exposed to the structural view of algebra but do not see how it is related to the algebra of the high school syllabus. The result is a dry and formal understanding of the axioms of algebra as "rules" or labels for ways in which operations work.

However, the vignettes show how some growth of the algebra of structure emerges from the algebra of computation. Newton's comment about algebra proceeding "backward" from arithmetic contains a hint of the notion of additive and multiplicative inverses, which are in a sense at the center of the group, ring, and field axioms. These axioms are descriptions of how binary operations work on sets, so the emphasis on operations, rather than on the numbers being combined, is a first step in creating algebraic structures.

The next step in understanding algebra is at once more concrete and more general than these small hints might suggest. An idea for this step was given by a modern master, the great mathematician and teacher I. M. Gelfand (personal communication 1997):

> Years ago, we thought of arithmetic as dealing with numbers and algebra as dealing with letters. But we sometimes use letters as well as numbers in discussing arithmetic.
>
> A more modern view distinguishes algebra from arithmetic in another way. In algebra we let letters represent other letters, and not just numbers. That is, a student can learn the algebraic identity $A^2 - B^2 = (A + B)(A - B)$ and think of it as representing such statements as $2499 = 50^2 - 1 = (50 + 1)(50 - 1) = 51 \times 49$. This is an arithmetic statement. But if we let $A = x^6$ and $B = y^6$, the same identity can represent the statement $x^6 - y^6 = (x^3 + y^3)(x^3 - y^3)$. Or, we could write $\cos^2 x - \sin^2 x = (\cos x + \sin x)(\cos x - \sin x)$. And so one algebraic identity spawns many others.
>
> In mathematical terms, we can say that arithmetic is largely the study of the field of rational numbers. Algebra, however, begins with a study of the field of rational expressions.

Perhaps some clarification is in order. Oddly, a deeper mathematical meaning sometimes emerges if we drain the objects we are investigating of other meanings. We can look at algebraic expressions as generalizations of arithmetic statements. As we do so, we inevitably begin to look at how one algebraic statement relates to another, sometimes without making reference to its meaning when numbers are substituted for the letters. That is, we can say that $(a + 3)(a + 7) = a^2 + 10a + 21$ without thinking of the multiplication or addition of real numbers. This is because we can think of the operations of addition and subtraction as directly combining two algebraic expressions: $a(a + 7) = a^2 + 7a$, or $3a + 7a = 10a$, and so on. These operations, on the set of algebraic expressions, have their own structure, independent of their meaning when applied to numbers.

For example, a beginning student, like Andrei, thinks of a polynomial as an expression with values, a function on a set of numbers. But mathematicians often study polynomials for their own sake, without thinking of them as taking on values. They might study, say, the set of polynomials in one variable with rational coefficients. The rational numbers here are not used as "values" of the unknown but as part of the notation of the polynomial itself. Computation with these polynomials may involve computation with rational numbers, but not the evaluation of the polynomial "at" a rational number.

Polynomials over the rationals have the structure of a ring. We can add, subtract, and multiply these polynomials, and we can divide them if we allow for division with remainder. Indeed, the textbooks of first-year algebra consist largely of exercises in which polynomials are not evaluated but combined as objects in their own right, as elements of a certain ring. The "meaning" of these symbols, in the sense of their representing some other objects, is then lost.

Likewise, we can form the set of polynomials in several variables—any letters or symbols we choose—without looking at what these symbols represent. This set also forms a ring. And if we take all possible fractions with polynomial numerators and denominators (except that we don't admit the zero polynomial as a denominator), we can make them into a field. We can add, subtract, multiply, and divide, just as we do with rational numbers. This set is the field of rational expressions referred to by Gelfand.

In a process largely transparent to both teacher and learner, a big part of algebra, after the first year of study, slowly turns into the study of the field of rational expressions without regard to their role in representing functions or even rational numbers. It is strange that this has not been noted in the literature, perhaps because it grows so naturally out of the pedagogy. Conscious attention to this way of looking at the process can help teachers identify problems of understanding, such as those experienced by the students portrayed above.

Dina, Elizaveta, Froim, Gabe, and Harriet are all working on acquiring this sense of algebra. Dina, on some level, probably sees the identity $x^2 - y^2 = (x + y)(x - y)$ as a statement about arithmetic, and the identity $4a^2 - 9b^2 = (2a + 3b)(2a - 3b)$ as another statement about arithmetic. But she cannot see the relationship between the two statements. This will come when she experiences many such examples and begins to recognize the similar elements in each.

A strategic pedagogic intervention in this process can help students on Dina's level. She is beginning to see the similarities among some of the problems, but she has not achieved fluency in exploiting the similarity. As soon as Dina can see that one or two examples have the same form as $A^2 - B^2$, the teacher can ask, "What plays the role of A? What plays the role of B?"

Strangely, the standard pedagogic literature does not make note of this device. In more elementary work, it is routine for teachers to suggest to students that they check the validity of an algebraic transformation by substituting numbers. The students then are thinking of the algebra of the field of rational numbers. The question "What plays the role of ... ?" is similar; it asks the students to substitute values in the field of rational expressions.

Hints like these can help Elizaveta, Froim, Gabe, and Harriet with their difficulties. Indeed, many of the problem sets in our intermediate algebra textbooks are organized along these lines. An algebraic "form" is given, and students must use it to generate many special cases. Although this can be interpreted as a routine exercise in algebraic manipulation, a conscious interpretation as work in the field of rational expressions can help teachers guide the students in acquiring these skills. Some examples follow of how this might happen.

Example 1: Algebraic Identities

This point of view can also explain some thorny issues in the mathematics of elementary algebra. One of these issues is the definition of an algebraic (or trigonometric) identity. The usual definition given is that an identity is an equation that is true when any value of the variable is substituted, so long as the two sides of the identity are defined for those values. So, the identity $(A + 3)^2 = A^2 + 6A + 9$ is true exactly because the corresponding statement about numbers is true, whenever a number is substituted for A.

But according to this definition, the following two equations are identities for the field of real numbers:

$\sqrt{x} = \sqrt{-x}$ (The only value for which both sides are defined, for real numbers, is $x = 0$, and for this one value, the two sides are equal.)

arccos x = **arcsec** x, defining both functions by the usual "principal value." (The only value for which both sides are defined, for real numbers, is $x = 1$, and for this one value, the two sides are equal.)

It is unlikely that we want these statements to be considered identities.

A better definition is obtained if we think of identities as statements in the field of rational expressions, or, in the examples above, fields of algebraic or trigonometric expressions. (Polynomials in $\sin x$ and $\cos x$ also form a ring, a generalization of the ring of polynomials in one or two variables, and can be studied "formally" in the same way.) That is, an identity can be considered as a statement that two expressions are equal, as elements of the field of rational (algebraic, trigonometric) expressions, if one can be transformed into the other using the operations within these fields.

If we think of identities in this way rather than as statements about fields of numbers, we clear up another difficulty. Algebra textbooks may state that $\frac{x^2 - 4}{x - 2} = x + 2$, except when $x = 2$ (when the left-hand expression is undefined). Considered as elements of the field of rational expressions, however, these two expressions are fully equivalent, without apology for a particular "value" of x. We are now not thinking of substituting numbers for them, so this exception does not occur. There would be an exception if the zero element of the field of rational expressions were involved as a denominator, but here it is not. (Although this distinction may elude many students, teachers can certainly understand it and use it to interpret and enrich their interactions with students.)

Example 2: The "Universal Distributive Law"

Harry thinks that $(a + b)^2 = a^2 + b^2$.

Inez thinks that $10^{a+b} = 10^a + 10^b$.

> *Jerzy thinks that* $\cos(a + b) = \cos a + \cos b$.
>
> *Kris thinks that* $\sqrt{a + b} = \sqrt{a} + \sqrt{b}$.

Any teacher of algebra can give examples ad infinitum of this phenomenon. It is very common and very difficult to correct. What's going on?

As with any common and persistent error, there are probably several reasons students make this mistake. The easiest way to explain the first two examples (Harry and Inez) is to say that the students are overgeneralizing the distributive law for addition and multiplication. But if this were true, it would mean that they have understood the distributive law as it applies to the operations of addition and multiplication and can generalize it to apply to the operations of addition and exponentiation. If Harry and Inez were doing this, then they would in fact be well on their way to a deeper understanding of algebra, and this error would be a simple growing pain, not the persistent difficulty it often is.

The last two examples (Jerzy and Kris) are a bit different. If this is an instance of overgeneralization, then the students have read a statement like $3(a + b) = 3a + 3b$ as a property of the function $f(x) = 3x$. They think the function is additive, and they are generalizing to the statement that all functions are additive. If this is true, then Jerzy and Kris are thinking of general properties of functions. But are they? Students who make such errors usually are not ready to record and discuss general properties of functions or operations. They often can discuss general properties of operations, but not as fluently as would be required to make a well-formulated, if incorrect, generalization.

It is more likely that all four of these students have been rushed into a situation where they simply don't understand what is going on. Typically, they have skipped over the stage in which algebraic expressions represent generalizations of arithmetic and have not yet intuited algebraic expressions as objects in their own right. So they are left with a set of symbols that have neither the meaning of general arithmetic nor the meaning of an element of the field of rational expressions. Thus they can do whatever they like with these symbols, and since there is a rule that "looks like" the false one they are formulating, they simply imitate it. The term *universal distributivity* is probably a misnomer. Rather, it is our way of describing a phenomenon that really has nothing to do with the application or generalization of an algebraic axiom.

Example 3: Algebraic "Radar"

> *Nell is simplifying an algebraic expression. She (mistakenly) writes:*
>
> $$(a + b)(a + b + c) = a^2 + 2ab + ac + b^2 + bc + c$$

"No," thinks Nell. "This can't be right. I am always multiplying two let-ters together, so I can never get the term c alone." So she corrects her work.

Oren is solving a system of three equations:

$$a + b = 7$$
$$b + c = 3$$
$$a + c = 12$$

At first he writes $a = 7 - b$. Then he starts substituting this value of "a" into the third equation.

"No," he thinks. "Everything that happens to a also happens to b and c. Why should I do something special to a?" So he tries a different technique. He adds all three equations:

$$2a + 2b + 2c = 22, \text{ so } a + b + c = 11.$$

Then, subtracting, in turn, each of the original equations from this last one, he easily solves the system.

These advanced students have learned a form of metacognition that I call "algebraic radar." They have developed a sense of what the next step in an algebraic computation should look like, and so they can correct errors as they go along. This capacity is allowed them because they are working in the field of rational expressions and are thinking about general properties of these expressions. Nell sees that her final expression should be *homogeneous* in *a, b,* and *c*: each term should be of the same degree. Oren sees that the original equations are *symmetric* in *a, b,* and *c* and has in-tuited a way to exploit this symmetry by treating all the equations in the same way.

Example 4: Algebra and Functions

It is sometimes argued that mathematics has meaning to students only when it is applied to real-life situations. This phrase begs its own question, for it doesn't explain what constitutes "real life." Sometimes it is assumed that real life means empirical fact, as reified by the empirical sciences, so that "meaningful mathemat-ics" becomes "applied mathematics."

A broader, more useful view might be that real life also encompasses the life of the mind, so that it includes mathematics that describes games or puzzles. And the life of the mind does not stop with games and puzzles. Mathematics itself acquires a reality for students, and mathematical objects become as real as falling stones, growing populations, or flowing water. So motivation for learning mathematics can eventually arise from questions within mathematics itself. That is, mathematics is, at a certain level, its own application.

This level is sometimes achieved as early as the middle of the high school curriculum. In algebra, this issue is usually played out in the subject's relationship to the study of functions. Young students learn to distinguish and describe patterns in numbers, and insights about patterns can grow into the notion of function. Eventually, students are introduced to the standard notation for functions of a real variable, and they start learning algebra.

As we have seen, algebra, as mathematicians use the term, is not the study of functions but rather the study of binary operations and of the structures they induce. Nonetheless, the description of functions and their properties continues to be an important application of algebra throughout the high school curriculum and into the undergraduate curriculum. At this stage, students are usually well on their way to working routinely with algebraic expressions in their own right, as elements of a field of rational (or algebraic, or trigonometric) expressions. The following are two examples of places in the curriculum where algebra is used to explore algebraic properties of functions.

> *Pedro is an average achiever in an average intermediate algebra class. His teacher asked: If $f(x) = x^2 - 5x + 7$, what is $f(x + 3)$? Pedro couldn't answer the question. He can compute $f(7)$ and $f(-2)$, and even $f(\sqrt{3})$. Mr. Nabob, the teacher, asks Pedro to compute $f(a)$, $f(2a)$, then $f(1 + \sqrt{3})$. With this assistance, Pedro can answer the question.*

Our standard notation for a function invites substitution. As we have seen, substitution of an expression for a variable is a crucial step in learning intermediate algebra. Pedro's teacher knows how to guide him through some steps that will give him access to this concept. Mr. Nabob is "scaffolding" the transition from $f(x)$ as a function of rational numbers, to a function on the real numbers, to a function on the set of rational expressions (here limited to a simple binomial). Concealed in the anecdote is the difficulty that the variable x in $f(x)$ "looks like" the x in $f(x + 3)$. Mr. Nabob has skillfully avoided this, and Pedro has made the leap. Some students might need another intermediary step, such as computing $f(a)$, $f(a + 3)$, and so on.

A good advanced question to give students like Pedro, after they've progressed a bit, involves turning around the usual examination question about functional notation: If $f(x+3) = x^2 + 2x + 6$, what is $f(x)$?

When Pedro has settled for himself the variable issue—and this is not a simple issue—the solution might be as follows:

Let $y = x + 3$, so that $x = y - 3$.

Then $f(y) = x^2 + 2x + 6 = (y - 3)^2 + 2(y - 3) + 6 = y^2 - 4y + 9$.

So $f(x)$ is simply $x^2 - 4x + 9$.

> Quentin, a student in an advanced algebra class, is struck by the following "coincidence" in formulas:
>
> (i) $\tan(x + y) = \dfrac{\tan x + \tan y}{1 - \tan x \tan y}$ (ii) $\text{arcan } A + \arctan B = \arctan\left[\dfrac{A + B}{1 - AB}\right]$
>
> (These formulas are valid for $-\pi/2 < x, y < \pi/2$, or any similar domain in which the tangent function is one-to-one and onto.)

Often, students cannot articulate what is going on in this situation. What Quentin is reacting to is that the fractions in the two formulas have the same form; if we make the substitution $A = \tan x$ and $B = \tan y$, they are identical. A deeper understanding of algebraic form will give us the reason for this. Here is how the formula is usually derived. Using the substitution suggested above, we have $x = \text{arctan } A$, $y = \text{arctan } B$. Then formula (i) can be rewritten as

$$\tan(\text{arctan } A + \arctan B) = \frac{A + B}{1 - AB}$$

This says that $\text{arctan } A + \arctan B$ is the "angle" whose tangent is $\frac{A + B}{1 - AB}$, which is just the assertion of the formula. More formally, on the chosen domain, two numbers are equal if and only if their arctangents are equal, so

$$\arctan\left(\tan(\text{arctan } A + \arctan B)\right) = \arctan\left[\frac{A + B}{1 - AB}\right].$$

Again, on this domain, $\arctan(\tan Q) = Q$, so we have

$$\text{arctan } A + \arctan B = \arctan\left[\frac{A + B}{1 - AB}\right].$$

The interesting point about this derivation is that it doesn't depend on the actual form of the expression

$$\frac{A + B}{1 - AB}.$$

We never clear denominators, reduce to lowest terms, or indeed manipulate fractions in any way.

The fact is that the derivation does not depend on the particular formula involved. We can generalize the derivation, and even the formula, to any function $f(x)$ that is one-to-one and onto on a certain domain. Indeed, suppose we can represent $f(x + y)$ using some algebraic expression in $f(x)$ and $f(y)$. Let us call this expression $M[f(x), f(y)]$. So in the situation we've just examined, $f(x) = \tan x$, and

$$M[f(x), f(y)] = \frac{f(x) + f(y)}{1 - f(x)f(y)}.$$

(In working with students, I tell them that M stands for "mess," or "some messy expression.") Then we have (iii)$f(x+y) = M[f(x), f(y)]$.

If we let $A = f(x)$, $B = f(y)$, then $x = f^{-1}(A)$ and $y = f^{-1}(B)$, and we can rewrite expression (iii) as $f(f^{-1}(A) + f^{-1}(B)) = M[f^{-1}(A), f^{-1}(B)]$. By assumption, f is one-to-one and onto for the chosen domain, so f^{-1} has the same value for both these numbers, or

$$f^{-1}\big(f(f^{-1}(A)+f^{-1}(B))\big)=f^{-1}\big(M[f^{-1}(A),f^{-1}(B)]\big),\ \text{or}$$
$$f^{-1}(A)+f^{-1}(B)=f^{-1}\big(M[f^{-1}(A),f^{-1}(B)]\big).$$

It is important for students to go back and see how the formula for the sum of arctangents is a special case of this general formula. For many students, the punch line to this argument comes when they are asked to apply it to the function $y=10^x$. What they get is simply the fact (with which they're already likely to be familiar) that $\log(x+y)=\log x+\log y$.

Conclusion

In this article, I have tried to show how difficulties students encounter in learning algebra, and pedagogical techniques to address them, are related to deeper mathematical insights. In order to implement these techniques, teachers need to know more mathematics than they expect their students to know. The question of teachers' content knowledge is an increasingly important one and worthy of our continued attention.

We have already seen, at least with algebra, that it is not obvious what particular content knowledge teachers will need. The remark by I. M. Gelfand quoted earlier may turn out to be only one of a series of such insights we will have about the mathematics of elementary and intermediate algebra.

In exploring this area, we have found that the cooperation of teachers and mathematicians has already proved crucial. Mathematicians often have important insights, some of which may be simple mathematically. But mathematicians, working alone, often do not see the significance of their insights. That is, mathematicians typically have answers, but they have not been asked the right questions. It is the role of the educator to ask the questions. Often the questions are less trivial than the answers. For the mathematician, it is simple to describe the algebra of functional notation. But to connect this algebra with the work of students in intermediate algebra requires that the teacher think hard about students' difficulties.

This article was written with the hope that cooperation between educators and mathematicians, which is now as rare as it is important, will become more common and more important in our dialogues about teaching and learning.

References

Boyer, Carl B. *A History of Mathematics.* New York: John Wiley & Sons, 1968. Reprint. Princeton, N.J.: Princeton University Press, 1985.

Carpenter, Thomas P., Megan Loef Franke, and Linda Levi. *Thinking Mathematically: Integrating Arithmetic and Algebra in the Elementary School.* Portsmouth, N.H.: Heinemann, 2003.

Kieran, Carolyn. "Learning and Teaching Algebra at the Middle School through College Levels: Building Meaning for Symbols and Their Manipulation." In *Second Handbook of Research on Mathematics Teaching and Learning,* edited by Frank K. Lester, Jr., pp. 707–62. Charlotte, N.C.: Information Age Publishing, 2007.

Sfard, Anna. "The Development of Algebra: Confronting Historical and Psychological Perspectives." *Journal of Mathematical Behavior* 14 (March 1995): 15–39.

Whiteside, Derek Thomas, ed. *The Mathematical Papers of Isaac Newton.* Vol. 5. London: Cambridge University Press, 1972.

ADDITIONAL READING

Falkner, Karen, Linda Levi, and Thomas P. Carpenter. "Children's Understanding of Equality: A Foundation for Algebra." *Teaching Children Mathematics* 6 (December 1999): 232–36.

6

The Three R's: Recursive Thinking, Recursion, and Recursive Formulas

Stanley J. Bezuszka
Margaret J. Kenney

You can see a lot just by looking.
—Yogi Berra

JUST as recursive thinking is fundamental to algebraic thinking and reasoning, so recursion and recurrence relations are fundamental core content in algebra. In this article the mathematical and pedagogical aspects of these topics are examined. Specifically, recursive formulas and explicit formulas are defined and compared, and the topics are illustrated through rich investigations with varying degrees of challenge.

Recursive Thinking

Recursive thinking is a vital part of algebraic thinking and reasoning at all levels. In general it begins informally in the routine behavior of young students when they first learn to recognize patterns through activities as ordinary as skip counting. Recursive thinking is also part of the reasoning and computations of adult buyers who use compound interest calculations to analyze costs of items that are purchased over time. Simply put, recursive thinking is a habit of mind that embraces step-by-step sequential change. When skip counting by twos, the young child recites the numbers 2, 4, 6, 8, 10, …, where the learned behavior may be supported physically by actual hops along a concrete number line in such a way as to emphasize that there is a particular starting point and that the successive hops are each the same length. In this example the starting point is 2 and the hop length is 2, and each new number reached is two more than the number preceding it. As children progress in school, their skip-counting abilities are nurtured through the use of a number line or a hundred chart, both of which are visualization and recitation aids. Older students can simulate this behavior with a calculator by first pressing 2 + 2, then ENTER (or the = key), followed by the + key, then 2, and then pressing ENTER repeatedly. With each new press of ENTER, a new term in the sequence, that is, an ordered list of terms, 2, 4, 6, 8, 10, ... appears in the display.

In the skip-counting process, "hopping" 2 over and over illustrates an action related to recursive thinking called *iteration*. Iteration, the continuing repetition of a specific action, is illustrated on the calculator with the repeated depression of the ENTER key. (Note that not all calculators are constructed in the same way, so that the description of the iteration process may differ slightly among models.) Middle school students can investigate iteration on their calculators using different starting numbers and different operations. At all levels, students need varied experiences in observing, continuing, and describing sequential patterns of different kinds. An important objective for all students to achieve is the ability to create, describe, and analyze their own sequential patterns.

Introducing and reinforcing recursive thinking, with sufficient time for discussion and reflection throughout the elementary school curriculum, helps prepare students to reason inductively in the middle grades. It is expected that students develop the ability to use inductive reasoning to make generalizations at the middle school level (National Council of Teachers of Mathematics [NCTM] 2000). It is incumbent on middle and secondary school mathematics programs to build on the prior experiences at the elementary school level and to take recursive thinking to the next stages of development. On the one hand, recursive thinking can be used to help students formulate and analyze conjectures. On the other hand, refining recursive thinking and taking a closer look at patterns and practices together supply students with a foundation for understanding and applying the important principle of mathematical induction in secondary school mathematics.

Recursion and Recursive Formulas

Recursion is a process that makes use of recursive thinking. Specifically, recursion is the method of recording and summarizing step-by-step sequential change. Each new step in the process is described in terms of the preceding step or steps. This step-by-step change is typically represented by a recurrence relation. Recursion and iteration, mentioned earlier, have a close relationship. Recursion focuses on looking back from the current step to previous steps, whereas iteration, the process of repeating the same procedure over and over, moves forward from the initial step.

To illustrate how step-by-step change can be portrayed simply, consider a sequence of shapes described recursively. Geometric attributes of these shapes can be used to generate a variety of numerical sequences. Such examples afford an opportunity to investigate both the visual and the numerical aspects of recursion. Figure 6.1 shows models of 1 × 2 rectangles sketched in increasing numbers and linked in steplike fashion. This sequence of $1(1 \times 2)$, $2(1 \times 2)$, $3(1 \times 2)$, $4(1 \times 2)$, ..., $n(1 \times 2)$ rectangles gives rise to several numerical sequences, each with a different recursive pattern. Subscript notation is a useful way to label terms in a sequence. Below, a_k is the number associated with the kth model.

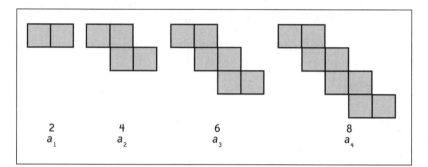

Fig. 6.1. Sequence of 1 × 2 rectangles

a)   Area change: a_k is the area associated with the kth model.

The sequence of square counts (or area) of each model in figure 6.1 is $a_1 = 2$, $a_2 = 4$, $a_3 = 6$, $a_4 = 8$, ... Observe that

$$a_2 = 2 + 2 = a_1 + 2,$$
$$a_3 = 4 + 2 = a_2 + 2,$$
$$a_4 = 6 + 2 = a_3 + 2.$$

Assuming this pattern continues and applying recursive thinking, we find that the nth term is $a_n = a_{n-1} + 2$, where $n \geq 2$.

The equation $a_n = a_{n-1} + 2$ is called the recurrence relation, and the set of the two equations $a_1 = 2$ and $a_n = a_{n-1} + 2$, with $n \geq 2$, is the recursive formula, where $a_1 = 2$ is the initial condition. The diagrams in figure 6.1 display clearly why each term is 2 more than the preceding term.

b)   Perimeter change: p_k is the perimeter associated with the kth model.

The sequence of perimeters of each model is $p_1 = 6$, $p_2 = 10$, $p_3 = 14$, $p_4 = 18$, ... In this example,

$$p_2 = 6 + 4 = p_1 + 4,$$
$$p_3 = 10 + 4 = p_2 + 4,$$
$$p_4 = 14 + 4 = p_3 + 4.$$

It appears that $p_n = p_{n-1} + 4$ is the recurrence relation and that $p_1 = 6$, $p_n = p_{n-1} + 4$ for $n \geq 2$ is the recursive formula. In this instance, $p_1 = 6$ is the initial condition. Students should study the models in figure 6.1 and use them to explain why the perimeter increases by 4 at each new step. Their analyses should start with the observation that each succeeding model has one more 1×2 rectangle than the one preceding it. If a prompt is needed, ask what the perimeter of the 1×2 rectangle is and how much it contributes to the perimeter of the model when it is attached. That is, the perimeter of a 1×2 rectangle is 6, and when it is added to the preceding figure, there is an overall loss of 2 in perimeter, leaving a net gain of 4.

c) Rectangle count change: s_k is the rectangle count associated with the kth model.

The sequence of rectangle counts for each model is $s_1 = 3$, $s_2 = 7$, $s_3 = 11$, $s_4 = 15$, ... To find the terms in this more complex recursive pattern, examine each model and count all possible rectangles. A scheme for determining s_2 and s_3 is given below.

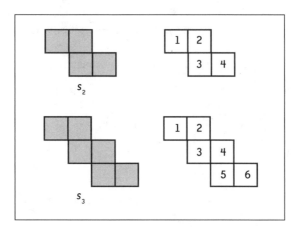

Fig. 6.2. Counting rectangles

$s_2 = 7$ can be determined as follows:

1. Number each square tile as shown in figure 6.2.
2. List the rectangles that are size 1×1.

    They are the tiles numbered 1, 2, 3, 4.   Subtotal: 4

3. List the rectangles that are size 1×2.

    They are the two-tile combinations 12 and 34.   Subtotal: 2

4. List the rectangles that are size 2×1.

    This is the two-tile combination 23.   Subtotal: 1

5. Add the subtotals to get $s_2 = 7$.

$s_3 = 11$ can be determined as follows:

1. Observe that every rectangle of s_2 is also a rectangle of s_3.

2. In addition, there are four new rectangles—two of size 1×1, one of size 1×2, and one of size 2×1, namely, tiles numbered 5 and 6, and the two-tile combinations 56 and 45.

Assuming the pattern continues, we find that $s_n = s_{n-1} + 4$ is the recurrence relation and $s_1 = 3$, $s_n = s_{n-1} + 4$ for $n \geq 2$ is the recursive formula, with $s_1 = 3$ being the initial condition. Note that this particular sequence as in (b) is such that each new term is 4 more than the preceding term. A difference of 4 between terms is correct here, since the 1×2 rectangle that is added to each model by itself has a count of three rectangles and it also forms one additional 2×1 rectangle when it is attached to the preceding model.

The sequences in (b) and (c) have the same recurrence relation. They are different sequences because their initial conditions differ. This result helps to emphasize the significant role the initial condition(s) plays in recursive formulas.

d) Least unit squares to add change: u_k is the least number of unit squares to be added to form a rectangle in the kth model.

The sequence of least number of unit squares to be added to each step pattern

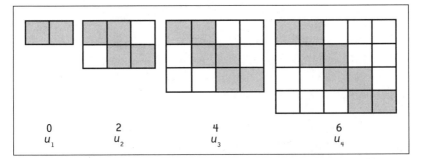

Fig. 6.3. Forming rectangles

to form a rectangle is $u_1 = 0$, $u_2 = 2$, $u_3 = 6$, $u_4 = 12$, ... See figure 6.3. Observe that

$$u_2 = 0 + 2 = u_1 + 2 = u_1 + 2 \cdot 1,$$
$$u_3 = 2 + 4 = u_2 + 4 = u_2 + 2 \cdot 2,$$
$$u_4 = 6 + 6 = u_3 + 6 = u_3 + 2 \cdot 3.$$

In this example, each new term is *not* the sum of the preceding term plus a constant. However, in the second addend there is an apparent pattern that leads to the recurrence relation $u_n = u_{n-1} + 2(n - 1)$. The recursive formula is $u_1 = 0$, $u_n = u_{n-1} + 2(n - 1)$ for $n \geq 2$, and $u_1 = 0$ is the initial condition. Each new rectangle increases by one unit each in length and width over its predecessor. If we assume that the pattern continues, the nth model is an $n \times (n + 1)$ rectangle. The expression u_n is the count of unshaded squares in the nth model. The count u_n equals the preceding count u_{n-1} plus $((n + 1) - 2) + (n - 1) = 2n - 2$ new unshaded squares appearing in the last row and column of the rectangular grid.

The recursive formulas in all the previous examples are additive. That is, each new term is the sum of the preceding term *plus* an additional amount. Other recursive formulas may be multiplicative. In such circumstances, each new term may be the product of the preceding term and a factor plus an additional amount. For example, suppose Penny Wise adds pennies to her piggy bank over a ten-day period as follows: She puts 2 pennies in her bank on day one, $4 = 2 \cdot 2$ pennies in on day two, $8 = 2 \cdot 4$ pennies in on day three, and so on. Each day, she puts in double the number of pennies that she put in on the preceding day. The recurrence relation that gives the number of pennies, s_n, to go in the bank on the nth day is $s_n = 2s_{n-1}$. In the product, the preceding term is one factor and the other is 2. The recursive formula is $s_1 = 2$, $s_n = 2s_{n-1}$ for $n \geq 2$, and $s_1 = 2$ is the initial condition.

Students in middle and secondary school mathematics classes should explore problems that use both types of recursive formulas. Some student materials incorporate user-friendly language and symbolic representation to promote an understanding of the recursive process, such as NEXT = NOW + 4 or NEXT = 2 * NOW. However, starting at about middle school, it is appropriate for students to adapt to the use of subscript notation in paper-and-pencil activities. By this time, many students are using similar notation on their calculators (Rubenstein 2002) and with spreadsheet software on their computers (Lannin 2004). The use of this notation offers a subtle buildup of the function concept with the underlying ordered pairs term number k, term value s_k. When students engage in the study of functions as part of their algebra sequence, they will expand their knowledge of recursive formulas and view sequences as explicitly or recursively defined functions.

Recursive Formulas versus Explicit Formulas

Middle and secondary school students who have been identifying and using patterns in the lower grades tend to routinely describe sequences recursively. Their prior experiences have prepared them to observe the step-by-step change, form tables of data to illustrate the change, and make verbal generalizations. Consequently, they are more comfortable with, and have a better understanding of, recursive formulas than explicit formulas. Students typically have difficulty finding explicit formulas or expressions that give s_n in terms of n (Driscoll 1999, p.100). Thus, it is important to address the issue of linking recursive with explicit formulas. Algebra students should explore problems and tasks that include making generalizations, justifying them, and representing the results with explicit formulas. Familiarity with explicit formulas is central to an understanding of functions.

Students learn that the recursive method has its limitations when they are asked to identify the terms of a sequence out of order. Implementing a systematic listing method to achieve a solution does not make sense when asked to give the 100th or 256th term of a sequence that has been defined recursively. Likewise, if students are asked if 328 or 611 is a term of a sequence that has been described recursively, they don't know how to proceed. Such questions can become the impetus for learning how to represent sequences with explicit formulas.

If an *explicit* formula cannot be deduced directly by students, then suggest that they use the *recursive* formula as a starting point for deriving it. Often, using the recursive formula in combination with some comparison technique, a repeated substitution procedure, or the method of differences will help students develop an explicit formula, or closed form as it is sometimes called. These strategies are described briefly and illustrated in the next section.

Comparison Strategy

A comparison of the terms in the recursively determined sequence with corresponding terms in another sequence whose explicit formula is already known can be a convenient way to derive an explicit formula. In order to have success in applying this strategy, the student should know some key sequences and their explicit formulas, and have some ability in manipulating algebraic expressions. Key sequences include multiples and powers of numbers as well as some figurate number sequences, like those of the triangular and square numbers. In fact, students can develop a page of sequences whose explicit formulas they know and then use it for reference as new sequences are encountered. For example, if the given sequence is $s_1 = 3$, $s_n = s_{n-1} + 4$ with $n \geq 2$, then

(1)   3   7   11   15   19   23   27 ...

can be compared with

(2)   4   8   12   16   20   24   28 ....

It is apparent that each term of the sequence in (1) is one less than the corresponding term of the sequence in (2). But (2) is the sequence of multiples of 4. By comparison, then, the explicit formula for the sequence in (1) is $s_n = 4n - 1$, $n \geq 1$,

Once determined, the explicit formula is fundamental for answering the types of questions posed earlier. The explicit formula can be used to determine s_n for arbitrary values of n. Here, the 100th term is $s_{100} = 4 \cdot 100 - 1 = 399$, and the 256th term is $s_{256} = 4 \cdot 256 - 1 = 1023$. The explicit formula can also be used to figure out if 328 or 611 is a term of the sequence s_n by deciding if $328 = 4n - 1$ or $611 = 4n - 1$ has a positive integer solution. The first equation does not have a solution in the positive integers, but $n = 153$ is a solution of the second equation. Thus, an important feature of the explicit formula is that it offers the means for going back and forth between a term's position in a sequence and its corresponding value.

Repeated Substitution Strategy

Another means of obtaining an explicit formula for a sequence represented recursively is to employ a successive substitution process. Thus, starting with the sequence of rectangle counts 3, 7, 11, 15, …with the recurrence relation $s_n = s_{n-1} + 4$,

$s_1 = 3$;

$s_2 = s_1 + 4 = 3 + 4$, by substituting for s_1;

$s_3 = s_2 + 4 = (3 + 1 \cdot 4) + 4 = 3 + 2 \cdot 4$, by substituting for s_2;

$s_4 = s_3 + 4 = (3 + 2 \cdot 4) + 4 = 3 + 3 \cdot 4$, by substituting for s_3;

$s_5 = s_4 + 4 = (3 + 3 \cdot 4) + 4 = 3 + 4 \cdot 4$, by substituting for s_4;

In order to make the leap to the generalization, students should compare the subscript number with what is varying in the expression on the right side of the equality. In the data above, the subscript number is 2 greater than the multiplier of 4. Assuming this pattern continues, we conclude as previously that $s_n = s_{n-1} + 4 = (3 + (n-2) \cdot 4) + 4 = 4n - 1$, $n \geq 1$ is an explicit formula.

Alternatively, if the data for the rectangle count are displayed in the horizontal format shown below, then each number in row 2 can be expressed as the starting number 3 plus the number of "4 hops" beyond 3. Thus, $15 = 3 + 3(4s)$, $19 = 3 + 4(4s)$, and so on. This arrangement is a visual process for achieving $s_n = 3 + (n-1) \cdot 4$.

n	1	2	3	4	5	6	7	8	9	10
rectangle count, s_n	3	7	11	15	19	23	27	31	35	39
		4	4	4	4					

The Method of Differences

The method of differences (or finite differences) is an effective algorithm for finding explicit formulas that are polynomial equations. The origin of finite differences can be traced back to the work of Isaac Newton (1642–1727) and others concerned with the development of calculus. The study of difference equations continues in importance today in many applied areas, including the study of chaos theory and discrete dynamical systems. The algorithm is illustrated in table 6.1 for the sequence 3, 7, 11, 15, …. In this approach a vertical representation of the data is typical. The columns in table 6.1 pertaining to the *given* sequence are the term numbers (n), the terms of the sequence (s_n), and the differences between successive terms. The columns in table 6.1 pertaining to an *arbitrary* sequence defined by a linear polynomial are the term numbers, the terms of the sequence, and the differences between successive terms. If the differences between successive terms in the given sequence are constant, as they are in table 6.1, the explicit formula will be a linear equation. Further, the constant in the first-differences column is actually the slope of the line. This is evident by observing that a, the slope of the linear equation $s_n = an + b$, is the constant in the first-differences column. Later in this article, this method is extended to a sequence whose first-differences column is not constant.

Table 6.1
First Differences Are Constant

n	s_n	1st diff.		n	$an + b$	1st diff.
1	3			1	$a + b$	
		4				a
2	7			2	$2a + b$	
		4				a
3	11			3	$3a + b$	
		4				a
4	15			4	$4a + b$	
		4				a
5	19			5	$5a + b$	

The difference between successive terms of the given s_n is the constant 4, and comparing first-differences columns, we clearly see that $a = 4$. Once a has been identified, match the terms in the first rows of the columns $an + b$ and s_n. Thus, from $a + b = 3$, it follows that $b = -1$, and once again the solution is $s_n = 4n - 1$. Students should investigate and find that b could have been determined by matching corresponding terms in any row of the columns $an + b$ and s_n.

As students begin to learn about recursive and explicit formulas in algebra, it is useful to record the data in the form of familiar input/output tables. For example, by studying the vertical arrangement of the terms of a given sequence as in column 3 of table 6.2, students should recognize that the pattern there is the recurrence relation, $s_n = s_{n-1} + 4$. Then by studying the data in table 6.2 horizontally by rows, students can deduce the explicit formula, $s_n = 4n - 1$. Note that column 2 has been inserted arbitrarily as a prompt for making the deduction.

When students understand how to move between recursive and explicit representations of data, they need to consider some probing questions. For example: If the explicit representation of the data can be found directly, should a recursive representation also be sought? For illustration, we examine a familiar problem that

Table 6.2
Input/Output Table

Input		Output
n	$4n$	s_n
1	4	3
2	8	7
3	12	11
4	16	15
5	20	19
6	24	23
7	28	27
8	32	31

occurs in many geometry textbooks. The problem is to determine the number of diagonals of a convex polygon. A natural selection for the input-to-output relationship is the number of sides of a polygon to the number of its diagonals. An explicit formula can be reached using the fact that a diagonal connects any two nonadjacent vertices. Try a hexagon. It has 6 vertices, and any one of the 6 vertices can be connected with $6 - 3$ other vertices, making $6(6 - 3)$ pairings that produce diagonals. Since a diagonal cannot be drawn to an adjacent vertex or to the vertex itself, 3 is subtracted from 6. But the product $6(6 - 3)$ counts each diagonal twice, once from each endpoint, so the actual diagonal count should be $6(6 - 3)/2$. Using inductive reasoning, we find that a reasonable generalization is that there are $n(n - 3)$ ways to partner vertices of an n-gon to make a diagonal and $n(n - 3)/2$ diagonals.

By also seeking a recursive formula here, we gain a deeper understanding of visual and numerical patterns, and the process stimulates related questions and connections. See figure 6.4.

Study column (a) in figure 6.4 to see how each succeeding polygon is an outgrowth of the preceding polygon and that it contains at least one more diagonal than the preceding one. In column (b) of the figure, note how the diagonal count of polygons contains at least the preceding diagonal count. In column (c), determine how each diagonal count of the new n-gon includes at least $n - 3$ new diagonals. The sequence of figures implies that the recursive formula for the number of diagonals of a convex polygon is $s_n = 1 + s_{n-1} + (n - 3) = s_{n-1} + (n - 2)$, for $n \geq 5$, and initial condition $s_4 = 2$. Note that $s_1 = s_2 = s_3 = 0$, since there are no diagonals in these instances. Also observe that the simplified recurrence relation for s_n does not offer the insight provided by the unsimplified version. Here, as in other situations represented algebraically, the simplification of an algebraic expression tends to obscure derivation and meaning.

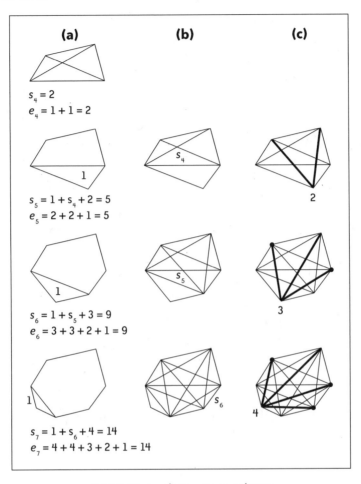

Fig. 6.4. Diagonals in a covex polygon

Examine the sequence e_n, an alternative sequence for the diagonal count. See figure 6.4, column (a). The sequence $e_4 = 1 + 1$, $e_5 = 2 + \underline{2 + 1}$, $e_6 = 3 + \underline{3 + 2 + 1}$, $e_7 = 4 + \underline{4 + 3 + 2 + 1}$ is the sum of the number of different diagonals that can be drawn from the first vertex to the $(n - 2)$nd vertex in a convex n-gon. In one problem, two distinctive patterns arise. The pattern $e_n = (n - 3) + \underline{(n - 3) + (n - 4) + \ldots + 3 + 2 + 1}$ is a nonrecursive but immediately recognizable pattern, since it includes the ubiquitous sum of consecutive positive integers $1 + 2 + 3 + \ldots + (n - 3)$. It can be shown that both sequences, e_n and s_n, have the same explicit formula derived earlier.

Yet another reason to reflect on the diagonals question and to examine figure 6.4 closely is the fact that the sides of the n-gon together with the diagonals are a visual representation of the action in the well-known handshake problem. In this problem, the number of handshakes among people in a group of n persons is counted. For example, the quadrilateral and its diagonals illustrate $(4 + 2)$ possible handshakes among 4 persons. A recursive approach shows how each new person (vertex) joining a group must shake hands with each of the preceding members of the group.

An analysis of recursive and explicit formulas should include a discussion about sequences that cannot be constructed readily using both or either type of formula. To illustrate and emphasize these remarks, ask students to give the first ten terms of the Fibonacci sequence. Undoubtedly they will use the recursive formula $F_n = F_{n-1} + F_{n-2}$, with $n > 2$ and $F_1 = 1$ and $F_2 = 1$, to produce the desired sequence: $1, 1, 2, 3, 5, 8, 13, 21, 34, 55, \ldots$. Most students are unaware there is also an explicit formula for the Fibonacci sequence, namely,

$$F_n = \frac{\left(\frac{1 + \sqrt{5}}{2}\right)^n - \left(\frac{1 - \sqrt{5}}{2}\right)^n}{\sqrt{5}},$$

which requires complex computation to find even the first few terms. Clearly, the Fibonacci sequence is one example where a recursive formula is preferred. Students should be asked to identify some commonly used sequences that cannot be represented using either recursive or explicit formulas. For a prime example, the prime number sequence cannot be represented recursively or explicitly!

Sample Activity Integrating Recursive and Explicit Formulas

Experiences that yield visual and numerical patterns offer opportunities to make connections between algebra and geometry. A problem set based on this premise appears in figure 6.5. As students work on determining solutions, they build on their prior knowledge of patterns and use recursive thinking to make conjectures. They discover that algebraic expressions help them to organize and summarize their thinking. They establish habits of mind for scrutinizing shapes and designs carefully to search for clues, connections, and links to familiar patterns. They learn to associate several different numerical sequences with a fixed sequence of geometric shapes. While exploring problems of this type, students have opportunities to increase their understanding of a central concept in mathematics, namely, function, and to achieve a more integrated view of mathematics. As a result of using activities like these with students, it is clear that classroom discourse is an important component of this activity. Students should be given time to work individually or in pairs on the problems and then discuss their different approaches and share their creative solutions with one another. Manipulatives, such as triangle tiles, can facilitate the construction of the shape sequences and support the development of insights about

Growing Triangles

The number of small triangular regions is listed under each figure.

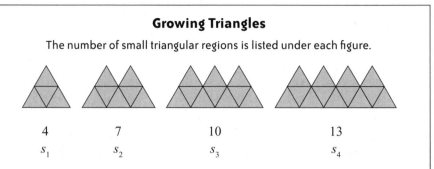

4	7	10	13
s_1	s_2	s_3	s_4

1. Sketch the next figure in the sequence and find s_5, the number of small triangular regions in the figure.

2. Complete the table below by listing the next five terms of sequence s_n.

n	1	2	3	4	5	6	7	8	9	10
Small triangular region count, s_n	4	7	10	13						31

3. Study the table in (2) or the sketches and use them to predict

    a) s_{20} b) s_{45} c) s_{100} d) s_n

4. Find a recursive formula for the small triangular region count, s_n.
5. Find an explicit formula for the small triangular region count, s_n.
6. Find a recursive formula for the total triangular region count, t_n. *Hint t_1 = 5.*
7. Find an explicit formula for the total triangular region count, t_n.
8. Explain how you would use the sequence of figures above to represent the sequence 1, 2, 3, 4,....

9. Let r_n be the sequence of the least number of small triangular regions to add to each figure to make one equilateral triangular region. The first few terms of the sequence are given in the table below.

n	1	2	3	4	5	6	7	8	9	10
Least small triangular region count to add, r_n	0	2	6	12						

    a) Draw the first four figures to verify that the counts in the table are correct.
    b) Complete the table by listing the next six terms of the sequence.

10. Find a recursive formula for the least number of small triangular regions to add count, r_n.

11. Find an explicit formula for the least number of small triangular regions to add count, r_n.

12. What other sequences of numbers could represent the original sequence of figures above? Explain your choices.

Fig. 6.5. Growing triangles

the recursive and explicit formulas. Some students require the hands-on images to see the step-by-step change that takes place. By analyzing the changes that occur from figure to figure, they are often able to "see" a recursive or explicit formula. For instance, one way to view the sketches in figure 6.5 so that the recursive pattern stands out is to observe that that each new sketch is the same as the preceding sketch plus a trapezoid that contains three new triangular regions. Let students try problem 3 (fig. 6.5), which calls for finding s_{20}, s_{45}, s_{100}, s_n on their own before suggesting a process for handling it. Comments on how to treat problems 4–7, 10, and 11 using visual, numerical, or algebraic approaches have occurred earlier in this article.

Students may also perceive patterns and reach conclusions by relying strictly on the numerical data. Some will look simultaneously at the two rows of the table in problem 9 (fig. 6.5) and "see" an explicit formula. After first focusing on $6 = 3 \cdot 2$ and on $12 = 4 \cdot 3$ and then checking the other instances, they will move to a general observation that any number in row 2 of table 6.3 is the product of the number above it and the number to the left in row 1.

Table 6.3
Row 1 and Row 2 Connection

Row 1	1	2	3 ←→ 4		5	6	7	8	9	10
Row 2	0	2	6	12	20	30	42	56	72	90

The reader may note that this is the second appearance of the sequence 0, 2, 6, 12, 20, ..., with $s_n = n(n - 1)$. This repetition suggests another type of investigation for students to explore, namely, given one numerical sequence, find different geometric models that can be associated with the sequence. In this instance, sequences of rectangle models and triangle models are connected with the same numerical sequence.

As mentioned earlier, the method of finite differences is an algebraic procedure that finds those explicit formulas that are polynomials (Bezuszka 1976). To apply finite differences to solve problem 11 (fig. 6.5), represent the data from problem 9 in column form and calculate both the first and the second differences. See table 6.4. This is necessary, since the first differences are not constant, whereas the second differences are constant.

In table 6.5, an arbitrary polynomial of degree 2 is given. The first differences of this quadratic are linear expressions, and the second differences are constant. This result implies that the explicit formula will be a quadratic equation. To find a, b, and c, match corresponding terms in tables 6.4 and 6.5.

$$2a = 2 \text{ implies } a = 1, \ 3a + b = 2, \text{ so } 3 + b = 2 \text{ implies } b = -1,$$
$$a + b + c = 0, \text{ so } 1 + (-1) + c = 0 \text{ implies } c = 0.$$

Table 6.4
Problem 9 Data

n	s_n	1st diff.	2nd diff.
1	0		
		2	
2	2		2
		4	
3	6		2
		6	
4	12		2
		8	
5	20		2
		10	
6	30		

Table 6.5
Second Differences Are Constant

n	$an^2 + bn + c$	1st diff.	2nd diff.
1	$a + b + c$		
		$3a + b$	
2	$4a + 2b + c$		$2a$
		$5a + b$	
3	$9a + 3b + c$		$2a$
		$7a + b$	
4	$16a + 4b + c$		$2a$
		$9a + b$	
5	$25a + 5b + c$		$2a$
		$11a + b$	
6	$36a + 6b + c$		

Substitute the values found for a, b, and c in the expression $an^2 + bn + c$ to get the explicit formula $r_n = n^2 - n = n(n - 1)$, $n \geq 1$, a result that was observed in the data in table 6.3. Likewise, sequences whose third and fourth differences are the first to

Table 6.6
Solutions to "Growing Triangles"

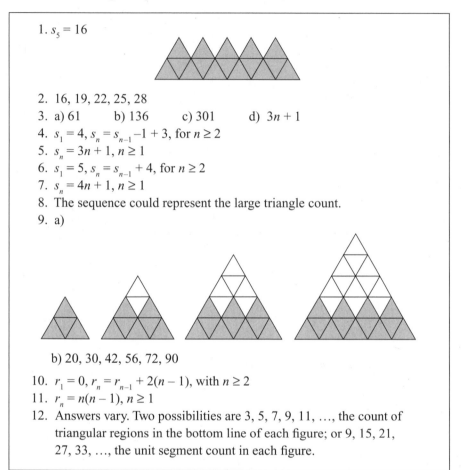

1. $s_5 = 16$

2. 16, 19, 22, 25, 28
3. a) 61   b) 136   c) 301   d) $3n + 1$
4. $s_1 = 4, s_n = s_{n-1} - 1 + 3$, for $n \geq 2$
5. $s_n = 3n + 1, n \geq 1$
6. $s_1 = 5, s_n = s_{n-1} + 4$, for $n \geq 2$
7. $s_n = 4n + 1, n \geq 1$
8. The sequence could represent the large triangle count.
9. a)

b) 20, 30, 42, 56, 72, 90
10. $r_1 = 0, r_n = r_{n-1} + 2(n - 1)$, with $n \geq 2$
11. $r_n = n(n - 1), n \geq 1$
12. Answers vary. Two possibilities are 3, 5, 7, 9, 11, …, the count of
triangular regions in the bottom line of each figure; or 9, 15, 21,
27, 33, …, the unit segment count in each figure.

be constant can be shown to have cubic and quartic polynomial explicit formulas, respectively. A brief but complete set of solutions to all the problems in the sample activity appears in table 6.6.

Conclusion

This article has emphasized the relationship between recursive and explicit formulas and suggests that they have complementary features. Recursive formulas offer the simplicity of understanding, whereas explicit formulas are useful for the identification of the terms of a sequence in any order. Recursive formulas are recommended as a starting point for learning how to derive explicit formulas. The use of examples that blend geometry concepts with number relationships and algebraic thinking are particularly recommended so that students have an opportunity to develop a rich and connected view of how algebra is a powerful tool and much more than generalized arithmetic. A next step to take in the discussion of recursive formulas and explicit formulas could be to explore connections with the principle of mathematical induction.

REFERENCES

Bezuszka, Stanley J. *Applications of Finite Differences*. Chestnut Hill, Mass.: Boston College Press, 1976.

Driscoll, Mark. *Fostering Algebraic Thinking*. Portsmouth, N.H.: Heinemann, 1999.

Lannin, John K. "Developing Mathematical Power by Using Explicit and Recursive Reasoning." *Mathematics Teacher* 98 (November 2004): 216–23.

National Council of Teachers of Mathematics (NCTM). *Principles and Standards for School Mathematics*. Reston, Va.: NCTM, 2000.

Rubenstein, Rheta N. "Building Explicit and Recursive Forms of Patterns with the Function Game." *Mathematics Teaching in the Middle School* 7 (April 2002): 426–31.

7

Algebraic Thinking and Geometric Thinking

Thomas Banchoff

GEOMETRY and algebra are not just two subjects that appear throughout the curriculum; they are also distinct ways of thinking about mathematical ideas. At all levels of education in mathematics, teaching and learning work better when both ways of thinking are involved and when they complement each other. During the past forty years, in my introductory and advanced courses in calculus and linear algebra, I have stressed the interplay between algebra and geometry, using diagrams to illustrate formulas and structures and using algebraic ideas to formalize geometric constructions. Some students already appreciate the power and beauty of the connections between geometry and algebra when they arrive at college; most, unfortunately, do not. In this article, I examine some of the ways that geometric thinking can combine with algebraic thinking to offer students more effective learning and retention of ideas, and I present several of my favorite examples.

Algebraic Formulas: Gaps in Expanding and Factoring

As a young calculus teacher, I was fairly happy with my students' grasp of quadratic equations. They could all recite the quadratic formula, and most could graph a parabola and even find its highest or lowest point. For many of them, that is about where their algebraic thinking and geometric thinking stopped. They could all expand and factor $a^2 - b^2 = (a - b)(a + b)$. That gave me two ways to approach finding the derivative of $y(x) = x^2$. The difference quotient is

$$\frac{(x+h)^2 - x^2}{h},$$

I would like to express special thanks to Michael Schwarz for rendering the illustrations for this article.

and there are two good ways to simplify it. One approach is to expand the square of the binomial to get

$$\frac{(x+h)^2 - x^2}{h} = \frac{(x^2 + 2xh + h^2 - x^2)}{h} = \frac{(2xh + h^2)}{h} = 2x + h.$$

The other approach is to factor the difference of the two squares to get

$$\frac{(x+h)^2 - x^2}{h} = \frac{[(x+h) - x][(x+h) + x]}{h} = \frac{h(2x+h)}{h} = 2x + h,$$

the same result as before. In either situation, we have an expression that goes to $y'(x) = 2x$ as h goes to zero.

Which of the two ways, I wondered, would be more effective as we went on to the next challenge, namely, the derivative of $y(x) = x^3$? Privately I hoped they would prefer the "difference of powers" method, since it works so well to give the first really good example of the chain rule, as follows: If $y(x) = [u(x)]^2$, then the difference quotient is

$$\frac{[y(x + h) - y(x)]}{h} = \frac{[u(x + h) - u(x)][u(x + h) + u(x)]}{h}.$$

The first two terms of the expression go to $u'(x)$ and the third term goes to $2u(x)$, so the derivative is $y'(x) + 2u(x)u'(x)$.

I surveyed my students in the most nonthreatening way I could imagine. I asked them to write the answers to two questions and not put their names on their papers. They also had as much time as they needed to write the answers. The questions were as follows:

1. Expand $(a + b)^3$.

2. Factor $a^3 - b^3 = (a - b)(?)$.

I was surprised at the results. For the first problem, expanding the cube of a binomial, only about half of the students gave the correct answer. Some recalled the solution and simply wrote it down, not always correctly. Others at least realized that they could solve the problem by multiplying out $(a + b)(a^2 + 2ab + b^2)$, which many tried, not always successfully. Others wrote, "I forget the formula."

The second problem was even more discouraging. Hardly anyone managed to come up with the right answer, although a number of them wrote variations involving almost random combinations of a^2, ab, and b^2 and with different algebraic signs and coefficients of 1 or 3. They included comments of the sort, "It's something like this." As far as I could tell, none of them thought to check an answer by multiplying out to see if a proposed answer was correct or to get an idea of why it might be wrong. Most left the problem blank.

"I forget the formula" is a response based on one wrong conception of what algebra actually is. Many students apparently think that "algebra is the study of formulas." What do you do with formulas? You memorize them for tests. What do you do then? You forget them until the next time you have to memorize them. There might be a hundred of these formulas, almost as unrelated as a collection of telephone numbers from different area codes. It is difficult for students to see which of these formulas might actually be useful sometime in the future and therefore worthwhile to try to memorize permanently.

At heart, algebra involves procedures. It may be convenient to remember the formula for cubing a binomial, but it is even better for students to have the confidence that they can reconstruct it as needed.

"It's something like this" is a response that indicates another false or incomplete view of algebra. If you do remember that a formula has a certain form, then you should have confidence that you can check to see if a conjectured formula makes sense by trying it on some examples. In the problem of the difference of cubes, you can multiply things out to see what the correct answer should be. You don't have to memorize the details if you can figure them out.

One student explained that he didn't know how to factor the difference of cubes because his teacher had told him that factoring wasn't important any more. I replied that his teacher was misinformed.

Algebra encompasses many topics, of course, and the ones described here are only two of them. Basically, I would like my students to become confident with algebraic procedures and to know how to check their work along the way. That is the kind of algebraic thinking I would like to see my students bring with them when they come to mathematics in college. I am much more interested in the habits of mind that they bring than the formulas and techniques they have learned how to use.

I suggest that one way to increase understanding and confidence is to emphasize the connections between geometry and algebra throughout the curriculum.

Algebraic Reasoning and Geometric Decompositions

In some dramatic examples, the interplay between algebra and geometry helps many students learn more effectively and remember better. The two problems already mentioned offer examples. How can geometric thinking assist in the algebraic thinking required for expanding powers and factoring differences of powers? As it happens, most students have at one time or another seen a diagram of a square with side $(a + b)$ expressed as a union of a square of side a, a square of side b, and two $a \times b$ rectangles. The analogous figure works in three-dimensional space, decomposing a cube with side $a + b$ into a cube of side a, a cube of side b, three $a \times a \times b$ slabs, and three $a \times b \times b$ columns.

As a check on these formulas and as a help in remembering them, a 3×3 square can be expressed as nine unit squares arranged in a 2×2 square, two 2×1 rectangles, and a unit square, with $9 = 4 + 4 + 1 = 2^2 + 2(2)(1) + 1^2$. In the instance of a $3 \times 3 \times 3$ cube, the decomposition gives a $2 \times 2 \times 2$ cube, three $2 \times 2 \times 1$ slabs, three $2 \times 1 \times 1$ columns, and a unit cube, with $27 = 8 + 12 + 6 + 1 = 2^3 + 3(2^2)1 + 3(2)1^2 + 1^3$. Students who have a good visual memory will profit from recalling both diagrams, especially when they are accompanied by interactive demonstrations.

In the example of factoring the difference of two squares, a square of side a with a square of side b removed, can be expressed as a union of two rectangles, one $(a - b) \times a$ and the other $(a - b) \times b$. These can be combined into an $(a - b) \times (a + b)$ rectangle, summarized as $(a^2 - b^2) = (a - b)(a + b.)$ See figs, 7.1 and 7.2.

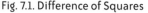

Fig. 7.1. Difference of Squares   Fig. 7.2. Difference of squares (spread)

What about the difference of cubes? That decomposition is less familiar, but it works just as well. We decompose a cube of side a with a cube of side b removed into three rectangular prisms, $(a - b) \times a \times a$, $(a - b) \times a \times b$, and $(a - b) \times b \times b$, summarized as $(a^3 - b^3) = (a - b)(a^2 + ab + b^2)$. (This decomposition also appears in *Math Made Visual* by Claudi Alsina and Roger Nelsen [2006, p. 20]. See fig. 7.3.)

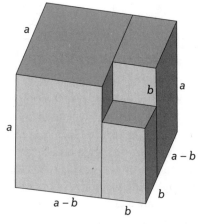

Fig. 7.3. Difference of cubes

Will students who see this demonstration remember it when they are challenged to reconstruct the factorization of the difference of cubes? Some will. Are there times when the same approach will help in solving other important problems? Yes.

One geometric problem that makes beautiful use of the factorization of the difference of cubes is the Egyptian triumph, the formula for the volume of an incomplete pyramid. The story is told in some detail in *Beyond the Third Dimension* (Banchoff 1990b) and in the "Dimension" chapter of *On the Shoulders of Giants* (Banchoff 1990a). It is summarized here.

If we have a trapezoid with height h, with top edge a and bottom edge b, and with the length of the top less than the length of the bottom, we can extend the two nonparallel sides to get a triangle with height $x + h$. We then have

$$\frac{x}{a} = \frac{(h+x)}{b}$$

and

$$x = \frac{ah}{(b-a)},$$

from which we can get

$$x + h = \frac{bh}{(b-a)}.$$

The area of the trapezoid is

$$\frac{[(h+x)b - xa]}{2} = \frac{(bh+ah)}{2} = \frac{h(b+a)}{2}.$$

See figure 7.4.

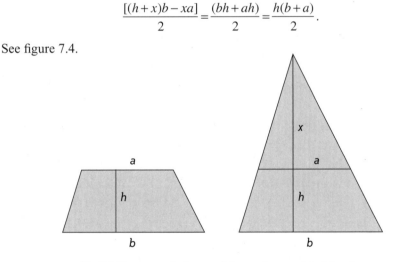

Fig. 7.4. The area of a trapezoid as an incomplete triangle

Likewise, if we have a truncated pyramid with height h and square base of side length b and square top of side length a, then the volume is given by

$$\frac{[(b^2(x+h)-a^2x]}{3}=\frac{\left[\dfrac{b^3h}{(b-a)}-\dfrac{a^3h}{(b-a)}\right]}{3}$$

$$=\left(\frac{h}{3}\right)\left(\frac{b^3-a^3}{b-a}\right)=\left(\frac{h}{3}\right)\left(b^2+ba+a^2\right).$$

The Egyptian pyramid designers' discovery of the same formula is one of the great achievements of ancient mathematics (see fig. 7.5).

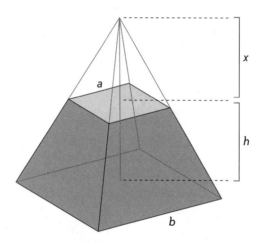

Fig. 7.5. Volume of incomplete pyramid

To return to the problem of finding the derivative of the cube of a function, if we have $y(x) = [u(x)]^3$, then the difference quotient is

$$\frac{y(x+h)-y(x)}{h}=\frac{[u(x+h)]^3-[u(x)]^3}{h}$$

$$=\frac{[u(x+h)-u(x)][(u(x+h))^2+u(x+h)u(x)+(u(x))^2]}{h}.$$

The first two terms of the expression go to $u'(x)$ and the third expression goes to $3u(x)^2$, so $y'(x) = 3[u(x)]^2u'(x)$.

The pattern is clear, and we can use the analogous formula for the difference of nth powers to construct a similar proof of the general power rule. If students are familiar with mathematical induction, it is possible to prove the result using the product rule, another rule in calculus that has a strong geometric counterpart. We will carry this out at the end of the next section.

Multiplication as Area and Volume

Stacking three-dimensional blocks is probably the first experience that most children have with decomposition demonstrations. The number of identical cubical blocks in a stack is the precursor of volume formulas to come up again and again throughout mathematics education.

Somewhat later, children become familiar with two-dimensional flat "puzzles" solved on a table or a floor. These days, children fairly quickly see not only the horizontal placement of flat patterns but also the vertical display on a computer screen. This is an ideal place to describe the processes involved in multiplication. On a blackboard (or whiteboard) or computer screen, there are natural coordinates—distance from the left edge and distance from the bottom. It is somewhat more natural to consider the length of the base multiplied by the height than the more usual length multiplied by width (since many people assume that the length is the larger of the two quantities, whereas there is no such bias with base and height). We see an array of square blocks as n columns, each with m blocks, or as m rows, each with n blocks. What appears on the vertical board then corresponds to the same display on the horizontal page of a workbook.

Commutativity is immediate when multiplication is viewed geometrically. For a rectangular array on the floor, it is just a question of counting the same set of blocks from two different points of view. If we picture the array on a transparency for an overhead projector, we find that it is easy to rotate the array by a quarter-turn, which preserves the total number of blocks while turning the $m \times n$ rectangle into an $n \times m$ rectangle. The fundamental intuition that rotation does not change the size turns into a statement that the product of two positive integers is independent of the order of the factors.

Note that commutativity is not so immediate for students whose primary introduction to multiplication is repeated addition of objects, where the first factor plays a different role from the second. Two times three pounds of sugar does happen to equal three times two pounds of sugar, but that result is not quite so obvious.

Multiplication becomes more subtle when the base and height are given by numbers that are not integers. With the area interpretation, students should have little trouble with $4 \times (1/2)$ or $(1/2) \times 4$. It is more difficult to deal with an expression like "1/2 of 4" and to recognize that it represents the same number as "4 of 1/2." The area interpretation also makes it easier to deal with $1/2 \times 3/4$ or products of decimals.

The distributive rule also works well with the area interpretation. Two rectangles with the same number of rows can be placed side by side to form another rectangle with the same number of rows, a fundamental demonstration of the distributive property, not just of whole numbers, but also for any numbers that can be represented as lengths of segments on the real line. We always have $(ah + bh) = (a + b)h$.

The next step is to multiply two sums, $(a + c)(b + d)$, and to express this as the union of four rectangles. Separating into two columns corresponds to $a(b + d) + c(b + d) = ab + ad + cb + cd$, and separating into two rows gives $(a + b)c + (a + b)d = ac + bc + ad + bd$, two different orderings of the four subrectangles. The latter ordering is the one memorialized in the famous FOIL rule: First (ab), Outer (ad), Inner (cb), and Last (cd). See figure 7.6.

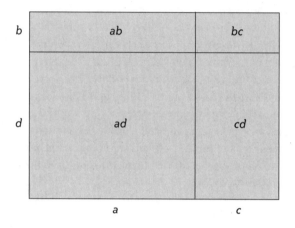

Fig. 7.6. Distributive law

When we want to find the rate of change of a product, we can always interpret it as the rate of change of the area of a rectangle as the sides are changing. If $x(t)$ and $y(t)$ are the sides of a rectangle, then the area is $A(t) = x(t) \cdot y(t)$. If $x(t)$ and $y(t)$ are increasing, then the rectangle with sides $x(t + h)$ and $y(t + h)$ contains the rectangle with sides $x(t)$ and $y(t)$. Removing the smaller rectangle from the larger leaves an area that can be expressed as the union of two rectangles. Algebraically, this corresponds to $A(t + h) - A(t) = x(t + h) \cdot y(t + h) - x(t) \cdot y(t) = (x(t + h) - x(t)) \cdot y(t + h) + x(t) \cdot (y(t + h) - y(t))$. Dividing by h and taking the limit as h goes to 0 gives the familiar formula $A'(t) = x'(t)y(t) + x(t)y'(t)$. Giving that algebraic argument and including the geometric picture amounts to bestowing on the student a powerful connection between algebraic and geometric thinking (see fig. 7.7).

Once we have worked out the product rule, we can set up the proof of the general power formula by induction: If $y(t) = [x(t)]^n$ has derivative $y'(t) = n[x(t)]^{n+1} \cdot x'(t)$, then $z(t) = [x(t)]^{n+1} = x(t)y(t)$ so $z'(t) = [x'(t)] \cdot y(t) + x(t) \cdot y'(t) = [x'(t)^n] + [x(t) \cdot nx(t)^{n-1} \cdot x'(t)] = [(n + 1)x(t)^n] \cdot [x'(t)]$, as expected.

When we have the product of three numbers, we can immediately think of the volume of a rectangular solid. A $3 \times 4 \times 2$ solid can be thought of as three 4×2 slabs, or as 3×4 slabs taken twice (see fig. 7.8).

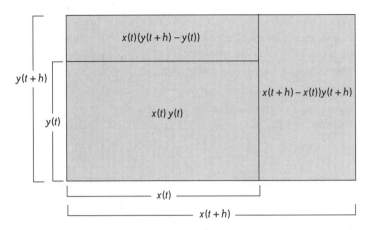

Fig. 7.7. Product rule

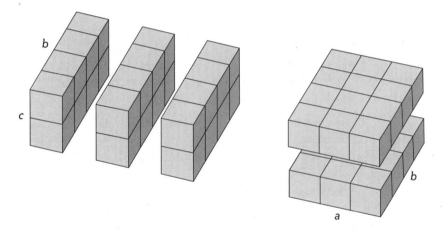

Fig. 7.8. Demonstrating the associative law: $a \times (b \times c) = (a \times b) \times c$

This elementary fact about arithmetic appears in the differential calculus when we consider $f(x) = (u(x) \cdot v(x)) \cdot w(x)$ and proceed to derive $f'(x) = [(u(x) \cdot v'(x)) \cdot w(x)] + [(u(x) \cdot v(x)) \cdot w'(x)] = [(u'(x) \cdot v(x)) \cdot w(x)] + [(u(x) \cdot v'(x)) \cdot w(x)] + [(u(x) \cdot v(x)) \cdot w'(x)]$.

Proofs in Algebra and Proofs in Geometry

When we combine algebraic thinking and geometric thinking, we get a different interpretation of the meaning of proof. In a sense, the geometric demonstration can show why an algebraic argument works, and an algebraic formulation of a geometric demonstration can reveal formal patterns that correspond to the geometric ones.

One theorem in geometry that is familiar to just about everyone is the Pythagorean theorem, memorized in the symbolic form $a^2 + b^2 = c^2$. There is a perfectly good geometric proof of this theorem based on reasoning with generic pictures.

We start the discussion with a specific picture based on a square subdivided into four small squares, each divided in two by a diagonal so that there are four triangles with their right angles meeting at the center of the original square. These four triangles determine a rotated square with area one-half the original square (see fig. 7.9).

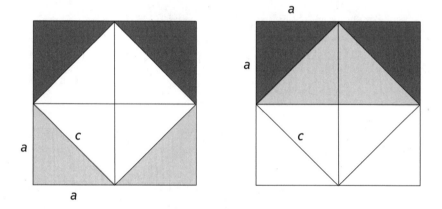

Fig. 7.9. Pythagorean theorem (special case): $c^2 = 2a^2$

The more general case refers to the square of side $a + b$ subdivided into two squares, a^2 and b^2, and two rectangles with area ab. We can subdivide each of these rectangles by a diagonal and move the four right angles of the resulting triangles to the corners of the original $a + b$ square, leaving inside a rotated square region with side equal in length to c, the longest side of each of these right triangles. The conclusion is that $a^2 + 2ab + b^2 = c^2 + 2ab$, so $a^2 + b^2 = c^2$ (see fig. 7.10).

This demonstration constitutes a proof. It is a convincing argument, and it is completely general. It works for any pair of positive real numbers a and b. The beauty of this geometric proof is that it can be appreciated at so many different levels. Elementary school students can arrange blocks in a tray. In middle school, students know formulas for the area of a square and a right triangle, and the sum of the different terms is a precursor to algebraic manipulations. High school students will see other proofs and use them in analytic geometry in the plane, and perhaps even in three dimensions. But everyone should see a proof like the one given in figure 7.10. With such a proof in mind, the formula can be used with confidence from then on. Slightly more subtle is the formula for the area of a parallelogram in the coordinate plane with vertices given by $(0, 0)$, (a, b), $(a + c, b + d)$, and (c, d) (see fig. 7.11).

If A denotes the area of this parallelogram, then $A + ab + cd + 2bc$ equals the

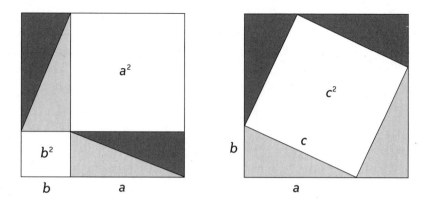

Fig. 7.10. Pythagorean theorem

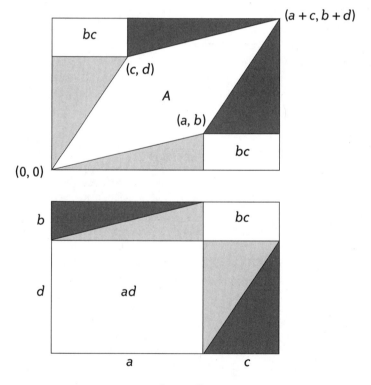

Fig. 7.11. Area of a paralleogram

area of the rectangle with sides $a + c$ and $b + d$, namely, $ab + ad + cb + cd$. It follows that the area of the parallelogram is $ad - bc$. The subtlety in this proof is that it works only if the slope of the line between $(0, 0)$ and (a, b) is less than the slope of the line between $(0, 0)$ and (c, d) so that we traverse the four vertices of the parallelogram in counterclockwise order. If the slope of the line between $(0, 0)$ and (a, b) is less than the slope of the line between $(0, 0)$ and (c, d) so that we traverse the four vertices of the parallelogram in clockwise order, that leads to a negative area, something that is not treated the first or second or third time through. But that is the subject of another article.

Conclusion

In this article, I have examined a number of mathematical topics that involve both algebraic and geometric aspects. Some are quite elementary, others are appropriate for middle and high school, and still others arise in college courses. Readers will be able to think of many more illustrations of this phenomenon that appear at different levels of education, some several times in progressively more sophisticated guises. If the connections between algebraic thinking and geometric thinking are emphasized each time they arise, then students can approach each new topic with greater understanding and with greater confidence. I appreciate the teachers who imbue their students with an appreciation of both algebra and geometry and their connections, and I look forward to more and more students who come to college wanting to continue those challenges—in algebra, geometry, and all the other subjects that depend on them.

REFERENCES

Alsina, Claudi, and Roger Nelsen. *Math Made Visual: Creating Images for Understanding Mathematics.* Washington, D.C.: Mathematical Association of America, 2006.

Banchoff, Thomas. "Dimension." In *On the Shoulders of Giants: New Approaches to Numeracy,* edited by Lynn Steen, pp. 11–60. Washington, D.C.: National Academy Press, 1990a.

———. *Beyond the Third Dimension: Geometry, Computer Graphics, and Higher Dimensions.* New York: Scientific American Library, 1990b.

Part 3

Studies on the Learning of Algebra

8

Patterns That Support Early Algebraic Thinking in the Elementary School

Elizabeth Warren
Tom J. Cooper

O VER a period of three years, we conducted an extensive longitudinal study in Australia aimed at ascertaining teachers' actions, activities, questions, and conversations that support the development of early algebraic thinking in the elementary school classroom. The study was conducted in five classrooms and consisted of teaching experiments focused on the development of an understanding of equivalence and equations, functional thinking, patterning, and generalized arithmetic. In this article, we report on one of those experiments involving repeating patterns and geometric growing patterns.

As we began our work, we were aware that students spend a great deal of time in their early years in school investigating repeating patterns, but they have little experience with geometric growing patterns. There are three major reasons for exploring geometric growing patterns in the elementary school classroom: (1) they are visual representations of number patterns, (2) they can be used as an informal introduction to the concept of a variable, and (3) they can be used to generate equivalent expressions.

The specific purpose of the study was to identify and characterize activities that help elementary school students distinguish repeating patterns from growing patterns, to establish relationships between data sets, to extend patterns, and to develop an awareness of the synergy between patterns and tables of values. The article is organized by mathematical idea and illustrated with activities and students' work. We begin by describing how we distinguished repeating patterns from growing patterns.

Identifying the Repeating Component in Patterns

A repeating pattern is defined as a pattern in which there is an identifiable unit that repeats, that is, a cyclical structure that can be generated by the repeated application of the smallest portion of the pattern. Growing patterns have discernible units commonly called *terms*, and each term in the pattern depends on the previous term and its position in the pattern. Many growing patterns involve the use of concrete materials arranged in a geometric configuration. See figure 8.1.

Repeating patterns

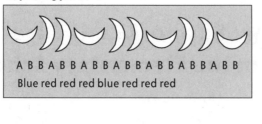

A B B A B B A B B A B B A B B A B B A B B
Blue red red red blue red red red

Growing patterns

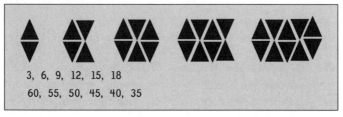

3, 6, 9, 12, 15, 18
60, 55, 50, 45, 40, 35

Fig. 8.1. Examples of repeating patterns and growing patterns

Number patterns (constructed from numbers) are of two types. Some number patterns are repeating patterns (e.g., 122122122 ...) in which the numbers are treated as shapes; their numerical values are not important. Other number patterns, like 3, 7, 11, 15, 19, ..., are growing patterns. The numbers have values, and differences between pairs of successive numbers in the pattern are important. In this article, we discuss growing patterns that always involve a constant change between successive elements in the pattern.

The Importance of the Repeating Component

We suggest that there are two different representations for repeating patterns, one that emphasizes the rhythm of the pattern and one that focuses on the repeat. For example, for the pattern consisting of the repeating component of one white tile and one black tile, many young students tended to see this as a continual chant, "White, black, white, black, white, black, white, black." Many students experienced difficulty identifying the repeating component and breaking the pattern into its repeating parts "white black, (pause) white black, (pause) white black, (pause)." Identifying the repeating component is important, since it allows students to differentiate the visual difference between a repeating pattern as illustrated above and a geometric growing pattern, such as white, black (pause); white, black, black (pause);

white, black, black, black (pause); where the black tiles are continually growing by one. Students can begin to see the distinction between these two presentations and thus (*a*) relate geometric growing patterns to growing number patterns, (*b*) explore repeating patterns as repeated addition, and (*c*) investigate repeating patterns as representations of division with a remainder.

Beginning to Distinguish the Visual Difference between a Repeating Pattern and a Growing Pattern

To help students distinguish between repeating and geometric growing patterns, we encourage them to make two copies of the same repeating pattern (e.g., blue, yellow, blue, yellow …), one beneath the other and ask them which color they would like to grow and by how much (see fig. 8.2).

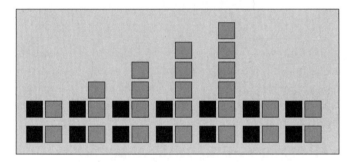

Fig. 8.2. An example of "growing the yellow tiles by 1"

The following excerpts are from conversations with five-year-olds engaged in an activity to distinguish between repeating and growing patterns and to convert a repeating pattern into a growing pattern.

Teacher: Let's make the yellow tiles grow. In the repeating part there is one yellow tile and one blue tile. How many tiles do we want the yellow tiles to grow by?

John: One tile.

Students were directed to put one more yellow tile under the yellow tile in the second repeat and to identify the total number of yellow tiles in this repeat (see fig. 8.2). They were then asked, "How is this different from the first set of elements?" Pointing to the yellow tile in the third repeat, the teacher asked, "How many yellow tiles will we need for this repeat? Remember it is growing by 1."

Many students simply added one extra yellow tile to the third repeat, making a total of two yellow tiles instead of three yellow tiles. The discussion then focused on whether it was the same as the second step or different. Eventually the students came to the conclusion that the third repeat needed three yellow tiles altogether and the fourth repeat required four yellow tiles. Matthew commented, "It's 1, 2, 3, 4, 5, 6, 7, 8, 9," each time pointing to the column of yellow tiles in each step. "Each one is growing by 1. In the other pattern [the repeating pattern] they are all the same. There is only one yellow tile in each."

Once this distinction was made, students were directed to make a growing pattern and to record the number of tiles under each step (see fig. 8.3).

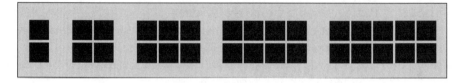

Fig. 8.3. A geometric growth pattern representing the number
pattern 2, 4, 6, 8

The results of our work with these students suggest that five-year-olds not only are capable of exploring repeating and growing patterns in parallel but also can separate a repeating pattern into its repeats and then allow the separated repeats to "grow." This is crucial in helping them develop language and visual representations that make the distinction between repeating and growing patterns.

Exploring Repeating Patterns as Repeated Addition

Physically splitting the repeating pattern into its repeating components also assisted older students (with an average age of 7 years, 6 months) to use repeating patterns to develop an understanding of repeated addition, multiplication, and division. For example, we placed the numeral 3 under each set as shown in figure 8.4 and asked, "How many tiles are in the first two repeats? The first five repeats? How did you work it out? How many groups of three are there? How many hearts? How many triangles? How many altogether? How did you work it out?" In these discussions, the students were beginning to engage in conversations about proportional reasoning.

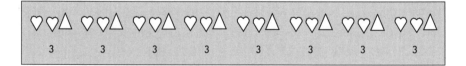

Fig. 8.4. Representing a repeating pattern as
repeated addition

Investigating Repeating Patterns as Division with a Remainder

We found that the repeating patterns can also assist in discussions on division, especially division with nonzero remainders. We pointed to the first heart (fig. 8.4) and said, "This is the first tile in the repeating pattern." Then we pointed to the triangle and asked, "What tile is this in the repeating pattern? (3rd) Which other tiles are triangles (6th, 9th, 12th, 15th, 18th, 21st, 24th, 27th)? How did you work it out? What is the shape of the 25th tile?" The following excerpt from conversations with students exemplifies some typical responses to this task.

Teacher: What is the shape of the 25th tile? Explain how you worked it out.

Sam: It is a heart because the 24th tile is a triangle, so it must be one more, which is a heart.

Jill: You know the 27th tile is a triangle, so it is two back. It must be a heart.

Penny: You divide 25 by 3 (three shapes in each repeat) and there is one left, so it is the first tile of the next repeat. It is a heart.

As suggested by these samples of results from our work, the activities helped young students to distinguish repeating patterns from growing patterns, to relate geometric growing patterns to corresponding number patterns, to bring out the mathematics embedded in repeating patterns, and to use repeating patterns to support conversations about multiplication and division.

Establishing Relationships among Data Sets

The aim of this next series of teaching activities was to identify actions that help elementary school students to reconceptualize simple repeating and growing patterns in ways that not only support reaching generalizations but also provide opportunities to develop an understanding of functional reasoning. Algebraic thinking is seen as thinking that focuses on identifying the underlying mathematical relationships that exist among data sets and expressing these relationships in everyday language and with notation systems. Through their explorations, students can begin to develop an understanding of two important ideas that underpin algebraic thinking, namely, the variable and equivalent situations. The following section illustrates the types of activities and questions that supported the development of this thinking. All the activities were conducted with students whose average age was 8 years, 6 months. The sequence was as follows.

Simple repeating patterns, such as ABBABBABB, were used and represented with red and green tiles that were cut from sheets of foam. The students worked in pairs, with each pair manipulating its own set of tiles. The pattern shown in figure

8.5 was created on the board. Students were asked to re-create this pattern with their own tiles and place a card over the pattern so that only the first set of elements (or tiles) that repeat was visible, as in figure 8.6.

Fig. 8.5. A repeating pattern

Fig. 8.6. Covering all the pattern except one repeat

We asked, "How many red tiles are there? How many green tiles are there? How many tiles are there altogether?" The set of tiles that repeats consists of one red and two green tiles. Next, we directed students to uncover enough of the pattern to show two sets of repeating tiles (see fig. 8.7), and then we asked, "How many red tiles are there? How many green tiles are there? How many tiles are there altogether?"

Fig. 8.7. Uncovering the pattern to show two repeats

This sequence of uncovering parts of the pattern and asking questions about the numbers of tiles was continued until five sets were visible. The students had now generated three data sets—namely, the number of repeats, the number of red tiles, and the number of green tiles—in that number of repeats. This reformulation of the repeating pattern allowed for an exploration of the concept of ratio. For example, for two repeats the ratio of red to green is 2 to 4, and for five repeats the ratio is 5 to 10. The actions of physically uncovering different numbers of repeats and counting the number of tiles in these repeats also supported the development of an understanding of the relationship between the number of repeats and the ratio it represented.

Some of the growing patterns that we used in our teaching experiments were constructed from tiles and fence patterns made from toothpicks. In all instances we chose patterns where the link between the step number and the pattern was made explicit by deliberate spacing. Figure 8.8 illustrates two growing patterns, one fence pattern and one tile pattern, that were presented to be explored by the students.

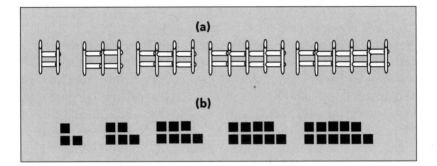

Fig. 8.8. Two geometric growing patterns used in the teaching phase

Students were directed to replicate each growing pattern. Then they were given cards marked with 1st, 2nd, and 3rd and told to place these cards under each step in the pattern. This procedure not only furnished a visual representation of the two data sets (i.e., the position and the number of tiles or fence posts in each position) but also allowed for discussions about what the 10th and the 12th steps would look like. The use of cards also allowed for the creation of patterns in which some steps were not given, as, for example, in presenting only the 1st, 5th, and 6th steps. We found that this helped students to begin to look for the link between the step number and the number of tiles in that step. For example, in the tile pattern in figure 8.8, the 6th step has 6 tiles in the top row and 7 tiles in the bottom row. Students were beginning to realize that the number of tiles in the top row is the same as the step number and the number of tiles in the bottom row is one more than the step number. Previously, their responses tended to be that, each time, the top row grows by one and the bottom row grows by two.

Extending Patterns

From these discussions we proceeded to activities that supported students in expressing generality and exploring the concept of a variable. We wanted students to be able to generalize relationships from a small number of countable repeats within a pattern to the extension of that pattern with many uncountable repeats. For example, for the RRGGGRRGGG pattern, we would ask the following questions:

If I had 10 red tiles, how many green tiles would I have? How many repeats are there?

If I had 30 red tiles, how many green tiles would I have?

If I had 60 green tiles, how many red tiles would I have? How many sets of

tiles would I have?

If I had 100 repeats, how many red tiles would there be? How many green tiles would there be?

Most students answered these questions quite easily.

For the growing patterns, students (average age 8 years, 6 months) were asked to construct elements of patterns that were beyond those that had been given. Students were given a step number on a card (e.g., the 20th step) and asked to create the element for that step number. They were then asked to describe the pattern according to the step number. For example, for the 20th step of the fence pattern, Sarah said, "The fence has 21 vertical posts and 2 groups of 20 horizontal posts. It has 61 posts altogether." We found that creating and describing steps for extended patterns is an important phase in helping students identify the rule for any step. For the fence pattern, the rule is *the number of vertical posts is one more than the step number and the number of horizontal posts is twice the step number.*

Using Tables of Values

The second phase of this set of activities involved recording data in a table. Previous research indicates that students commonly look down a table to find patterns. For example, they tend to say that the number of green tiles is increasing by 1 or the total number of tiles is increasing by 3. We refer to this as the recursive approach to functional thinking (in this example, the additive strategy) (Warren 1996). Another kind of functional thinking involves searching for patterns across the rows of the table, that is, identifying the relationship between pairs of data sets (the explicit functional approach). Both types of thinking are important in mathematics. Since specific language is seen to assist students in their interpretations of mathematical situations (Warren 2003), students created a table representing the repeating pattern, RRGRRGRRG (two red tiles followed by one green tile) and were asked to identify three patterns *down* the table and three patterns *across* the table. The table consisted of three columns. In the first column they recorded the number of repeats. In the second and third columns they recorded the number of red and green tiles, respectively, for the number of repeats. Samples of students' responses are given in figure 8.9. We found that by restricting the number of responses offered for *down* the table patterns to three, students were encouraged to look across the table. The aim of this activity was to facilitate students' use of their "across" rules to generalize patterns in the table of values.

For growing patterns the introduction of explicit language and questions helped students identify the relationship between the two data sets, that is, the step number and the number of tiles or posts in each step. A distinction was made between a growing rule (i.e., a recursive approach) and a position rule (i.e., an explicit functional approach). The following excerpt exemplifies some typical classroom dialogue about the tiling pattern in figure 8.8(b):

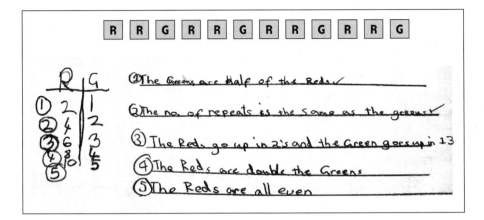

Fig. 8.9. Students' responses to describing the patterns in the table for repeating patterns

Teacher: Tell me about this pattern. How can we describe this pattern according to its step number?

Mat: It is growing by 2 each time, one for the top and one for the bottom.

Teacher: We call this a *growing rule*, since this tells us how the pattern is growing. I want you to look at the step number and the tiles in each step and tell me how they are related.

Sue: The top row has the same number as the step number, and the bottom row has one more.

Teacher: Well done. That is a *position rule*. (Notice that Sue used the step number in her description.)

From the results of our research we contend that tables of values facilitate students' systematic search for an explicit pattern rule. The common strategy used was systematic guessing and checking by testing addition, subtraction, multiplication, division, a combination of multiplication and addition, and a combination of multiplication and subtraction, in that order. This helped students find a general rule, but that rule was often stated specifically. For example, for the fence pattern (see fig. 8.8(a)) the rule students identified was *three times the step number and add 1*. One of the difficulties encountered by students occurred when they established the general rule from the table of values rather than from the physical situation. In this instance, they could not necessarily relate the rule back to the pattern or express the rule in a variety of ways. For example, for the pattern in figure 8.8(b):

Teacher: What is the general rule?

Jill: You multiply the step number by 2 and add 1.

Teacher:	How did you find this?
Jill:	Just kept guessing and checking. Two times 2 add 1 is 5.
Teacher:	How is this rule related to the pattern? Which part is the multiply by 2? Which part is the add 1?
Jill:	I don't know.

The question with which many researchers have struggled is the relationship between the visual pattern and the table of values. In our research, the table of values seemed to help students find the general rule. However, if students experience difficulties in relating the rule to the visual representation, one must ask why use the visual representations in the first place? What role do visual representations play in developing students' understanding of the concept of a variable? Why don't we simply search for patterns in tables of values, thus reducing the difficulty of the task and making it accessible to more students (Warren 2005a)? Or we might ask if it is appropriate to rush into using the table of values representation. We shall return to this issue later in this article.

Beginning Notation Systems

Although the use of symbols to generalize relationships is not common practice in the elementary school or even seen as appropriate in many classrooms in the Australian context, we decided to see how generally our students could think. We posed the following questions: "If I have *n* repeats, how many red tiles do I have? How many green tiles? How many tiles in all?"

The discussion consisted of three phases. First, students were asked: "For this repeating pattern, if I had an unknown number of sets of tiles, how would I work out how many red tiles, green tiles, and total number of tiles I had?" A typical response was, "You would double the number of sets and that would be how many green ones." We then asked: "How could we write this? What symbols could we use for the unknown?" Some students suggested that we use a square with a question mark in it ?⃞ to represent the unknown. Most were comfortable with this notational system, and some wrote: 2*x*. Finally, the decision was made to use letters to represent the unknown. Many students were not as comfortable with this notation system and continued to express generalities using the box notation. The same sequence of questions was used in our discussions of growing patterns.

The students were also introduced to representing the comparison between the two parts, the number of red tiles and the number of green tiles, as a ratio. For the repeating pattern RRGGGRRGGGRRGGGRRGGG, a fourth column was added to the table and the ratio of red tiles to green tiles was recorded as 2 to 3, 4 to 6, 12 to 18, 40 to 60, and so on. Figure 8.10 gives examples of some of the students' responses to the question, "For *n* repeats, what is the ratio of red tiles to green tiles?" For response (d), Sarah added another "arm" to *n* for the reds, saying, "We have *m* [sounding an m sound] reds because there is another arm on the *n* for the number of red tiles and ⌒ [sounding a long nnn sound] because there are 2 arms on the *n* for the number of green tiles." As evidenced by responses like these, students as young as eight years can engage in conversations about ratios and can begin to express these ideas using abstract notation.

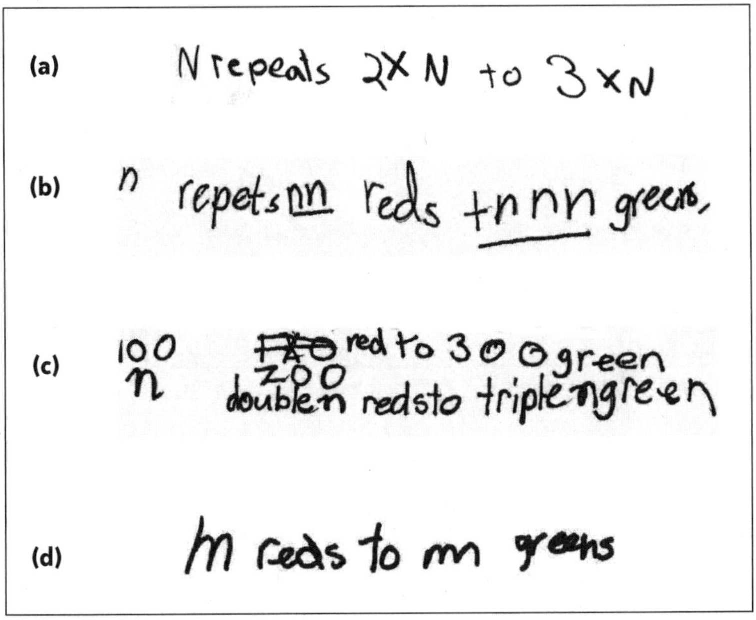

Fig. 8.10. Students' responses to "If I had *n* repeats, what is the ratio of reds to greens?"

Developing an Awareness of the Synergy between Patterns and Tables of Values

In order to explore the role of the actual physical representation in growing patterns in one of our classrooms, we decided to restrict our discussion of expressing generality by not introducing the recording of data in tables of values. We relied on students' visual identification of the relationship between the pattern and the step number in order to reach a general rule. We found that initially this was a struggle for students, since it relied on a number of skills that are not commonly related to the algebraic domain, namely, the ability to visually separate a pattern into its component parts and then to relate these parts to the step number. This required explicit classroom discourse. The discussions were supported by the use of concrete manipulatives, allowing students to construct and deconstruct patterns. Students were encouraged to publicly share and defend their thinking. This led to different ways of describing the pattern, which in turn led to different expressions for the same relationship. The following excerpts illustrate the type of discourse and actions that supported the development of a discussion about equivalent expressions. The dialogue relates to the fence pattern shown in figure 8.8(a). The fence pattern proved to be an important stimulus for discussions. Students could "act out" the construction of the fence as they described their solutions.

Teacher: What would the fence look like for step 5? For step 5, the fence is 5 panels long. How many posts would we need?

Henry: Horizontal is double the step number, and vertical is one more than the step number. So it is 2 times 5, add 5, and add 1.

Henry rearranged his posts to support his description (see fig. 8.11).

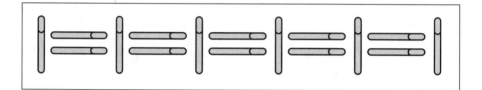

Fig. 8.11. Henry's rearrangement of the posts

Teacher: What if the fence is 58 panels long? How many fence posts would we need?

Henry: It would be double 58 for the horizontal posts and 58 plus 1 for the vertical posts. So it would be 2 times 58, add 58, and add 1.

Teacher: How would I make this fence?

Henry: You would put all the vertical posts in and then all the horizontal posts.

Teacher: How else could I make the fence?

Billy: You could put the post in, then 2 rails and a post, then another post with 2 rails and a post.

Billy rearranged his "posts" to show this (see fig. 8.12).

Teacher: How many posts do I have to carry each time?

Billy: Three and those three things [*pointing to the group of three posts*] you would have to do 58 times.

Teacher: So I take the 58 and multiply it by 3. Does that give me every post I need?

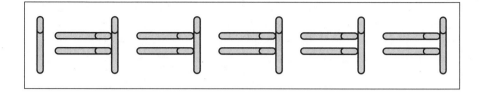

Fig. 8.12. Billy's rearrangement of the posts

Billy: No, you have missed the first one. So it is 58 times 3 and add 1.

Teacher: So we have two ways of writing this, 2 times 58 add 58 add 1, and 58 times 3 add 1. Are they the same? Why are they the same?

This dialogue continued for different fence constructions, consisting of 1, 2, 3, and 4 rails and finally to discussions of expressions such as $2n + n + 1$ and $3n + 1$ and whether they are equivalent. The most difficult aspect of this series of activities was the deconstruction and reconstruction of the pattern and expressing the component parts as related to the step number. Yet it was within this activity that discussions about equivalent expressions occurred. For example, *Is $2n + n + 1$ the same as $3n + 1$? Why?*

Thus, we suggest that the geometric pattern has an important role to play in helping students explore both equivalent ratios and equivalent expressions. However, it does call on an array of different thinking skills not commonly found in the algebraic domain, namely, visual and spatial thinking. The table of values helps in efficiently reaching generalized rules, and the visual patterns support discussions about equivalence. It is the synergy between both representations that results in rich dialogues about variables, equivalent expressions, and equivalent ratios. We believe a continual mapping from one to the other is imperative to support these understandings.

Concluding Comments

The characteristics that underpinned all our classroom work were (*a*) believing that young students can engage in conversations about generalizations and express these generalizations using notational systems, (*b*) using materials that exemplify the mathematical ideas being explored, (*c*) choosing activities with numbers that are within the cognitive domain of the students with whom we are engaged, (*d*) encouraging students to share and defend their understandings with other students, (*e*) asking directive questions that target the heart of the mathematics embedded within the activity, (*f*) introducing explicit language that helps students formulate verbal responses, (*g*) using a range of representations to illustrate the same mathematical idea, (*h*) encouraging students to visualize the patterns in more than one way, and (*i*) allowing students to be "wrong."

We have presented four important actions that support the development of algebraic thinking in elementary school classrooms through patterning activities. The first involves decomposing a repeating pattern into its repeats, since this helps young students make the visual distinction between repeating and growing patterns. It also supports the natural progression from repeating to growing patterns and effectively links geometric growing patterns to number patterns.

The second incorporates physical representation of the data sets that are under discussion with regard to expressing generality. The uncovering of successive repeats for the repeating patterns and the introduction of cards with positional language (e.g., 1st step, 2nd step, 3rd step) to place under the steps of the growing patterns certainly helped focus students on the fundamental elements of the discussion, the two data sets and the relationship between them.

The third action entails creating extended patterns, recording these data in tables of values, and using explicit discussions, language, and symbols to help young students begin to express generality. In particular, the use of "across" rules, position rules, "down" rules, and growing rules helped students see the distinction between covariational and single-variational thinking.

The fourth embodies recognizing the synergy between the visual pattern and the tables of values and recognizing the importance each plays in expressing generality and in creating multiple expressions for the same relationship. Most students found it difficult to manipulate visual patterns to represent different expressions of generality. Activities focusing on deconstructing and reconstructing the pattern itself facilitated this process.

Although we acknowledge that many students experienced difficulties in expressing generalizations in everyday language and writing these generalizations using abstract notational systems, we believe these activities were instrumental in helping young students commence this journey, and that it is in the experimentation and conversations that growth occurs.

REFERENCES

Warren, Elizabeth. "Interactions between Instructional Approaches, Students' Reasoning Processes and Their Understanding of Elementary Algebra." Ph.D. diss., Queensland [Australia] University of Technology, 1996.

———. "Language, Arithmetic and Young Children's Interpretations." *Focus on Learning Problems in Mathematics* 25, no. 4 (2003): 22–35.

———. "Young Children's Ability to Generalize the Pattern Rule for Growing Patterns." In *Proceedings of the 29th Conference of the International Group for the Psychology of Mathematics Education*, vol. 4, edited by Helen Chick and Jill Vincent, pp. 305–12. Melbourne, Victoria: University of Melbourne, 2005.

9

Using Number Sentences to Introduce the Idea of Variable

Toshiakira Fujii
Maxwell Stephens

THIS article uses students' growing knowledge of arithmetical operations in the elementary school as the basis for the development of ideas about variable numerical quantities. Relating numerical and symbolic expressions provides an important bridge between arithmetic operations and the idea of variable, which students need to cross continually during their elementary, middle, and junior high school years.

Building on What Students Know

In the early years of elementary school, the focus for almost all teaching of number is on developing a strong foundation in counting and numeration. What is neglected is the use of students' knowledge of number and operations with numbers as the bases for developing ideas about variables as representing varying quantities. Carpenter and Levi (1999) draw attention to this "artificial separation of arithmetic and algebra," which, they argue, "deprives children of powerful schemes for thinking about mathematics in the early grades and makes it more difficult for them to learn algebra in the later grades" (p. 3).

In their study, Carpenter and Levi (1999) introduced first- and second-grade students to the concept of true and false number sentences. When some first and second graders were asked to decide whether a number sentence such as $78 - 49 + 49 = 78$ was true, Carpenter and Levi reported that some students needed to treat it as a calculation because the numbers were large. By contrast, other students interviewed in the same study said, "Of course it is true. The result has to be 78 because you have taken away 49 and then given it back." These responders were then asked, "Is it only true if you take away 49 and then give back 49?" Some students gave responses such as, "You will still get 78 if you took away another number and then added the same number back."

It was never the intention of Carpenter and Levi to introduce first- and second-grade students to a formal algebraic expression, $x - y + y = x$. What they wanted students to understand is that the sentence $78 - 49 + 49 = 78$ belongs to a type of number sentence that is always true regardless of the number that is taken away and then added back. This is a good example of what Blanton and Kaput (2001) mean when they urge teachers, especially in the elementary grades, to grow "algebra eyes and ears" (p. 91). Here especially, teachers can assist students in identifying particular numbers that can vary without affecting the truth of the expression. These expressions provide an important bridge between arithmetic and the idea of a variable. This approach offers a counterbalance to the common treatment of algebra in the elementary and middle or junior high school, where the concept of finding an *unknown* dominates students' and teachers' thinking.

Number sentences, such as $\square + 8 = 23$, and $63 - \square = 49$, introduce students to the task of finding the value of unknown numbers. Later, these sentences can be expressed using literal symbols in forms such as $x + 8 = 23$ and $63 - y = 49$. Here x and y do not act as variables. An emphasis on single-value, missing-number sentences in the elementary and middle school years can create difficulties later on when students meet variable quantities. As Radford (1996) points out, "While the unknown is a number which does not vary, the variable designates a quantity whose value can change" (p. 47). Even when literal symbols are used, many students still rely on computational or guess-and-check methods to solve these problems.

Quasi-Variable Thinking

Students' *general* explanations of why number sentences like $78 - 49 + 49 = 78$ are true and their ability to generate specific instances of what they will later see as a general relationship ($78 - a + a = 78$) have been described by Fujii and Stephens (2001), Fujii (2003), and Lins and Kaput (2004) as *quasi-variable* thinking. This type of thinking recognizes that young students are not able to grasp the full *range of variation* that is implied by the formal expression $78 - a + a = 78$, where a can represent rational and negative numbers, not just counting numbers. Further, students usually say that the number being subtracted (from 78) must be a number less than 78. This is a further feature of *quasi-variable* thinking. Such upper limits or boundary values, typically applied by students to number sentences, do not apply to formal algebraic statements where the range of the variable can be unlimited. Later it will be argued that the explicit use of boundary values, far from being an impediment to students' thinking about variable number quantities, actually seems to help them to recognize and deal with variable quantities embedded in number sentences.

To facilitate their understanding of the $78 - a + a = 78$ relationship, ask students to consider if a sentence like $78 - 49 + 49 = 78$ could still be true if the first number was other than 78. Invite them to write some other sentences like the one above but using different numbers. Ask older students to find the value of the missing number in a sentence such as $78 - 49\frac{3}{4} + \square = 78$. Create a further challenge by asking, "If you know that the sentence $78 - 49 + 49 = 78$ is true, what number makes the sentence $78 - 49 + \square = 79$ true?" The goal in these examples is to have students attend to the *structure* of the sentence in order to decide what numbers make the sentence true, not to carry out all the calculations indicated in order to determine the values of the missing numbers.

Peter's Method

We used an interview-dialogue with second- and third-grade students in Japan and Australia to introduce individual students to families of number sentences involving addition and subtraction. Our aim was to see how well students were able to identify features of variability in the number sentences that had their origin in a method actually used by Peter to subtract 5. The dialogue shown in figure 9.1 uses a similar approach to that used by Carpenter and Levi (1999) and Carpenter and Franke (2001) when asking children to judge if a number sentence is true or false, and to explain their thinking.

The structured questions used in Peter's method are not part of the taught curriculum. They are used to create a scenario for students that will encourage them to offer their own explanations of what Peter did. The interview was used with approximately thirty students in grades 2 and 3 (mostly third grade) in Australia and Japan. Students interviewed were chosen from five schools and from a range of abilities as advised by the classroom teachers. The questions are shown and read to the students. See figure 9.1.

For the interview-dialogue to be successful, second- and third-grade students need to be able to subtract 10 from two- and three-digit numbers. Some have difficulty with this. Other students have difficulty rewriting the questions in a form that matches Peter's method. When asked to explain why Peter's method works, some say it works because it gives the right answer. Sometimes, students prefer to discuss their own methods of subtracting 5. For example, in dealing with $32 - 5$, Thomas (8 years, 3 months, and in the middle of grade 2) said, "5 is $2 + 3$. So, I first take away the 2 from 32 giving 30, and then take away 3, giving 27." Some students, like Thomas, prefer to use their own methods and find it difficult to engage with Peter's method. No criticism of this kind of thinking is implied. The interview does not point students in one direction or the other. If for some reason students are unable to engage with Peter's method, the interview does not continue. For those who can continue, the interview-dialogue lasts for about twenty to thirty minutes with students giving responses both orally and in writing.

After applying Peter's method for $53 - 5$ and for $84 - 5$, students are asked to use Peter's method to create and write some examples of their own for subtracting 5. If successful, they are then asked to explain why it works. Alan (8 years, 10 months,

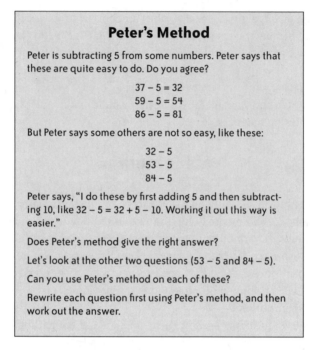

Peter's Method

Peter is subtracting 5 from some numbers. Peter says that these are quite easy to do. Do you agree?

$$37 - 5 = 32$$
$$59 - 5 = 54$$
$$86 - 5 = 81$$

But Peter says some others are not so easy, like these:

$$32 - 5$$
$$53 - 5$$
$$84 - 5$$

Peter says, "I do these by first adding 5 and then subtracting 10, like $32 - 5 = 32 + 5 - 10$. Working it out this way is easier."

Does Peter's method give the right answer?

Let's look at the other two questions ($53 - 5$ and $84 - 5$).

Can you use Peter's method on each of these?

Rewrite each question first using Peter's method, and then work out the answer.

Fig. 9.1. Introducing Peter's method

at the end of grade 2) gave the following explanation: "Instead of taking away 5, he [Peter] adds 5 and then takes away 10. If you add 5, you need to take away 10 to equal it out." After explaining why Peter's method works for subtracting 5, students are asked to consider how Peter might use his method to subtract 6 (see fig. 9.2.).

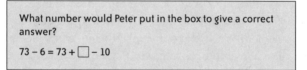

What number would Peter put in the box to give a correct answer?

$73 - 6 = 73 + \square - 10$

Fig. 9.2. Peter's method continued

If students successfully answer this question, they are asked to create and write some other examples showing how Peter's method could be used to subtract 6 and to explain why Peter's method works for subtracting 6. If they are successful with this, the interview concludes with the prompts and questions shown in figure 9.3.

Alan answered the last question in figure 9.3 about how the method works by saying, "For any number you take away, you have to add the other number, which is between 1 and 10, that equals 10; like 7 and 3, or 4 and 6. You take away 10, and that gives you the answer." From his response, it is evident that Alan understands the *allowable range of movement* of the number being taken away, and he imposes

Peter says that his method also works for subtracting 7—and 8 and 9.

Can you show how Peter's method works for the following three questions?

Rewrite each of the questions first using Peter's method, and then work out the answer.

$$83 - 7$$
$$123 - 8$$
$$235 - 9$$

Can you explain why this method always works?

Fig. 9.3. Peter's method concluded

a boundary condition, namely, that the number being subtracted has to be less than 10. He also identifies the connection between the number being subtracted and the number that Peter then adds on. He also sees that the initial numbers, 83, 123, or 235, can be left out of an explanation of why Peter's method always works.

Zoe (8 years, 4 months, and at the start of grade 3) gave an explanation that focuses on the equivalence between subtracting a number (less than 10) and Peter's method. She said, "Whatever the number is you are taking away, it needs to have another number to make 10. You add the number to make 10, and then take away 10. Say, if you had $22 - 9$, you know $9 + 1 = 10$, so you add the 1 to 22 and then take away 10."

Tim (9 years, 1 month, and at the start of grade 3) said, "Here is an explanation for all numbers. Whatever number he [Peter] is taking away (assumed to be less than 10), you plus the number that would make a 10, and you take away 10. The bigger the number you are subtracting, the smaller the number you are plussing. They all make a 10 together."

Kou, a Japanese student (9 years, 6 months, and at the beginning of grade 3) explained, "It does not matter what number is being taken away, when the adding number makes 10, the answer is always the same, whether the subtracting number is increasing or decreasing." Tim and Kou discern the pattern of variation between the "adding number" and the "subtracting number"—as one becomes bigger, the other must become smaller.

Like Alan, these students are also able to "ignore" the value of the "starting number" for the purpose of their explanation. They also show that they are comfortable with "a lack of closure" (see Collis 1975), that is, leaving the expression in *uncalculated* form. Their explanations capture in their own language the equivalence between the expressions that experts would represent as $a - b$ and $a + (10 - b) - 10$. These students are able to explain why Peter's method *always* works "whatever number he is taking away" (Tim), "whatever the number is you are taking away"

(Zoe), "for any number you are taking away" (Alan), "there is always a number to make 10" (Adam), or "whether the subtracting number is increasing or decreasing" (Kou). The number being subtracted is *understood* by these students to be any counting number between 1 and 10.

However, there are students who need to close the sentence by first calculating the results of 83 −7, 123 − 8, and 235 − 9, and then calculating the missing number by writing, for example, 76 = 83 + ☐ − 10. Although they often correctly calculate the values of the missing numbers, these students are rarely able to explain why Peter's method *always* works. These students cannot ignore the "starting number" and are reluctant to leave expressions in uncalculated form. As a result, they usually do not discern any pattern of variation between the number that they are taking away and the number that was added on. Being able to keep numbers on either side of the equal sign in uncalculated form is also crucial for explaining why number sentences like 78 − 49 + 49 = 78 are always true. The present elementary school curriculum does little to shift students who are inclined to "close" away from this kind of thinking.

Peter's method is only an *easier* method if students are confident in subtracting 10. Some third-grade students still use counting back by ones to subtract 10, and therefore they find it difficult to keep track of the numbers. These students, overloaded by the demands of the calculations, can see no underlying pattern in Peter's method.

When trying to explain why Peter's method *always* works, some students do no more than recapitulate the specific solutions that they have computed. These students need to move beyond review and summarization. They need to explain why Peter's method *always* works, as Adam (aged 8 years, 6 months, and at the start of grade 3) did when he said, "If the number is under 10, there is *always* a number to make 10, so you can *always* add on (that) number and take away 10."

All successful explanations of Peter's method by the previously named students make it clear that the number being subtracted and the number being added in the rewritten sentence *together* add to 10. In this way, students understand that the *range of movement* of the two numbers is limited and that the value of one is complementary to the other.

Extending Peter's Method

So far in Peter's method, the numbers being subtracted have all been counting numbers less than 10. That feature was changed in the following extensions of Peter's method that we used with twenty Japanese and Australian students from grade 4 through grade 8. The students were taken *first* through the original interview-dialogue for Peter's method and *then* through the extensions using larger numbers as well as fractions and decimals. Our intention was to investigate how a similar interview-dialogue, using a mix of number sentences and some simple symbolic representations, could be used with older students to gain insight into how they think about equivalent number sentences and about patterns of variation between some of the numbers used in these sentences.

A First Extension

In this first extension, shown in figure 9.4, students were introduced to Susan, a hypothetical student who has decided to replace the examples used in Peter's method, such as 32 – 5, 32 – 6, 32 – 7, 32 – 8, and so on, with 32 – ▼ to represent the different numbers being subtracted. Symbols like ▼ and ● (shown below) were *always* referred to in ways that made it clear that they were standing for numbers. They were never called "triangle" or "circle." The written dialogue was shown and read to students, with vocalizations shown in parentheses. Students gave verbal responses to the following prompts. The words in parentheses were present in the teachers' version of the dialogue.

> Susan said it this way: "Instead of writing 32 – 5, 32 – 6, 32 – 7, 32 – 8, and so on, I decided to write the symbol ▼ to stand for the numbers 5, 6, 7, 8, and so on. So, I wrote 32 – ▼ (read as: "32 minus some number") to represent all of these."
>
> Susan then says: "So instead of 32 – ▼ ("32 minus some number"), Peter says 32 + ● – 10" (read as: "32 plus some other number minus 10").
>
> How does Peter find the value of the second number, ● ?
>
> What do these two numbers add up to? What can you say about ▼ + ● = ?
>
> (Pause for an answer to this question. Then ask: Could ▼ ("the first number") stand for a fraction like 7½ or a decimal fraction like 5.2?

Fig. 9.4. A first extension of Peter's method

The symbol ▼ is intended as no more than a placeholder for the different numbers that Peter has used. From the examples above, it is clear to students that ▼ is bounded and must represent a number less than 10. All students could see how this symbolic representation was connected to the specific number sentences used in figure 9.4 and could explain the relationship between the number being subtracted, ▼, and its complementary number ● in the equivalent sentences 32 – ▼ and 32 + ● – 10. When asked to consider if ▼ could represent a fraction or a decimal, students showed how Peter's method could work for 32 – 7½ by saying that they would need to add 2½ and then subtract 10. With 5.2, they explained that they would need to add 4.8 and then subtract 10. The use of decimals and fractions helps students to see that the values of ▼ and ● in ▼ + ● = 10 vary and are not restricted to counting numbers.

Here, ▼ and ● are summarizing symbols. They act as *quasi-variables*, defined by Lins and Kaput (2004) as "numbers within a number sentence or group of number sentences that indicate an underlying mathematical relationship that remains true whatever the numbers used are" (p. 58). The idea behind the term *quasi-variable* is not a new one in the teaching of algebra. In his history of mathematics, Nakamura (1971) introduces the expression "quasi-general method" (pp. 88–90) to capture the same meaning. In this extension of Peter's method, students need to work with specific number sentences before they meet ▼ and ● . Only then should they be invited to use these summarizing symbols to express in more general terms what they have already presented in their own explanations.

A Second Extension

This extension, which appears in figure 9.5, was used with all students to gauge their abilities to apply and extend Peter's method to situations in which the number being subtracted is nearly 100. This extension was shown and read to students, who could give oral or written responses.

> Can we look at how Peter's method could be used for subtracting numbers like 95, 96, and 97?
>
> Suppose Peter had 251 − 95; what do you think he might do to make it easier?
>
> What would he do if he had 251 − 96.5?
>
> What do you think he would do if he had 251 − 93⅓?

Fig. 9.5. A second extension of Peter's method

A successful response to $251 - 95$ required students to be able to write the original sentence as $251 + 5 - 100$. That is, $256 - 100 = 156$. After completing the subtractions involving 96 and 97, students were asked to consider how Peter's method would work if the numbers involved were decimals or fractions. (Simple decimals and fractions are typically introduced by about grade 4.) Older students had no difficulty transforming the final two computations by adding 3.5 and 6⅔, respectively. The inclusion of decimals and fractions is important for establishing an idea of *variable*.

Although explicit variation of the starting number was not considered, several students gave explanations that indicated that they had considered this possibility. For example, one student began his explanation by stating, "Whatever number you are starting with." Other students used diagrams that clearly implied that they understood Peter's method to be independent of the starting number (minuend).

A Third Extension

This extension, shown in figure 9.6, builds on the arithmetical transformations that students encountered in the preceding extension, namely, $251 - 95$, $251 - 96$, $251 - 93\frac{1}{3}$, and so on. The words in parentheses were present in the teacher's version of the dialogue.

Remember what Susan did before. Now, instead of writing different sentences like $251 - 95$, $251 - 96$, $251 - 97$, and $251 - 98$, Susan again uses the symbol ▼ to represent all of these. What do you think she would write? (Pause for students to write $251 - ▼$.)

(After they have written this, say:) Susan then rewrites the sentence $251 - ▼$ to show how Peter would subtract numbers like 95, 96, 97, 98, and so on.

She uses a second symbol, ●, to write $251 + ●$ .... (Be careful to read this as: "251 plus some other number.") Can you complete this sentence?

How is the value of the second number, ●, connected to the value of the first number, ▼? (Point to, but do not verbalize, the symbols.)

What do these two numbers add up to? What can you say about ▼ + ● = ?

Could you use this reasoning to show how Peter would solve $251 - 83$?

Fig. 9.6. A third extension of Peter's method

For the third extension, students were expected to record their responses. Being able to write the symbolic expression $251 - ▼$ was intended to assist students in appreciating that ▼ represents a number close to 100 that is being "taken away" from 251. All students successfully completed the second question by writing $251 + ● - 100$. This symbolic term is intended to represent numbers in the several equivalent number sentences that students created in the preceding extension. In this extension, students need to consider the relationship between ▼ and ●, where ▼ is assumed to be a number that is less than (but close to) 100. Here again, students understood that the two numbers represented by ▼ and ● operated within clearly set boundaries.

Students made statements like this: "The two numbers together add to 100." They could see that ▼ and ● are defined by the relationship ▼ + ● = 100, where 100 serves as an upper boundary value for ▼ and ●. In dealing correctly with the final question, which asked them to apply Peter's method to $251 - 83$, students could see that the number being subtracted might be chosen more widely than the actual numerical examples used to introduce this third extension, while still being consistent with the relationship ▼ + ● = 100.

Unexpected Responses

Sometimes students responded in ways that were not anticipated. The interview-dialogue was never treated as a sequence where only some responses were accepted. From the outset, Peter's method requires students to see that $53 - 5$ can be rewritten as equivalent to $53 + 5 - 10$. Some students interpret the relationship between 5 and 10 as a doubling relationship. In this instance, students may think that $73 - 6$ should be replaced by $73 + 6 - 12$. These students have introduced a different dimension of variation—one that is mathematically correct but that may not achieve the computational simplicity that Peter achieved. Two students, one in grade 3 and one in grade 4, did this. As shown in figure 9.7, Keiko (grade 4) used a version 1 to show her doubling relationship and a version 2 to show the "standard" version of Peter's method.

$83 - 7 = 83 + 7 - 14 = 76$	version 1
$83 - 7 = 83 + 3 - 10 = 76$	version 2
$123 - 8 = 123 + 8 - 16 = 115$	version 1
$123 - 8 = 123 + 2 - 10 = 115$	version 2
$235 - 9 = 235 + 18 - 9 = 226$	version 1
$235 - 9 = 235 + 1 - 10 = 226$	version 2

Fig. 9.7. Keiko's two versions of Peter's method

Having written both versions for $235 - 9$, Keiko then checked the result of $235 + 9 - 18$ using a standard computational algorithm. She said, "Peter's method, which uses $235 + 1 - 10 = 226$, is actually easier." Keiko noticed the greater computational difficulty of her formulations only after the last example, when she had to subtract 18. Students must be allowed to explore and evaluate such alternative transformations in order to appreciate the elegance and simplicity of one method versus another.

Yoshi, a student in grade 4, said, "In the case of subtracting 6, to add 4 and subtract 10 is okay because subtracting 6 is equivalent to $+ 4 - 10$. I don't think this method is new for me. *But* now I see how to make *any* subtraction simpler." Yoshi then gave the following illustration: "For example, subtracting 27 could be made easier by adding 3 and subtracting 30. That is something I have learned that is new."

Naomi (grade 6) made a similar observation. Asked why Peter used 10 and 100, she said that these numbers made it easier to calculate. She added, "If we had (were subtracting) a smaller number instead of 95, we could use 50 or 60." Asked to explain what she would do if she had to calculate $251 - 48$, Naomi said that she would write $251 - 48 = 251 + 2 - 50 = 203$. She then used a traditional subtraction algorithm to check that $251 - 48$ gave the same result. Interestingly, she did not use the fact that $51 - 48$ is 3, allowing one to write $251 - 48 = 203$.

The ability to move beyond the given boundaries of Peter's method and to work with what several students referred to as "clean" or "round" numbers was an unexpected further dimension of variation.

Sometimes students responded with a degree of generality that was not expected. For example, Yoshi (grade 4) gave a symbolic response when asked, "Can you explain why Peter's method always works?" Yoshi wrote $\square - 10 = - \blacktriangle$, explaining that this was always true for any two numbers less than 10, provided that $\square + \blacktriangle = 10$. He wrote a similar symbolic representation in the third extension, where the boundary value was 100. Yoshi clearly understood how the two numbers varied regardless of whether their boundary value was 10 or 100.

Leo (grade 6) said that Peter's method was not confined to subtracting numbers less than 10, or to subtracting numbers less than (and near to) 100, or even to subtracting numbers less than (and near to) 1000. Leo pointed out that Peter's method and its extensions were instances of a pattern that "always works." When asked how this pattern could be expressed, Leo wrote $\square - \bullet = \square + (\blacktriangle - \bullet) - \blacktriangle$, saying that any subtraction could be converted into "an easier subtraction" by choosing a "cleaner" number $\blacktriangle$ (greater than the original number $\bullet$ being taken away), adding the difference ($\blacktriangle - \bullet$), and then subtracting $\blacktriangle$.

After calculating $83 - 7$, $123 - 8$, and $235 - 9$, Satoshi (grade 7) wrote the symbolic expression $M - n = M + (10 - n) - 10$ to explain why this method always works. After the second extension, Satoshi wrote:

$$M - n = M + (100 - n) - 100.$$

When asked to say whether it might be true for a number that was not a power of 10, Satoshi said that it was possible "in an abstract sense." The interviewer was hoping that Satoshi might choose to simplify a calculation like $M - 37$ by writing an equivalent sentence like $M - n = M + (40 - n) - 40$. Rather, Satoshi gave as an example, "Instead of $83 - 5$, you could write $83 + (51 - 5) - 51 = 83 + 46 - 51$". He added that this was not an easy calculation.

Other students in grades 7 and 8 used x and y to write expressions similar to those used by Satoshi. Some used x and y to show, for example, that $251 - x$ could be written as $251 + y - 100$ where $y = 100 - x$; or they wrote $251 - x = 251 + (100 - x) - 100$. It might be said that these students *already* have a notion of variable, but we argue that these forms of completely generalized thinking do not emerge out of the blue. They are solidly based on students' grasp of the underlying structure of specific number sentences. Take away the experience of working with specific number sentences, and these elegant generalizations are less likely to emerge.

Discussion and Summary

The number sentences described throughout this article can be seen as a kind of "proto-algebra" where the sentences become objects for exploring patterns of variation that could be, but are not necessarily, represented by algebraic expressions. Many number sentences have this potential, but how this potential can be realized depends on how students are supported to see these possibilities for variation.

A *first* step in looking beyond *particular* number sentences to seeing *generalizable* patterns implicit in these sentences is helping students leave number sentences in uncalculated (unexecuted) form.

A *second* step is to avoid premature generalization. Even in Peter's method, where the aim is to have students see that subtracting 5 is equivalent to adding 5 and subtracting 10, the numbers 5 and 10 are still seen by many students as particular numbers, and not as a part of a pattern. When asked to consider $73 - 6 = 73 + \Box - 10$, some students can immediately explain that the number pairs 5 and 5, and 6 and 4, are part of a pattern with both numbers adding to 10. Other students need practice applying Peter's method to $83 - 7$, $123 - 8$, and $235 - 9$ before being able to articulate the relationship between the number being subtracted and the number to be added before subtracting 10. In extending Peter's method, larger numbers are used, as well as decimals and fractions, in order to illustrate underlying patterns of generalized thinking. Even when students are working with numbers, they still need many carefully selected examples of the underlying general relationship.

A *third* step in developing students' ideas of variable numbers is to acknowledge the importance to students of boundary values implied by specific numerical expressions. By experiencing the boundary conditions implicit in Peter's method and its extensions, many students were able to explore *numerically* and to articulate important patterns of *variation* implicit in the mathematical relationships $a - b = a + (10 - b) - 10$ and $a - b = a + (100 - b) - 100$ long before they might be expected to know these formal algebraic expressions.

A *fourth* step in developing students' understanding of a variable is the use of representative symbolic "terms" as a way of summarizing multiple numerical expressions that students have already met. We agree with Brown and Drouhard (2004) that working *with* and *on* symbolic representations is very powerful in drawing the attention of students to the relationships among numbers and to their boundary values. Even when students were invited to use summarizing symbols, such as ● and ▼, these appeared to retain the boundary values of the originating number sentences. Simple symbolic expressions, like those using ▼ and ● and based on number sentences that students have met, enabled students to attend to and explore patterns of variation embedded in Peter's method and to extend its range of application. However, these symbols do not have a meaning on their own, as they will in later algebra. Their meaning is anchored in, but not completely restricted to, the specific number sentences from which they are derived and to which students are able to return to confirm the meaning attached to them. Students need a lot of experience before they are able to detach "symbols" from specific number sentences that give them meaning.

As this article shows, students need to be able to move forward and backward across the bridge connecting number sentences and generalizations that can be derived from them, whether these generalizations are stated verbally or symbolically. That bridge permits "proto-algebra" to take place. Some students are never introduced to such a bridge in their school experience with number sentences. Some are able to make a bridge of their own devising. For others, a bridge is made available for a short time but is withdrawn too quickly, leaving them to cope with symbols that have lost their connection with number sentences.

Teachers' vision of arithmetic has for so long been restricted to thinking of it primarily as computation. The potentially algebraic nature of number sentences as discussed in this article can furnish a strong bridge to the idea of variable. It can also strengthen students' understanding of basic arithmetic. In the twenty-first century, the mathematics curriculum in the elementary and middle school years must address these two objectives.

References

Blanton, Maria, and James J. Kaput. "Algebrafying the Elementary Mathematics Experience." In *Proceedings of the 12th ICMI Study Conference: The Future of the Teaching and Learning of Algebra,* edited by Helen Chick, Kaye Stacey, Jill Vincent, and John Vincent, pp. 87–95. Melbourne, Victoria, Australia: University of Melbourne, 2001.

Brown, Laurinda, and Jean-Philppe Drouhard. "Responses to 'The Core of Algebra.'" In *The Future of the Teaching and Learning of Algebra: The 12th ICMI Study,* edited by Kaye Stacey, Helen Chick, and Margaret Kendal, pp. 35–44. Boston: Kluwer Academic Publishers, 2004.

Carpenter, Thomas P., and Megan Franke. "Developing Algebraic Reasoning in the Elementary School: Generalization and Proof." In *Proceedings of the 12th ICMI Study Conference: The Future of the Teaching and Learning of Algebra,* edited by Helen Chick, Kaye Stacey, Jill Vincent, and John Vincent, pp. 155–62. Melbourne, Victoria, Australia: University of Melbourne, 2001.

Carpenter, Thomas P., and Linda Levi. "Developing Conceptions of Algebraic Reasoning in the Primary Grades." Paper presented at the annual meeting of the American Educational Research Association, Montreal, Quebec, April 1999.

Collis, Kevin. *A Study of Concrete and Formal Operations in School Mathematics: A Piagetian Viewpoint.* Hawthorn, Victoria: Australian Council for Educational Research, 1975.

Fujii, Toshiakira. "Probing Students' Understanding of Variables through Cognitive Conflict Problems: Is the Concept of a Variable So Difficult for Students to Understand?" In *Proceedings of the Joint Meeting of PME and PME-NA,* edited by Neil A. Pateman,

Barbara J. Dougherty, and Joseph Zilliox, vol. 1, pp. 49–65. Honolulu: University of Hawaii and PME, 2003.

Fujii, Toshiakira, and Max Stephens. "Fostering an Understanding of Algebraic Generalization through Numerical Expressions: The Role of Quasi-Variables." In *Proceedings of the 12th ICMI Study Conference: The Future of the Teaching and Learning of Algebra,* edited by Helen Chick, Kaye Stacey, Jill Vincent, and John Vincent, pp. 259–64. Melbourne, Victoria, Australia: University of Melbourne, 2001.

Lins, Romulo, and James J. Kaput. "The Early Development of Algebraic Reasoning: The Current State of the Field." In *The Future of the Teaching and Learning of Algebra: The 12th ICMI Study,* edited by Kaye Stacey, Helen Chick, and Margaret Kendal, pp. 47–70. Boston: Kluwer Academic Publishers, 2004.

Nakamura, Koshiro. *History of Mathematics: From the Perspective of Constructing Mathematics.* [In Japanese.] Tokyo: Kyoritsu Zensho, 1971.

Radford, Luis. "The Roles of Geometry and Arithmetic in the Development of Elementary Algebra: Historical Remarks from a Didactic Perspective—Perspectives for Research and Teaching." In *Approaches to Algebra,* edited by Nadine Bednarz, Carolyn Kieran, and Lesley Lee, pp. 39–53. Dordrecht, Netherlands: Kluwer Academic Publishers, 1996.

10

Developing Algebraic Thinking through Explorations in Multiplication

Jae Meen Baek

IN THE eyes of too many students and adults, traditional algebra has been experienced as manipulations of symbols that do not have any mathematical meaning or relevance to their everyday lives. Students' understanding of these symbol manipulations is often fragmented and separated from their earlier mathematical activities, and they do not see mathematical connections between the use of algebraic symbols and the content of other mathematical domains.

In recent discussions of reform efforts in mathematics education, several researchers highlight the importance of teaching and learning algebra with understanding by making connections between children's arithmetic problem solving and algebraic reasoning (Carraher et al. 2006; Kaput 2000; National Council of Teachers of Mathematics [NCTM] 1994, 2000). In particular, Carraher and his colleagues and Kaput identify algebra in the elementary school as a *generalization* of arithmetic and quantitative reasoning. They view early algebra as a move from arithmetic with particular numbers toward generalizing relations in a set of numbers.

Several researchers argue that children in the elementary grades demonstrate intuitive understanding of algebra in their problem-solving processes for arithmetic problems (Blanton and Kaput 2003; Carpenter, Franke, and Levi 2003; Schifter 1999). Kaput (2000) asserts that acknowledging informal algebraic thinking in children's earlier mathematical activities would allow for deeply reformed algebra. Carpenter, Franke, and Levi provide a framework and examples of how to integrate arithmetic and algebra in elementary grades by focusing on fundamental properties of numbers and operations that children implicitly use in arithmetic problem solving, and they discuss how learning the fundamental properties in arithmetic can build foundations for more formal algebra.

This article extends the research by focusing on invented strategies for multiplication as a vehicle for fostering children's algebraic reasoning. First described are findings of my research on children's intuitive knowledge of the distributive and associative properties embedded in their multiplication strategies. Observations were made in five classrooms in grades 3–5. This is followed by a discussion of ways in which classroom teachers and I collaborated to use the children's informal understanding of the properties as a means to improve their multiplication procedures and algebraic reasoning. Specifically, we helped the students generalize their knowledge of the fundamental properties. The article concludes with a discussion of the benefits of instruction that focuses on integrating arithmetic and algebra in the elementary grades.

The Distributive and Associative Properties Embedded in Multiplication Strategies

Recent research on children's mathematical thinking shows that children develop a wide range of sophisticated strategies for multiplication using their intuitive understanding of the distributive and associative properties (Ambrose, Baek, and Carpenter 2003; Baek 1998, 2005; Caliandro 2000; Fosnot and Dolk 2001; Kamii 1994; Lampert 1986). On the basis of this research of children's understanding of multiplication, numbers, and fundamental properties, I constructed a classification scheme for children's multiplication strategies. The classification scheme reveals that children develop different levels of strategies, ranging from *direct modeling* to *adding*, *doubling*, *partitioning*, and then to *compensating* strategies (for more descriptions of each multiplication strategy type, see Ambrose, Baek, and Carpenter 2003; Baek 1998, 2005). In this section, I present several examples of children's strategies at different levels of sophistication and provide analyses of their informal understanding of the distributive and associative properties.

The first example illustrates Justin's strategy during a problem-solving interview. Justin, a third grader, solved the following problem:

> A new bookstore in Nicky's neighborhood sold 40 books on its first day of opening. If they sell 40 books every day for 30 days, how many books will they sell?

When he started, Justin had planned to directly model the problem using base-ten blocks, setting up 30 groups of four ten-rods. After he set up 10 groups of four ten-rods (see fig. 10.1), he paused.

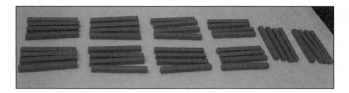

Fig. 10.1. Justin's strategy for 10 groups of 40

Interviewer:	Why are you stopping?
Justin:	I am trying to think of something. [*Points to the ten groups of four ten-rods*] I already have ten here.
Interviewer:	You mean ten groups of 40s?
Justin:	Yes, ten groups of 40s. And if I stack another 10 of those and another 10 of those.... [*Starts to count the 10 groups of 40 blocks by 40*], 40, 80, 120, ..., 400. 400 times 30 equals....
Interviewer:	Why 400 times 30?
Justin:	Wait, I mean 400 times 3.
Interviewer:	Why 400 times 3?
Justin:	Because it is 30 and you have..., [*pause*], I don't know.

Justin discontinued his explanation and proceeded to calculate 400×3 by adding 400 three times (fig. 10.2). He explained that 400 three times would compute all 30 days of book sales.

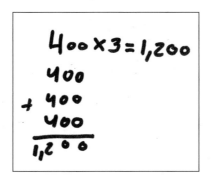

Fig. 10.2. Justin's strategy for 30 groups of 40

Although he could not articulate his reasoning, it appears that when Justin talked about computing 10 groups of 40 three times, he intuitively knew that 40 books a day for 30 days is the same as 40 books a day for 10 days times 3. "Yes, 10 groups of 40s. And if I stack another 10 of [40s] and another 10 of [40s]." Symbolic representation of the strategy helps to clarify Justin's intuitive understanding of the associative property.

$$30 \times 40 = (3 \times 10) \times 40$$
$$= 3 \times (10 \times 40) \qquad \text{[Associative Property]}$$

In the next example, Lindsey, a fourth grader, was presented with the following problem:

Mrs. V has 35 sets of wooden blocks. Each set has 23 blocks. How many wooden blocks does Mrs. V have?

As figure 10.3 shows, Lindsey computed the number of blocks in 6 sets of 23, doubled the number of blocks in 6 sets to get 12 sets, and doubled 12 sets to get 24 sets. She then added the number of blocks in 12 sets and in 24 sets to get the number of blocks in 36 sets. She subtracted the number of blocks in 1 set to get her final answer for the total number of blocks in 35 sets.

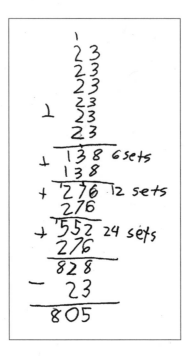

Fig. 10.3. Lindsey's strategy

Lindsey's strategy looks rather simple, relying on only addition and subtraction processes. However, when we consider how she partitioned the number of groups, we can see that her strategy was based on the distributive and associative properties. Lindsey used a strategy for 36 groups of 23 instead of 35 groups of 23, and she compensated by making a necessary adjustment in the last step. When figuring out 36 groups of 23, Lindsey treated 36 groups as 24 groups plus 12 groups, and she used her knowledge of 24 as a double of 12, and 12 as a double of 6. Her strategy can be symbolically represented as follows:

$$12 \times 23 = (2 \times 6) \times 23$$
$$= 2 \times (6 \times 23) \qquad \text{[Associative Property]}$$
$$24 \times 23 = (2 \times 12) \times 23$$

$$= 2 \times (12 \times 23) \qquad \text{[Associative Property]}$$
$$36 \times 23 = (24 + 12) \times 23$$
$$= (24 \times 23) + (12 \times 23) \qquad \text{[Distributive Property]}$$
$$35 \times 23 = (36 - 1) \times 23$$
$$= (36 \times 23) - (1 \times 23) \qquad \text{[Distributive Property]}$$

Holly, a fourth grader, demonstrated her understanding of the distributive property by partitioning both factors to solve the same block problem. She partitioned 35 into 30 and 5, and 23 into 20 and 3, and computed four partial products. She explained, "5 times 3 is 15, 5 times 20 is 100, 30 times 3 is 90, and 30 times 20 is 600." Then Holly added the partial products. (See fig. 10.4.)

Fig. 10.4. Holly's strategy. (*Note:* The circle around "1" was added to show her regrouping in the addition procedures.)

Holly's partitioning strategy can be symbolically represented as follows:

$$35 \times 23 = (5 + 30) \times (3 + 20)$$
$$= (5 \times 3) + (5 \times 20) + (30 \times 3) + (30 \times 20)$$
$$\text{[Distributive Property]}$$

Like several other children who partitioned both factors in this way, Holly had difficulty explaining why the partitioning strategy worked. When she was questioned, Holly said, "I did it in steps. I don't know why it works." It is interesting to compare Holly's explanation to Emilie's explanation for a similar partitioning method, which follows.

Emilie, a third grader, was given this problem:

> An elementary school has 24 classes. If there are 32 children in each class, how many children are there at the school?

Emilie began describing her strategy by saying, "I broke 24 into two 10s and one 4, so I multiplied 32 to each of them." As figure 10.5 shows, Emilie first partitioned

24 into 10, 10, and 4. She again partitioned 32 into 30 and 2. She multiplied 10, 10, and 4 by 30 and by 2, and created six partial products. She explained that she knew the answers of the partial products as number facts. "I got 300 for each 10, and 120 for 4, (pause), and next I did 2 times 10 is 20, 2 times 10 is 20, and 2 times 4 is 8."

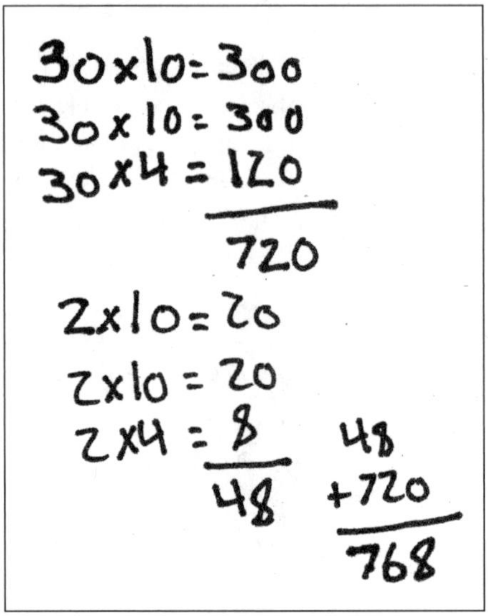

Fig. 10.5. Emilie's strategy

Emilie used the distributive property several times. First, she partitioned 24 into two 10s and 4, and again partitioned 32 into 30 and 2. Compared to Holly, children who partitioned both factors one at a time like Emilie could explain why the partitioning works. A symbolic representation of Emilie's strategy in which she used the distributive property to create the partial products is shown below.

$$32 \times 24 = 32 \times (10 + 10 + 4)$$
$$= (30 + 2) \times (10 + 10 + 4)$$
$$= (30 \times (10 + 10 + 4)) + (2 \times (10 + 10 + 4))$$
$$\text{[Distributive Property]}$$
$$= (30 \times 10) + (30 \times 10) + (30 \times 4) + (2 \times 10) + (2 \times 10) + (2 \times 4)$$
$$\text{[Distributive Property]}$$

Sara, a fifth grader, was presented with the following problem:

Mrs. P had 23 bags of M&M candies for Halloween. Each bag had 177 M&M's. How many M&M's did Mrs. P have?

Sara started with 10 groups of 177 and doubled it to determine the partial product of 20 groups. (See fig. 10.6.) Then she computed 3 groups of 177 in the second line by finding 2 groups of 177 and adding 177 to the product. She determined the total number by adding the partial products for 20 groups and 3 groups of 177.

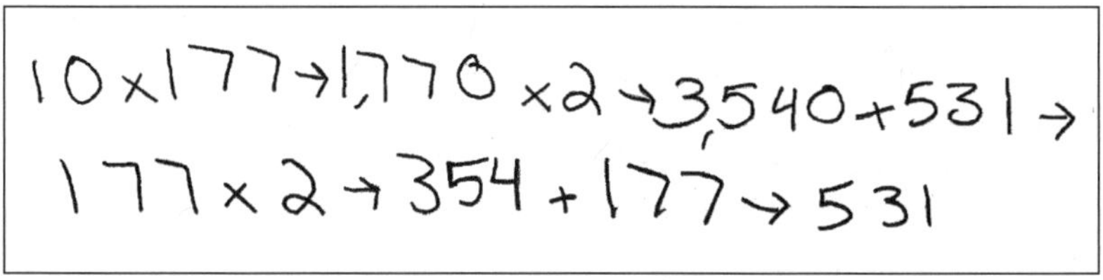

Fig. 10.6. Sara's strategy

The symbolic representation of Sara's strategy clearly reveals her use of the distributive and associative properties:

$$
\begin{aligned}
23 \times 177 &= (20 + 3) \times 177 \\
&= (20 \times 177) + (3 \times 177) \qquad \text{[Distributive Property]} \\
&= ((2 \times 10) \times 177) + (2 + 1) \times 177 \\
&= (2 \times (10 \times 177)) + (2 + 1) \times 177 \\
&\qquad\qquad\qquad\qquad \text{[Associative Property]} \\
&= (2 \times (10 \times 177)) + (2 \times 177) + (1 \times 177) \\
&\qquad\qquad\qquad\qquad \text{[Distributive Property]}
\end{aligned}
$$

As can be seen, strategies generated by children demonstrate that they have an informal understanding of the distributive and associative properties, and they are capable of using this understanding to construct efficient strategies for multiplying with multidigit factors. In the next section, I describe instructional strategies aimed at fostering children's algebraic reasoning by making their informal understanding of the distributive and associative properties more explicit.

Instruction That Fosters Children's Algebraic Thinking

The collaborating teachers and I sought to design and implement instructional strategies that facilitate children's development of fluent multiplication strategies and algebraic reasoning. First, we assisted children in making sense of the concept of multiplication, so that they could develop their own strategies. Then, we focused on making children's implicit understanding of the fundamental properties more explicit, so that they could use the properties, generalize them, and thereby think more algebraically.

To help children make sense of the operation, the teachers introduced multiplication problems in real-world contexts. Children were routinely encouraged to explain and discuss problem situations, solution strategies, and their reasoning about the strategies, and to learn from one another. In particular, the collaborating teachers guided children to pay attention to the meaning of their computational processes by referring back to the problem context. For example, if children wrote 10×177, 10×177, 3×177 for Sara's M&M problem, the teachers would ask them to explain the strategy according to the number of bags and M&M's, so that children could go back to the problem context and explain 10 bags of 177 M&M's, another 10 bags, and 3 more bags. It helped children keep track of their partitioning processes and partial products.

After children were observed developing strategies based on the distributive or associative properties, the teachers nurtured children's algebraic reasoning by having them discuss and generalize these properties. This algebra-focused instruction employed three main strategies: representing children's strategies in more algebraic ways, providing problems that promote the partitioning of one or both factors, and presenting *true/false* (T/F) and *open number sentences* that explicitly examine the distributive and associative properties. Many of the T/F and open number sentences were adapted from Carpenter, Franke, and Levi (2003). How these instructional strategies were implemented is described in the following episodes that took place in Ms. J's third-grade classroom in an urban school.

At the beginning of the school year, Ms. J presented students with multiplication word problems such as this one:

> Angelo earns $1 a day for walking dogs. How much will he earn in 9 weeks?

After Ms. J observed that many of her third graders started to partition one of the factors in the problem, she introduced number sentences that explicitly represent the distributive and associative properties. She used these number sentences to turn children's attention from computational procedures to the properties embedded in their strategies. This modeling of number sentence representations, in turn, helped children generalize their understanding of the distributive and associative properties and apply the properties to other problems.

As an example, consider the response of Kiyahn, a third grader, to the walking the dog problem (see fig. 10.7).

Kiyahn:	14 plus 14 is 28, 14 plus 14 is 28, 28 plus 7 is equal to 35. 28 plus 35 is equal to 63.
Ms. J:	Okay. We are going to write multiplication number sentences that go with Kiyahn's [strategy]. This is 9 times 7, but she's got numbers, 14, 14, 14, 14, and 7. What does 14 stand for?
Lizett:	2 times 7 and plus 2 times 7 and another 2 times 7 and another 2 times 7 and plus 7.

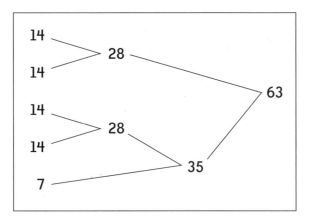

Fig. 10.7. Kiyahn's strategy

Ms. J:	[*Writing* $(2 \times 7) + (2 \times 7) + (2 \times 7) + (2 \times 7) + 7$ *on the board, following Lizett's explanation.*] How do we know this is 9 times 7?
Victoria:	[*Pointing at* 2×7] 2 times 7 is 2 weeks, and 2 weeks, and 2 weeks, and 2 weeks, and 1.
Lizett:	[*Pointing at the 2 in* 2×7] 2, 4, 6, 8, and 9.
Ms. J:	So what you are saying is, that is 9 times 7, because there are nine 7s up here?
Children:	Yes.
Ms. J:	So each 7 stands for what?
Children:	7 dollars.

In this episode, Ms. J modeled the representation, $(2 \times 7) + (2 \times 7) + (2 \times 7) + (2 \times 7) + 7$, for Kiyahn's strategy of $14 + 14 + 14 + 14 + 7$, as she guided children to pay more attention to the number of 7s in each partial product. It is important to note that Ms. J did not introduce any new strategies to the students. Instead, she demonstrated a new *representation* for Kiyahn's strategy, one that would represent Kiyahn's implicit distributive property more explicitly.

Children soon started to adapt Ms. J's more formal representations in their representations. You can see an example in Reggie's strategy for the following problem:

Kiyahn has 8 plates of brownies. Each plate has 9 brownies. How many brownies does she have?

As can be seen in figure 10.8, Reggie first solved for 4 plates with 9 brownies in each plate. He partitioned the 4 plates into 2 plates of 9 and another 2 plates of 9. He used his answer for 4 plates of 9 to solve for 8 plates of 9 brownies. He explained his strategy for 8 groups of 9 to the class by saying, "36 is four 9s, add another four 9s is equal to eight 9s." This strategy demonstrates that Reggie could not only partition 8 groups into 4 groups using his informal understanding of the distributive property but also adapt the teacher's number sentence representations, and he represented the distributivity in his partitioning strategy more formally.

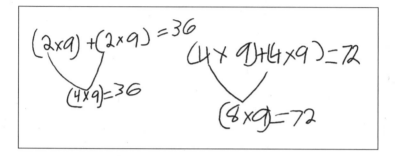

Fig. 10.8. Reggie's partitioning strategies

It would also have been mathematically appropriate to represent Reggie's strategy by highlighting the associative property. However, more collaborating teachers chose to represent children's strategies by notating the distributivity as $8 \times 9 = (4 + 4) \times 9 = (4 \times 9) + (4 \times 9)$ instead of notating the associativity as $8 \times 9 = (2 \times 4) \times 9 = 2 \times (4 \times 9)$.

In other instances, we provided several pairs of numbers for the same word problem. The pairs of numbers were selected in a way that children could easily "scaffold" from one problem to the next. Consider the following problem:

> Michael has ___ bags of pennies. Each bag has ___ pennies. How many pennies does Michael have?

Children solved this problem for three pairs of input: (4, 6), (8, 6), and (8, 16). Many children noticed the relationships among the pairs of numbers and took advantage of those relationships to solve the problems. Figure 10.9 illustrates how Minerva solved the problems using the distributive property.

Minerva solved the first problem, 4×6, by adding 2 groups of 6 twice. Then she used the product of 4×6 to figure out 8×6 by partitioning 8×6 into 4×6 and 4×6. Then she used the product of 8×6 to compute 8×16 by partitioning 8×16 into 8×10 and 8×6. This problem exemplifies how teachers' selections of problem structures and related numbers can encourage children to explore and construct strategies based on the distributive property.

The last instructional strategy that we implemented in this third-grade classroom was the use of a series of true/false and open number sentences. The goal of

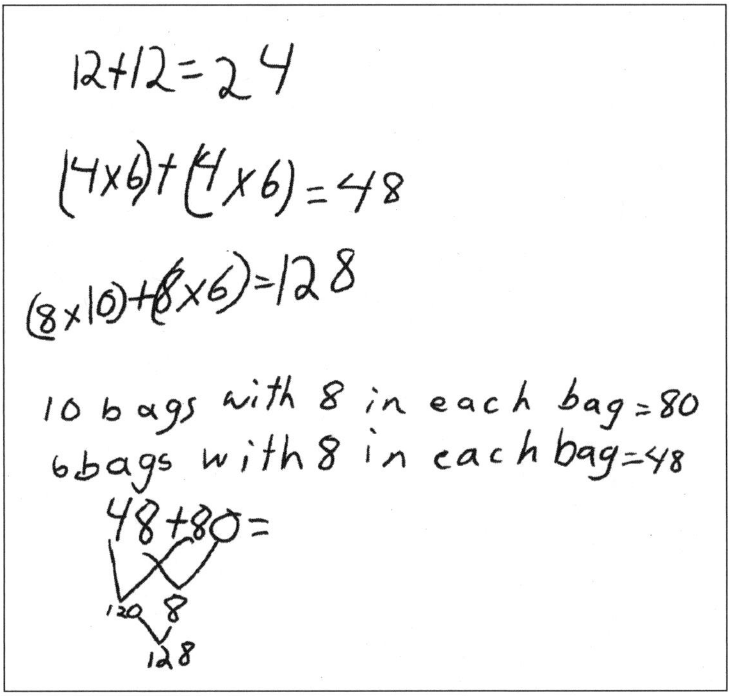

$$12 + 12 = 24$$

$$(4 \times 6) + (4 \times 6) = 48$$

$$(8 \times 10) + (8 \times 6) = 128$$

10 bags with 8 in each bag = 80
6 bags with 8 in each bag = 48

48 + 80 =

120   8

128

Fig. 10.9. Minerva's strategies for 4 × 6, 8 × 6, and 8 × 16

these T/F and open sentences was not to help the students compute products correctly but to help them investigate the distributive or associative properties explicitly, so that they could generalize the properties. For example, after children shared their strategies for word problems about 6 groups of 8 and 8 groups of 8, Ms. J presented this series of T/F and open number sentences:

Ms. J: [*Pointing at* $(2 \times 8) + (2 \times 8) = 16 + 16$ *on the board*] Is it true or false?

LeJuan: True, because two 8 is 16 and two 8 is 16.

Lizett: $(2 \times 8) + (2 \times 8)$ is 32 and $16 + 16$ is 32.

Carlos: 8 plus 8 is 16, so 2 times 8 is 16, and 8 plus 8 is 16, and 2 times 8 is 16.

Ms. J: [*Writing* $4 \times 8 = (2 \times 8) + (2 \times 8)$ *on the board*] True or false?

Students: True.

Ms. J: What does this 2 stand for?

Reggie: Two boxes of eight.

Ms. J: So how many boxes are there?

Students: Four.

Ms. J: [*Writing* $32 + 16 = (4 \times 8) + (a \times 8)$ *on the board*] What is a?

Michael: Two, because 4 times 8 is 32, and 2 times 8 is 16.

Ms. J: [*Writing* $(4 \times 8) + (2 \times 8) = b \times 8$ *on the board*] What is b?

Students: Six.

This interaction demonstrates that children have a good understanding of distributivity and the symbolic representation of the property. It also shows that children could justify the distributivity by explaining the partial products as the number of boxes. Reggie explained that 2×8 is like 2 boxes of 8, and students could see that 2 boxes and 2 boxes make 4 boxes.

The teachers and I decided to use these T/F and open number sentences because they allow children to focus more on the properties than on the computation procedures or answers. When Ms. J presented $(4 \times 8) + (2 \times 8) = b \times 8$, the focus was not on the answer for $(4 \times 8) + (2 \times 8)$ but on the distributive property that 4 groups of 8 plus 2 groups of 8 is the same as 6 groups of 8.

Conclusion

Instruction that focuses on the distributive and associative properties in children's multiplication strategies can play an important role in fostering algebraic thinking at the elementary school level in two significant ways. First, it can help children generalize and justify underpinning mathematics in their strategies and, in turn, develop algebraic reasoning (Carraher et al. 2006; Kaput 2000; Lannin 2005). A discussion of the distributive and associative properties, which children already informally use in their multiplication strategies, allows teachers to provide students with opportunities to generalize if partitioning one or both of the factors into smaller numbers *always* works and to justify *why* it works. In this process, children learn that it is important in algebra to know what it means to generalize properties that work for specific cases and how to justify why they work for any numbers.

Second, students who generalized and justified the distributive and associative properties in arithmetic problem solving are better prepared to learn formal algebra. For example, students who justified $16 \times 8 = 10 \times 8 + 6 \times 8$ will be able to apply the same line of reasoning to solve formal algebra problems such as $16y = 10y + 6y$. Students who were able to use the distributive property to solve for $23 \times 35 = (20 + 3) \times (30 + 5) = (20 \times 30) + (20 \times 5) + (3 \times 30) + (3 \times 5)$ will be able to use that knowledge to solve algebra problems like $(a + b) \times (c + d) = ac + ad + bc + bd$.

In conclusion, results of the study of children's problem-solving strategies and the pedagogical techniques described in this article suggest that children can develop powerful algebraic reasoning many years before the formal study of algebra. The instructional practices presented can help children make their informal understanding of mathematical properties more explicit, so that they can develop more sophisticated strategies for solving arithmetic problems. Explicit discussions of important mathematical concepts and properties can, in turn, help children to generalize and justify them, and develop algebraic reasoning. These instructional strategies stimulate and nurture students' abilities to represent their strategies using algebraic representations, thus strengthening the relationship between arithmetic and algebra. I argue that persistent efforts to develop students' algebraic reasoning in arithmetic problem-solving contexts will help students recognize generalized arithmetic in algebra, so that algebra is no longer meaningless symbol manipulations.

REFERENCES

Ambrose, Rebecca, Jae Meen Baek, and Thomas P. Carpenter. "Children's Invention of Multidigit Multiplication and Division Algorithms." In *The Development of Arithmetic Concepts and Skills,* edited by Arthur J. Baroody and Ann Dowker, pp. 302–36. Mahwah, N.J.: Lawrence Erlbaum Associates, 2003.

Baek, Jae Meen. "Children's Invented Algorithms for Multidigit Multiplication Problems." In *The Teaching and Learning of Algorithms in School Mathematics,* 1998 Yearbook of the National Council of Teachers of Mathematics (NCTM), edited by Lorna J. Morrow, pp. 151–60. Reston, Va.: NCTM, 1998.

———. "Children's Mathematical Understanding and Invented Strategies for Multidigit Multiplication." *Teaching Children Mathematics* 12 (December 2005/January 2006): 242–47.

Blanton, Maria L., and James J. Kaput. "Developing Elementary Teachers' 'Algebra Eyes and Ears.'" *Teaching Children Mathematics* 10 (October 2003): 70–77.

Caliandro, Christine K. "Children's Inventions for Multidigit Multiplication and Division." *Teaching Children Mathematics* 6 (February 2000): 420–24.

Carpenter, Thomas P., Megan L. Franke, and Linda Levi. *Thinking Mathematically: Integrating Arithmetic and Algebra in Elementary School.* Portsmouth, N.H.: Heinemann, 2003.

Carraher, David W., Analucia D. Schliemann, Barbara M. Brizuela, and Darrell Earnest. "Arithmetic and Algebra in Early Mathematics Education." *Journal for Research in Mathematics Education* 37 (March 2006): 87–115.

Fosnot, Catherine Twomey, and Maarten Dolk. *Young Mathematicians at Work: Constructing Multiplication and Division.* Portsmouth, N.H.: Heinemann, 2001.

Kamii, Constance. *Young Children Continue to Reinvent Arithmetic: Third Grade Implications of Piaget's Theory.* New York: Teachers College Press, 1994.

Kaput, James J. *Transforming Algebra from an Engine of Inequity to an Engine of Mathematical Power by "Algebrafying" the K–12 Curriculum.* Dartmouth, Mass.: National Center for Improving Student Learning and Achievement in Mathematics and Science, 2000. ERIC Document Reproduction No. ED 441664.

Lampert, Magdalene. "Knowing, Doing, and Teaching Multiplication." *Cognition and Instruction* 3 (1986): 305–42.

Lannin, John K. "Generalization and Justification: The Challenges of Introducing Algebraic Reasoning through Patterning Activities." *Mathematical Thinking and Learning* 7 (2005): 231–58.

National Council of Teachers of Mathematics (NCTM). "A Framework for Constructing a Vision of Algebra." Algebra Working Group Draft Document. Reston, Va.: NCTM, 1994.

———. *Principles and Standards for School Mathematics.* Reston, Va.: NCTM, 2000.

Schifter, Deborah. "Reasoning about Operations: Early Algebraic Thinking in Grades K–6." In *Developing Mathematical Reasoning in Grades K–12*, 1999 Yearbook of the National Council of Teachers of Mathematics (NCTM), edited by Lee V. Stiff, pp. 62–81. Reston, Va.: NCTM, 1999.

11

"What Is Your Theory? What Is Your Rule?" Fourth Graders Build an Understanding of Functions through Patterns and Generalizing Problems

Joan Moss
Ruth Beatty
Samantha Barkin
Gina Shillolo

IN AN urban public school, grade 4 students are clamoring to get their chance at the computers. The energy is palpable. Why are the students excited? Because they want to read how students in another school, whom they have never met, have responded to their proposals for theories and rules for a series of patterning and generalizing problems. These students have been collaborating using a communal database to solve challenging mathematical problems without any teacher input.

The students from these two linked classrooms were participants in a pilot study that is part of an ongoing research project investigating patterning as a support for learning mathematical functions (Moss, Beatty, and McNab 2006). The goals of this multiyear project are to address some of the well-known difficulties that students encounter when trying to develop functional rules for patterns—difficulties that include the use of limited strategies and the lack of rigor when identifying and justifying rules. A special feature of this project is the inclusion of a Web-based discourse platform, Knowledge Forum (Bereiter and Scardamalia 2003), to provide students with an authentic context to collaborate in finding solutions to generalizing problems. In particular we were interested in investigating whether the collaborative nature of Knowledge Forum would support students in attempting to provide evidence and justifications for their conjectures.

In this article we focus on how students communicated with one another on Knowledge Forum between the two classrooms. We present examples of their contributions to two of the problems that were posted on the Knowledge Forum database to illustrate how students found rules for generalizing problems and how they explained their reasoning using evidence-based discourse. We begin, however, with a general discussion of the use of patterns as a means of developing algebraic understanding, briefly outline the methods of our study, and describe the instructional sequence prior to using the Knowledge Forum database.

Patterns: Potentials and Pitfalls

Abstracting patterns is one route to a structural knowledge of mathematics (e.g., Steen 1988; Mason 1996; Warren 2000). In recent years increasing numbers of mathematics educators, policymakers, and researchers have proposed that patterning and algebra become part of the elementary school curriculum (e.g., Carraher et al. 2006; Greenes et al. 2001; Ministry of Education and Training [MOET] 2000; National Council of Teachers of Mathematics [NCTM] 2000). From a mathematical perspective, the introduction of patterns in the early years has many potential benefits for students. Patterns offer a powerful vehicle for understanding the dependent relations among quantities that underlie mathematical functions (e.g., Mason 1996; Lee 1996; Ferrini-Mundy, Lappan, and Phillips 1997), as well as a concrete and transparent way for young students to begin to grapple with the notions of abstraction and generalization (Watson and Mason 2002). Patterning activities are now pervasive in elementary school curricula in many countries. The National Council of Teachers of Mathematics recommends that students participate in patterning activities from a young age with the expectation that they will be able to describe numeric and geometric patterns, generalize patterns to predict what comes next, provide rationales for their predictions, and represent patterns with drawings, tables, symbols, and graphs (NCTM 2000).

Although the potential of patterns is well articulated, there is little systematic research that addresses how young children work with patterns or how patterning does, in fact, support young students in developing an understanding of functions and generalizations. Existing research on patterning as a route to generalizing and rule finding has been conducted only with older populations with the overwhelming consensus that the route from perceiving patterns to finding useful rules and algebraic representations can be difficult (e.g., English and Warren 1998; Lannin 2005; Kieran 1992; Noss, Healey, and Hoyles 1997).

Linear Generalizing Problems: The Trapezoid Table Problem

To illustrate the difficulties students have with the kinds of problems typically used in patterning research and in mathematics textbooks, consider the *linear generalizing problem* presented in figure 11.1 (Stacey 1989; Lee 1996). The example is shown with both a drawing and a table of values. Students are asked to find a rule to predict how many chairs (dots) would fit around any number of trapezoid tables when the tables are positioned as shown; each element (table arrangement) in the pattern has one more table than the immediately previous arrangement (Blanton and Kaput 2003).

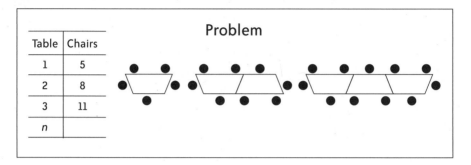

Fig. 11.1. Tabular and figural representations of the Trapezoid Table problem

The goal of this and other linear generalizing problems is to allow students to explore the relationship between the independent variable (in this example, the number of tables) and the dependent variable (in this instance, the number of chairs). In "natural language," for every table there are three chairs with an additional two chairs at either end. Arithmetically, multiply the number of tables by 3, and add 2. In algebraic language, if the number of tables is represented by x, then the number of chairs can be expressed as a function of x, or $f(x) = 3x + 2$.

Difficulties

Studies have found that students find this type of problem challenging and typically respond in a limited way. One of the difficulties lies in the propensity of students (and adults) to use recursive strategies for identifying and describing generalizations. In this example, the focus is on the variation within a single data set (e.g., adding 3 for each new table) rather than on the relationship between two data sets (e.g., finding the number of seats for any number of tables) (Warren 2000). Although this recursive approach allows students to predict the elements in the next couple of positions of a series, it does not foster the ability to perceive the relationship across the two data sets in order to find the underlying functional rule, which numerous researchers suggest is fundamental for algebraic thinking (Kieran 1992).

Another often reported problem is the difficulty students have working with functions of the form $y = mx + b$, which have both a multiplicative and a constant component; in the example of the trapezoid tables, $m = 3$ and $b = 2$, so $y = 3x + 2$. Students who fail to take into account both components often incorrectly use a "whole object strategy," which involves the incorrect use of proportional reasoning to find a functional relationship. A student using proportional reasoning to predict the number of seats for 6 trapezoid tables might double the seats for 3 tables and predict that 22 chairs would fit.

The proclivity of students to find rules that are incorrect (using whole-object reasoning) or limited (using recursive reasoning) is related to a more fundamental problem noted by researchers, namely, the lack of ability or inclination that students demonstrate in their explanations of pattern rules. Although the expectations from NCTM (2000) and Canadian curriculum documents are clear in their expectations that at least by grade 4, students should make conjectures and construct and justify their solution strategies (MOET 2000). Studies investigating the kinds of justifications students offer for patterning problems reveal that often their explanations are limited and reflect a tendency to value simplicity over accuracy. Several researchers have reported that even when students find incorrect rules for patterns, they tend to commit to their first conjecture despite invalidating data (e.g., Stacey 1989; Mason 1996; Lee 1996).

The research that we have been conducting addresses these difficulties associated with pattern learning. Specifically, we have studied different contexts to support students in their learning of functions through patterns. In our view it is important to find ways of maximizing the potential of patterning activities, since not only are patterns part of the curriculum but we know, at least for very young children, that patterns are widely enjoyed (Seo and Ginsburg 2004).

The Present Study

The study described here, the pilot study in our multiyear project (Moss, Beatty, and McNab 2006), was conducted in the spring of 2004. As will be elaborated in this article, we designed a brief instructional sequence, based on developmental principles (Moss and Case 1999), to help students gain an integrated understanding of numeric and geometric sequences as a means of developing a conception of functions. The second part of the instruction involved students' solving problems on the Web-based collaborative discourse platform, Knowledge Forum.

The participating grade 4 students ($n = 34$) were from two schools, one a university-based laboratory school and the other an inner-city public school. The students did not know one another and came from different socioeconomic backgrounds and different mathematics instruction experiences. The university lab school had a more reform orientation, whereas the downtown school maintained a more traditional approach.

Before the lesson sequence began, we conducted a brief informal assessment with students in each class to get an understanding of their abilities to work with patterns. We found that all the students used recursive strategies to find rules and that most could not identify underlying functional rules for patterns.

The Lessons: Moving between Numeric and Geometric Patterns

Although the scope of this article does not allow for a full discussion of the lesson design, the lessons did play an important role in developing core understandings that were foundational to the students' problem solving on Knowledge Forum. Thus we present a brief description of the six 40-minute lessons[1] that took place in both classrooms prior to students' collaboration on Knowledge Forum.

Numeric Patterns

The lessons began with a guess-my-rule type of game (Willoughby 1997; Rubenstein 2002). In our version of this game, one student took on the role of "robot" and had to apply a previously chosen function rule to randomly selected input numbers offered by their classmates in order to produce output numbers. The challenge for the rest of the students was to identify the relationship between the two data sets (input and output numbers) and to express this relationship as a rule. The students were introduced to a modified version of a function table (see fig. 11.2) where they were able to keep track of the input and output numbers and then record their conjectures about the functional relationship between the two sets of numbers. The functions that we introduced in this game were of the forms $f(x) = mx$ and $f(x) = mx + b$. In the second lesson, the "Guess My Rule" game was extended so that students could play in pairs and challenge their classmates to guess rules of their own invention. Because the input numbers were always presented out of sequence, students were not able to look solely at the output data set for a recursive pattern but instead needed to consider the relationship between the two sets of data in order to "guess the rule."

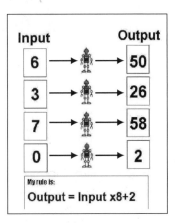

My rule is:

Output = Input x8+2

Fig. 11.2. Modified function table for the Robot game

Geometric Representations of Functions

The next set of lessons required students to build geometric growing patterns using position cards and pattern blocks. We began by demonstrating how to use pattern blocks to represent a multiplicative function in a geometric growing sequence. We then posed problems in which students were asked to make predictions about

---

1. The lessons were taught by student teachers in both classrooms who are the third and fourth authors of this article.

the number of elements or tiles in subsequent positions of the pattern, as, for example, the fifth or eleventh position. By asking for these "far" predictions, we encouraged the students to think beyond "What comes next?" to "What is the functional rule for building this pattern?" The position cards helped students to understand the functional relationship between one data set (the position number of a pattern as represented by the cards) and the other data set (the number of blocks used in that position). Later, when building composite functions, the students used two colors of pattern blocks (fig. 11.3) to visually represent "the part of the pattern that grows" and "the part of the pattern that stays the same." Figure 11.3 shows a geometric representation of the pattern $f(x) = 2x + 3$, where the coefficient is represented by the lower blocks that increase by 2 at every position and the constant, +3, by the top three blocks that "stay the same" at every position.

Fig. 11.3. Geometric growing sequence with position cards

The pattern-building lessons concluded with student-designed challenges. Students constructed the first three elements of a growing pattern following a rule of their choice and then challenged their classmates to guess their pattern rules. Although brief, these pattern-building lessons allowed the students to *see* the kinds of functional relationships they had been working with numerically in the "Guess My Rule" game.

Problem Solving Using Knowledge Forum

For the final two weeks of the study, students from the two classrooms were linked electronically and invited to collaborate to develop solutions for six problems posted on Knowledge Forum. Before presenting examples of students' discussions, the features of Knowledge Forum and how it works are described.

Knowledge Forum was established by the learning theorists Carl Bereiter and Marlene Scardamalia (1989) on the basis of their early work in intentional learning. When students work on Knowledge Forum, they have the potential to contribute their own ideas to the collaborative discussions in the form of "notes" or to respond to the ideas of others in notes referred to as "build ons." The notes are automatically labeled with the author's user name and the note's title, and students begin their notes by selecting one of a variety of prompts, such as *my theory, I need to understand, new information,* or *a better theory.* An important feature of Knowledge Forum that sets it apart from other threaded discourse systems is that students work on the database independently of their teachers. Thus it is not the teacher who asks for clarification or revision of the students' ideas or conjectures; rather, it is the students themselves who take on this responsibility. Generally, Knowledge Forum is used for students in science. Our intention was to explore the potential of this Web-based discourse platform for use by students in mathematics.

For the remainder of this article, we present verbatim examples of students' responses to generalizing problems that we posted on Knowledge Forum. The problems we posted were different from the types of patterns the students had encountered during the instructional sequence. New problems included both linear and quadratic functions that were embedded in different contexts. To illustrate students' thinking, we have chosen to highlight two of the problems, the Lunchroom Table Problem (a version of the Trapezoid Table Problem) and the Handshake Problem, both of which are well known for the challenges they present to students.

The Lunchroom Table Problem

We begin with some examples of notes and discussion contributed to the Lunchroom Table Problem that are representative of the notes posted by students in both classrooms. Figure 11.4 illustrates how the problem was presented in the database.

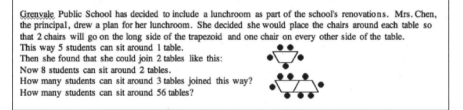

Grenvale Public School has decided to include a lunchroom as part of the school's renovations. Mrs. Chen, the principal, drew a plan for her lunchroom. She decided she would place the chairs around each table so that 2 chairs will go on the long side of the trapezoid and one chair on every other side of the table. This way 5 students can sit around 1 table.
Then she found that she could join 2 tables like this:
Now 8 students can sit around 2 tables.
How many students can sit around 3 tables joined this way?
How many students can sit around 56 tables?

Fig. 11.4. The Lunchroom Table Problem

Given the wide range of mathematical experiences and achievement levels across the two classrooms, it was not surprising to find that the strategies the students proposed varied significantly in mathematical sophistication. However, as will be shown by the first three examples, even when the students' reasoning was based on basic counting strategies, they were able to maintain their consideration of the contributing value of the constant and did not resort to whole-object reasoning. Sejal and Dave, whose note is presented below, found the rule $f(x) = 3x + 2$ (which they describe as "times three plus two" or "× 3 + 2") using a concrete representation and counting. They used the graphic tools of Knowledge Forum to represent their strategy and then used their drawing as a scaffold to create an algebraic rule.

Sejal and Dave: Our Way

We used 56 shape blocks and put them together [see fig. 11.5] and counted the places where chairs went and think the rule is × 3 + 2.

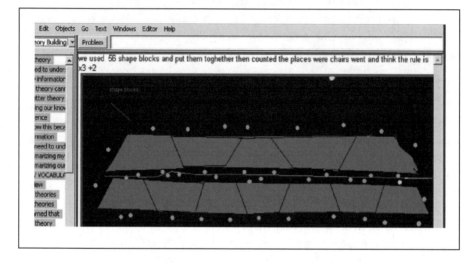

Fig. 11.5. Sejal and Dave's representation using Knowledge Forum

Another, more sophisticated counting strategy is shown in Niroshan's note. He responded to Sejal and Dave's note using the scaffold "my theory" and entitled his note, "Another answer."

Niroshan: Another Answer

My theory: *I got another answer that I did in my head and I got 170. First I drew 5 tables and put three people at each one. I didn't count the ones at the very end. I counted 15 people. I kept on adding 5 tables until I got to 55 (I times 15 by eleven). Then I needed to add another 3 people for the last table to make 56 tables. Then I added two for the very ends that I didn't count before and I got 170.*

As can be seen from his "another answer," Niroshan performed complicated mental calculations by chunking groups of 5 tables of 15 people to reach his total for 55 tables and then added one more table to find the total for 56. What is impressive is that throughout these laborious calculations, he recognized that his solution still required the additional two chairs (the constant) at the end of the connected tables.

Ferdie's contribution to the same discussion also shows his understanding of the need to incorporate the constant.

Ferdie: 170 People

*I also think that it was 170 people at 56 tables. My **evidence** is that I multiplied 56 × 3 and then I added 2. The 2 was for the sides.*

From the visual cue in the diagram, these students (and most others) interpreted the constant as the two chairs at the ends of the line of tables. In the exchanges that follow, Alonzo presents a different idea of what constitutes the constant in the function.

Alonzo: Lunchroom Tables

The answer is 170. The rule is however many tables you join together you take away two multiply the number by 3 then add 8.

Jalisa tries to replicate his approach and fails, and Alonzo then expands on his original conjecture of a rule to explain where she went wrong.

Jalisa: Different Answer

I got another answer. I got 172.
***New information:** I tried it [your rule] and I got confused.*

Alonzo: I Explained Better

Sorry you must have misunderstood. What I meant was multiply 3 and 54 together and then add 8. because you get the 8 from the tables at the sides that way you lose 2 tables then multiply 54 and 3. Does that make sence to you? If it doesn't please build on to me and tell me what you don't get.

Although Alonzo maintains his own unique solution to this problem throughout the exchange, he expands on his solution in response to Jalisa's inquiry. Additionally, despite his belief in his answer, Alonzo concludes his second note by asking Jalisa to verify the strategy and respond with any inaccuracies. As often reported, this kind of rigor in developing evidence and justification when working with generalizing problems is not often encountered, even among much older students.

The Handshake Problem

This same commitment to explaining conjectures of rules and clarifying strategies can be seen in students' discussions for the next problem. Figure 11.6 presents the Handshake Problem.

Imagine you are at a huge party. Everyone starts to shake hands with other people who are there. If 2 people shake hands, there is 1 handshake. If 3 people are in a group and they each shake hands with the other people in the group, there are 3 handshakes. If 4 people are in a group and they each shake hands with the other people in the group, there are 6 handshakes. How many handshakes would there be if there were 10 people in the group? How many handshakes would there be if there were 100 people in the group?

Fig. 11.6. The Handshake Problem appearing on Knowledge Forum

The Handshake Problem, which has been shown to be difficult for much older students (e.g., Cooper and Sakane 1986), requires students to figure out the quadratic rule to use to determine the total number of handshakes if everyone shakes hands with everyone else, exactly once, in any sized group. The following verbatim exchange, evolving over the course of five notes among four students, shows how they reasoned their way to their solutions, despite the fact that none of them had prior instruction in either the order of operations or the use of parentheses.

Rafe: My Theory

My theory is the first person who shakes hands with the all the other people. So if there's 10 people, the first person would shake 9 people's hands. Then the next person would shake 8 people's hands. And it goes on and on and on. The last person shakes 0 hands.

So for a 100, the first person would have 99 handshakes. And you go on and on and add all the number together and that will be the answer.

Mira: To Get the Answer

I agree with you. I think that a faster way to get the answer to a question like that is to take the number of people, so say there were 8 people, you would go 8 × 8 − 1 divided by two, because each person gets one handshake less than the person befor, so it's sort of like −1.

Hamsyani: The Rule

I am going to try your theory with threes $3 \times 3 - 1$ divided by 2, = 4, but we know the answer is 3. How come I got four? (Please answer).

Mira, realizing that Hamsyani was not able to understand her rule, restates her rule but this time inserts extra spaces between $3 \times$ and $3 - 1$ to clarify that the rule includes $3 \times (3 - 1)$, not $3 \times 3 - 1$.

Mira: Your Question Is Answered

You got 4 because I made a mistake. It's actuly $3 \times 3 -1$ wich is eczactly like 3×2 divided by 2. That equles 3. I only did -1 so you'd know how I got 2.

In his explanatory note, Jenorth incorporates natural language into the expression of a functional rule in order to explain the basis of each of the quantities included in Mira's rule.

Jenorth: Explanation of Mira's Note

The number of people $- 1 \times$ the number of people take 50% of that number and that is the answer. 10 people $- 1 = 9$. Then 9×10 (because there are 10 people) divide by 2 (90 divided by 2 = 45) and 45 is the answer.

We can see in this exchange that the students, with no assistance from a teacher, are grappling with mathematical ideas that they had not previously encountered. Not only is it impressive that these students are able to find a rule for this very difficult problem, but again we see how these students are motivated to search for and test new ideas and explanations for these ideas, both their own and those of their fellow collaborators.

Overall Contributions to Knowledge Forum

In our analyses of the students' contributions to the Knowledge Forum database for the six problems, we discovered that the students in both of these very different grade 4 classrooms contributed equally to the Knowledge Forum discussions. Furthermore, we discovered that two-thirds of all the "build on" notes that were contributed in response to another note either directly requested additional information or demonstrated, through additional evidence, the strengths or deficiencies of the theories posted in students' original notes. This finding indicates that the social environment encouraged by the database favored not simply "right answers" but emphasized evidence-based reasoning.

Conclusion

From the previously described examples, we see that students were able to use the Knowledge Forum database as a platform for developing their understanding of, and ability to articulate, functional relationships across data sets, to use a variety of strategies to develop rules, and although not explicitly asked to do so, to establish a community practice of offering explanations and evidence to support their conjectures.

One of the important consequences of connecting the classrooms through Knowledge Forum was the creation of a common goal among the participants of finding useful solutions to the difficult generalizing problems. Because the participants were unknown to one another, they were less able to accept or reject ideas according to the author's social standing or classroom credibility. The students' only frame of reference was the mathematical validity of the notes and discussions that took place on Knowledge Forum.

The database abounds with detailed descriptions of students' efforts to justify their conjectures of rules. It was the students who assumed responsibility for contributing to the mathematical knowledge base by finding algebraically useful rules and progressively moving their understanding forward by furnishing evidence and justifications. Not only did the database support rigorous mathematical thinking, but it also appears to have fostered a democracy of participation.

References

Bereiter, Carl, and Marlene Scardamalia. "Intentional Learning as a Goal of Instruction." In *Knowing, Learning, and Instruction,* edited by Lauren Resnick, pp. 361–92. Hillsdale, N.J.: Lawrence Erlbaum Associates, 1989.

———. "Learning to Work Creatively with Knowledge." In *Powerful Learning Environments: Unravelling Basic Components and Dimensions,* edited by Erik De Corte, Lieven Verschaffel, Noel Entwistle, and Jerome van Merriënboer, pp. 55–68. Oxford, England: Elsevier Science, 2003.

Blanton, Maria L., and James J. Kaput. "Developing Elementary Teachers' 'Algebra Eyes and Ears.'" *Teaching Children Mathematics* 10 (October 2003): 70–77.

Carraher, David W., Analucia D. Schliemann, Barbara M. Brizuella, and Darrell Earnest. "Arithmetic and Algebra in Early Mathematics Education." *Journal for Research in Mathematics Education* 37 (March 2006): 87–115.

Cooper, M., and H. Sakane. "Comparative Experimental Study of Children's Strategies with Deriving a Mathematical Law." In *Proceedings of the Tenth International Conference for the Psychology of Mathematics Education,* pp. 410–14. London: University of London, Institute of Education, 1986.

English, Lyn D., and Elizabeth A. Warren. "Introducing the Variable through Pattern Exploration." *Mathematics Teacher* 91 (February 1998): 166–70.

Ferrini-Mundy, Joan, Glenda Lappan, and Elizabeth Phillips. "Experiences with Patterning." *Teaching Children Mathematics* 3 (February 1997): 282–88.

Greenes, Carole, Mary Cavanagh, Linda Dacey, Carol Findell, and Marion Small. *Navigating through Algebra in Prekindergarten–Grade 2.* Reston, Va.: National Council of Teachers of Mathematics, 2001.

Kieran, Carolyn. "The Learning and Teaching of School Algebra." In *Handbook of Research on Mathematics Teaching and Learning,* edited by Douglas A. Grouws, pp. 390–419. NewYork: Macmillan Publishing Co., 1992.

Lannin, John K. "Generalization and Justification: The Challenge of Introducing Algebraic Reasoning through Pattern Activities." *Mathematical Thinking and Learning* 7 (2005): 231–58.

Lee, Lesley. "An Initiation into Algebraic Culture through Generalization Activities." In *Approaches to Algebra: Perspectives for Research and Teaching,* edited by Nadine Bednarz, Carolyn Kieran, and Lesley Lee, pp. 87–106. Dordrecht, Netherlands: Kluwer Academic Publishers, 1996.

Mason, John. "Expressing Generality and Roots of Algebra." In *Approaches to Algebra: Perspectives for Research and Teaching,* edited by Nadine Bednarz, Carolyn Kieran, and Lesley Lee, pp. 65–86. Dordrecht, Netherlands: Kluwer Academic Publishers, 1996.

Ministry of Education and Training (MOET). *The Ontario Curriculum Grade 1–8 Mathematics.* Toronto, Ont.: Queen's Printer for Ontario, 2000.

Moss, Joan, Ruth Beatty, and London McNab. "Design for the Development and Teaching of an Integrated Patterning Curriculum." Paper presented at the annual meeting of the American Educational Research Association, April 2006.

Moss, Joan, and Robbie Case. "Developing Children's Understanding of the Rational Numbers: A New Model and an Experimental Curriculum." *Journal for Research in Mathematics Education* 30 (March 1999): 122–47.

National Council of Teachers of Mathematics (NCTM). *Principles and Standards for School Mathematics.* Reston, Va.: NCTM, 2000.

Noss, Richard, Lulu Healy, and Celia Hoyles. "The Construction of Mathematical Meanings: Connecting the Visual with the Symbolic." *Educational Studies in Mathematics* 33 (July 1997): 203–33.

Rubenstein, Rheta. "Building Explicit and Recursive Forms of Patterns with the Function Game." *Mathematics Teaching in the Middle School* 7 (April 2002): 426–31.

Seo, Kyoung-Hye, and Herbert Ginsburg. "What Is Developmentally Appropriate in Early Childhood Mathematics Education? Lessons from New Research." In *Engaging Young Children in Mathematics: Standards for Early Childhood Mathematics Education,* edited by Douglas H. Clements and Julie Sarama, pp. 91–104. Mahwah, N.J.: Lawrence Erlbaum Associates, 2004.

Stacey, Kaye. "Finding and Using Patterns in Linear Generalising Problems." *Educational Studies in Mathematics* 20 (March 1989): 147–64.

Steen, Lynn A. "The Science of Patterns." *Science* 240 (April 1988): 611–16.

Warren, Elizabeth. "Visualisation and the Development of Early Understanding in Algebra." In *Proceedings of the 24th Conference of the International Group for the Psychology of Mathematics Education* (PME), edited by Maria van den Heuvel-Panhuizen, vol. 4, pp. 273–80. Hiroshima, Japan: PME, 2000.

Watson, Anne, and John H. Mason. "Student-Generated Examples in the Learning of Mathematics." *Canadian Journal of Science, Mathematics, and Technology Education* 2 (February 2002): 237–49.

Willoughby, Stephen S. "Functions from Kindergarten through Sixth Grade." *Teaching Children Mathematics* 3 (February 1997): 314–18.

12

Developing Algebraic Thinking in Earlier Grades: Some Insights from International Comparative Studies

Jinfa Cai
John Moyer

IT IS widely accepted that to achieve the goal of "algebra for all" in the United States, students in elementary and middle school should have experiences that prepare them for more formal study of algebra in the later grades (National Council of Teachers of Mathematics [NCTM] 2000). However, curriculum developers, educational researchers, and policymakers are just beginning to explore what these earlier experiences might be (Cai and Knuth 2005; Carpenter, Franke, and Levi 2003; Kaput 1999; Mathematical Sciences Education Board 1998; NCTM 2000; Schifter 1999). In other countries (e.g., China, Russia, Singapore, and South Korea), students begin the formal study of algebra much earlier (Cai et al. 2005). The purpose of this article is to describe what we can learn from international comparison studies about developing algebraic thinking in earlier grades. We believe that international perspectives can increase our knowledge and our ability to develop students' algebraic thinking in elementary and middle schools in North America.

In this article we share two major insights from international studies. The first insight relates to the transition between arithmetic and algebra. The second focuses on the generalization of concrete representations and strategies. These two insights are based on the belief that students in earlier grades are capable of thinking algebraically and should be expected to do so. However, teachers need to support students' development of algebraic thinking in the early grades as a way to help them make a smooth transition between arithmetic and algebra and appreciate the usefulness of generalized approaches to solving problems.

We Should Expect Students in Elementary Grades to Think Algebraically

Expecting students in elementary grades to think algebraically is not an issue among researchers these days. According to recent research on learning, there are many obvious and widely accepted reasons for maintaining this expectation (Cai et al. 2005). Nonetheless, we raise the question in order to offer a less obvious reason for developing algebraic ideas in the earlier grades, namely, that resistance to algebra in middle and high school would be reduced if we could remove the misconception that arithmetic and algebra are disjoint subjects. Traditionally, most school mathematics curricula separate the study of arithmetic and algebra—arithmetic being the primary focus of elementary school mathematics and algebra the primary focus of middle and high school mathematics. There is a growing consensus, however, that this separation makes it more difficult for students to learn algebra in the later grades (Kieran 1992, 2004).We are also aware that the need to develop algebraic thinking in earlier grades is not as accepted as the need to learn arithmetic (Usiskin 1995). Even those who have taken an algebra course and have done well can live productive lives without ever using it. Although one can make an eloquent argument in favor of studying algebra at the secondary school level (e.g., Usiskin 1995), we believe that resistance to algebra can be more effectively addressed by helping students form algebraic habits of thinking while they are in elementary school. If students and teachers routinely spent the first six years of elementary school simultaneously developing arithmetic and algebraic thinking (with differing emphases on both at different stages of learning), arithmetic and algebra would come to be viewed as inextricably connected. The study of algebra in secondary school would become a natural and nonthreatening extension of the mathematics of the elementary school curriculum.We are not claiming that the way to develop algebraic ideas in earlier grades is to simply push the traditional secondary school algebra curriculum into the elementary school program. Rather, developing algebraic ideas in the earlier grades requires fundamentally reforming how arithmetic should be taught (Carpenter et al. 2005). It also requires developing a better understanding of the factors that make the transition from arithmetic to algebra difficult for students.

What is algebraic thinking in earlier grades? Although there is no clear consensus about the answer to this question, there is a general agreement that algebraic thinking in earlier grades extends beyond arithmetic and computational fluency to attend to the deeper underlying structure of mathematics (Cai and Knuth 2005). The development of algebraic thinking in the earlier grades requires the development of particular ways of thinking that result from analyzing relationships between quantities, noticing structure, studying change, generalizing, problem solving, modeling, justifying, proving, and predicting (Kieran 2004).

Fostering Interconnections between Arithmetic and Algebra

The transition from arithmetic to algebra is difficult for many students, even those who are quite proficient in arithmetic, because it requires them to make many adjustments (Kieran 2004; Kilpatrick, Swafford, and Findell 2001). Kieran suggests that a successful transition from arithmetic to algebra requires five adjustments: (1) a focus on relations and not merely on the calculation of numeric answers, (2) a focus on operations as well as their inverses and on the related idea of doing and undoing, (3) a focus on both representing and solving a problem instead of merely solving it, (4) a focus on both numbers and letters rather than on numbers alone, and (5) a refocus on the meaning of the equal sign. These five adjustments represent a shift from arithmetic toward developing ideas fundamental to the study of algebra.

Three Ideas from Chinese and Singaporean Curricula

Our analysis of elementary school curricula in other countries showed that making connections between arithmetic and algebra is a common goal (Cai et al. 2005). In the remainder of this section we present three ideas from Chinese and Singaporean curricula that may help students make the adjustments needed to develop algebraic ways of thinking in earlier grades.

The first idea. The first idea is to relate reverse operations to equation solving. In Chinese elementary schools, addition and subtraction are introduced simultaneously in the first grade, and the subtraction operation is introduced as the reverse of addition (Cai 2004a; Cai et al. 2005). Students are guided to think about the following question: "$1 + ( ) = 3$?" In order to find the number in ( ), subtraction is introduced: $3 - 1 = 2$. Throughout the first grade, students are consistently asked to solve similar problems. In the second grade, multiplication and division with whole numbers are introduced. Division is first introduced as equal sharing. Division is also introduced as the reverse of multiplication: "What multiplied by 2 equals 8?" That is, "If $( ) \times 2 = 8$, what is the number in ( )?" The idea of equation and equation solving permeates the introduction of both subtraction and division. Similar approaches are taken in both the Singaporean and South Korean curricula (Lew 2004; Ng 2004).

The second idea. The second idea is "pictorial equation solving" as illustrated in the Singaporean curriculum (Ng 2004; Ng and Lee n.d.). It is common to use pictures to model problem situations in the first and second grades. Later, these pictures are replaced with the more abstract rectangles. To help third, fourth, and fifth graders engage with algebra word problems while avoiding the necessity of using algebraic equations, students are taught to use rectangles to solve algebra word problems involving whole numbers. Algebra word problems involving fractions and ratios are introduced in the fifth and sixth grades. More detailed descriptions of "pictorial equation solving" can be found in Ng (2004) and Ng and Lee (2006).

Figure 12.1 depicts four examples of pictorial equation solving taken from Beckmann (2005a, p. 599; 2005b, pp. 436–38), who selected them from the Singaporean curriculum (Curriculum Planning and Development Division [CPDD] of Singapore 2000a, 2000b). The examples are illustrative of the levels of algebraic problem solving that are fostered in grades 3–6. Each example includes a diagram whose structure can be described as a pictorial equation. The first example gives a third-grade problem and supplies a pictorial equation that can be used to find the cost of 1 kg of prawns. From the diagram, the student can see that 3 kg of prawns cost \$47 – \$20 = \$27. Using this result, the student can compute the cost of 1 kg of prawns by dividing \$27 by 3 kg. The algebraic equation $3x + \$20 = \$47$ can be seen directly in the strip diagram, where one small white strip represents x, which, in turn, represents the cost of 1 kg of prawns.

The second example illustrates a fourth-grade problem. Unlike the problem in Example 1, this problem is more algebraic than arithmetic. Suhua's rectangle or unit is the generator of all relationships presented in the problem. Meifen's rectangle is dependent on Suhua's, with Meifen's share represented by a unit identical to Suhua's plus another rectangle representing the relational portion of \$600 more. In the model drawing, a pictorial equation representing the problem is formed. If the letter x replaces Suhua's unit, then the algebraic equation $(x + \$600) + x = \$2000$ is produced.

Example 3 illustrates the increased difficulty of algebraic problem solving in grade 5. Not only are fractions used in the problem, but the fractions themselves are based on two different wholes. The larger whole, which is the unknown unit, is the amount of money Encik had at first. It is represented by the upper strip in each pair, which is divided into two darker rectangles (2/5) and three white rectangles (3/5). The smaller whole is the amount of money that remained after Encik paid his wife. It is represented by the lower strip in each pair. Its position and length show that the smaller whole is equal to 3/5 of the larger whole. Using the bottom pair of strips, students see that the smaller whole is \$600, and that each of the five rectangles in the larger whole equals 1/3 of the smaller whole. Therefore, the larger whole, which represents the money Encik had at first, is (\$600 ÷ 3) × 5 = \$1000. The pictorial equation reflects the following algebraic equation: $1/2 \, (3/5 \, x) = \$300$, where x represents the money Encik had at first.

The fourth example is taken from the Singaporean sixth-grade curriculum. It illustrates a still higher level of algebraic problem solving, namely, problem solving that involves equations with variables on both sides of the equal sign. Such equations are the precursors to systems of linear equations. The "Before" part of the pictorial equation shows that at first Raju had 3 times as much money as Gopal. The "After" part of the diagram shows that Raju and Gopal had equal amounts of

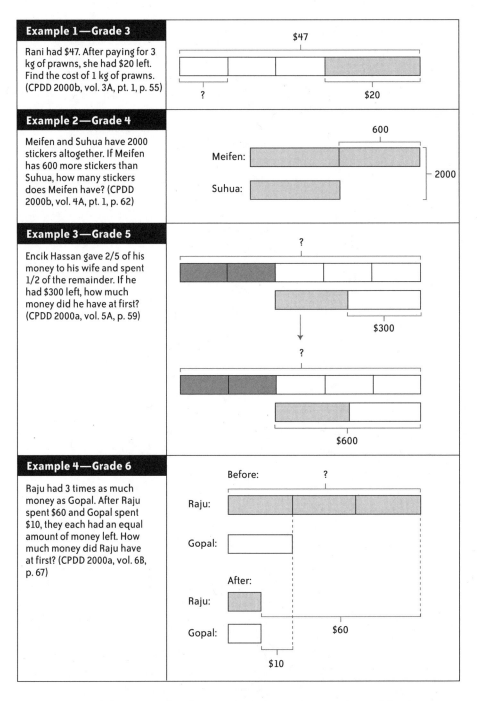

Example 1—Grade 3	$47
Rani had $47. After paying for 3 kg of prawns, she had $20 left. Find the cost of 1 kg of prawns. (CPDD 2000b, vol. 3A, pt. 1, p. 55)	? $20
Example 2—Grade 4	600
Meifen and Suhua have 2000 stickers altogether. If Meifen has 600 more stickers than Suhua, how many stickers does Meifen have? (CPDD 2000b, vol. 4A, pt. 1, p. 62)	Meifen: Suhua: 2000
Example 3—Grade 5	?
Encik Hassan gave 2/5 of his money to his wife and spent 1/2 of the remainder. If he had $300 left, how much money did he have at first? (CPDD 2000a, vol. 5A, p. 59)	$300 ? $600
Example 4—Grade 6	Before: ?
Raju had 3 times as much money as Gopal. After Raju spent $60 and Gopal spent $10, they each had an equal amount of money left. How much money did Raju have at first? (CPDD 2000a, vol. 6B, p. 67)	Raju: Gopal: After: Raju: Gopal: $60 $10

Fig. 12.1. Four examples of using pictorial equations to solve problems

money left after they spent $60 and $10 respectively. Using the pictorial equation, students see that two of Raju's "Before" rectangles represent $60 – $10 = $50. Therefore each of Raju's "Before" rectangles represent $50 ÷ 2 = $25. Finally, since his "Before" money is represented by 3 rectangles, Raju had 3 × $25 = $75 at first. The pictorial equation reflects the algebraic equation $3x – \$60 = x – \$10$, where x represents the money Gopal had at first. The solution to the equation (x = $25), however, is not the answer to the problem. Like the pictorial equation, the final step in the solution is to evaluate $3x$, the expression representing the money Raju had at first.

The third idea. The third idea is to use both arithmetic and algebraic approaches to solve problems. This idea can be seen clearly in Chinese classrooms where solving a problem in multiple ways is a common practice. For example, teachers will present two arithmetic and three algebraic ways to solve the following problem:

> Liming Elementary School had exactly enough funds to buy 12 basketballs that cost 24 yuan each. Before buying the basketballs, the school spent 144 yuan of the funds for some soccer balls. How many basketballs can the school buy with the remaining funds?

Arithmetic solutions:

Solution 1:   Begin by computing the original funding and subtract the money spent on soccer balls: $(24 \times 12 – 144) \div 24 = 144 \div 24 = 6$ basketballs.

Solution 2:   Begin by computing the number of basketballs that can no longer be bought: $12 – (144 \div 24) = 6$ basketballs.

Algebraic solutions:

Solution 3:   Assume that the school can still buy x basketballs: $(24 \times 12 – 144) = 24x$. Therefore, $x = 6$ basketballs.

Solution 4:   Assume that the school can still buy x basketballs: $24 \times 12 = 24x + 144$. Therefore, $x = 6$ basketballs.

Solution 5:   Assume that the school can still buy x basketballs. $12 = (144 \div 24) + x$. Therefore, $x = 6$ basketballs.

Note that Solutions 3 and 4 correspond to Solution 1, and Solution 5 corresponds to Solution 2.

There are three objectives in teaching students to solve problems both arithmetically and algebraically: (1) to help students attain an in-depth understanding of quantitative relationships by representing them both arithmetically and algebraically; (2) to guide students to discover the similarities and differences between arithmetic and algebraic approaches so that they can make smooth transitions from arithmetic to algebraic thinking; and (3) to develop students' thinking skills as well as flexibility in using appropriate approaches to solve problems. Post, Behr, and Lesh (1988) indicated that first-describing-and-then-calculating is one of the principal features that make algebra different from arithmetic. Comparisons between the arithmetic and algebraic approaches can highlight this unique feature.

The Chinese curriculum (Division of Elementary Mathematics 1999a, 1999b) we analyzed uses both arithmetic and algebraic problem solving to help students make the transition from arithmetic to algebraic thinking. During the transition period, Chinese students solve many problems like the ones given in this section. The students are required to solve the problems algebraically, despite the fact that all of them can be solved arithmetically. As might be expected, at the beginning of the transition period, students often do not understand why they need to learn an equation-solving approach to solve problems. However, after a period of time using both approaches, students come to see the advantages of using equations to solve these types of problems.

Relation to Kieran's Five Adjustments

The three ideas presented in this section could be incorporated into U.S. curricula to help students make four of the five adjustments suggested by Kieran (2004). The first idea, of incorporating the Chinese reverse-operation approach to subtraction and division, can help students make two of the adjustments suggested by Kieran: (1) focus on relations and not merely on the calculation of a numerical answer, and (2) focus on inverses of operations, not merely on the operations themselves, and on the related idea of doing and undoing. The second idea, of incorporating the Singaporean use of pictorial equation solving, can help students (3) focus on both representing and solving a problem rather than on merely solving it. The third idea, of incorporating the Chinese practice of using both arithmetic and algebraic approaches to solve problems, can help students (4) focus on both numbers and letters, rather than on numbers alone.

None of the Asian curricula we analyzed (Cai et al. 2005) addresses Kieran's fifth proposed adjustment of a refocusing on the meaning of the equal sign. In the United States, Carpenter, Franke, and Levi (2003) have analyzed many of the misunderstandings about equality that students develop. For instance, many students think that an equal sign means that they should record the answer to a computation problem. Recently, some U.S. curricula have incorporated activities that serve to focus students' attention on the relational properties of equality. By way of illustration, in one program, grade 3 students discuss the equivalence of subtraction expressions, such as those in the equation $104 - 78 = 106 - 80$, and grade 5 students justify the correctness of equations like $65 \times 24 = 130 \times 12$ in which one factor is halved and the other factor is doubled (TERC forthcoming). In both examples the first number to the right of the equal sign is not the result of the computation on the left.

Concrete Representations and Generalization

Formal algebraic representation, one of the important characteristics of algebraic thinking, is related to generalization and symbolism. A letter symbol can be used not only as a placeholder for an unknown (e.g. $3x + 5 = 8$) but also as a generalized representative of a range of values (e.g., $s = 2t + 3$). International studies found that U.S. sixth-grade students tended to use concrete, arithmetic problem-solving strategies, and by contrast Chinese students tended to use abstract, algebra-based problem-solving strategies involving letter symbols as generalized representatives of ranges of values (Cai and Hwang 2002). This is best illustrated in responses to the odd-number pattern problem (fig. 12.2).

Odd-Number Pattern Problem

When asked to solve a problem involving a pattern of odd numbers (see fig. 12.2), a considerable percentage of U.S. students used concrete, arithmetic strategies, but many Chinese students used abstract, algebraic strategies. Employing a concrete, arithmetic strategy, U.S. students noticed that each time the doorbell rang two more guests entered than on the previous ring. They made a table or a list by adding enough 2s sequentially to answer all the questions. Using an algebraic strategy, some Chinese students noticed that the number of guests who entered on a particular ring of the doorbell equaled two times that ring number minus one (i.e., $y = 2n - 1$, where y represents the number of guests and n represents the ring number). Others noticed that the number of guests who entered on a particular ring equaled the ring number plus one less than the ring number (i.e., $y = n + (n - 1)$).

The U.S. and Chinese students had almost identical success rates (70%) when they were asked to find the number of guests who entered on the 10th ring. When they were asked to identify the ring number when 99 guests would enter the party, the success rate for Chinese students was 43 percent and for U.S. students it was 24 percent. This difference in success rate appears to be due to the fact that more Chinese than U.S. students used algebraic strategies to solve the problem. Indeed, fully 65 percent of Chinese students choosing an appropriate strategy for Question 3 used an algebraic strategy, compared to only 11 percent for the U.S. sample. The majority (75%) of U.S. students chose arithmetic strategies, compared to 29 percent of the Chinese students. Algebraic strategies (e.g., solving for n: $99 = 2n - 1$) are more efficient than arithmetic strategies (e.g., repeatedly adding 2 until 99 is reached or making an exhaustive table or list) to answer the third question, which involves "undoing" (i.e., finding the ring number when the number of entering guests is known). Making a list is a viable (although cumbersome) arithmetic strategy for finding the ring number when 99 guests enter, but the exclusive use of arithmetic strategies in problems of this type may impose limitations on the development of students' algebraic reasoning ability. Therefore, teachers should help students develop strategies that go beyond arithmetic. Although initially students should be encouraged to con-

Sally is having a party.

The first time the doorbell rings, 1 guest enters.
The second time the doorbell rings, 3 guests enter.
The third time the doorbell rings, 5 guests enter.
The fourth time the doorbell rings, 7 guests enter.

The guests keep arriving in the same way. On the next ring a group enters that has 2 more persons than the group that entered on the previous ring.

A. How many guests will enter on the 10th ring? Explain or show how you found your answer.
B. Write a rule or describe in words how to find the number of guests that entered on each ring.
C. 99 guests entered on one of the rings. What ring was it? Explain or show how you found your answer.

Fig. 12.2. An odd-number pattern problem

struct their own representations of mathematical concepts, rules, and relationships, they eventually should be taught to use generalized solution strategies.

Why U.S. Students Are Inclined to Use Arithmetic Strategies

The findings from cross-national studies indicate the ineffectiveness of using only arithmetic strategies to develop students' mathematical thinking and substantive content knowledge. Why were U.S. students less likely than Chinese students to use generalized, algebraic problem-solving strategies? One possibility is that U.S. teachers less frequently encourage their students at earlier levels to move to more algebraic representations and strategies. A common belief held by many U.S. teachers is that visual representations and concrete materials facilitate students' conceptual understanding (Burrill 1997) and that concrete representations and manipulatives are the basis for all learning. However, research shows that the use of manipulatives or concrete experiences does not guarantee students' conceptual understanding (e.g., Baroody 1990). The purpose of using concrete, visual representations is to help bring about students' conceptual understanding of the abstract nature of mathematics, but concrete experiences do not automatically lead to generalization and conceptual understanding. Unfortunately, U.S. teachers whose lessons were observed in the cross-national studies made little or no attempt to help students make the transition from concrete, visual representations to symbolic representations (Cai and Lester 2005).

Although the reasons given above may explain why U.S. students tend to use concrete, arithmetic strategies rather than generalized, algebraic strategies to solve problems, they do not explain why U.S. teachers less frequently encourage their students to use generalized strategies than Chinese teachers do. Part of the answer may lie in differences between U.S. and Chinese teachers' expectations. One study showed that U.S. teachers do not expect their grade 6 students to use algebraic problem-solving strategies, whereas Chinese teachers do (Cai 2004b). The Chinese make generalized problem solving a top priority throughout their curriculum, in part because Chinese teachers expect their sixth-grade students to reason abstractly and in part because they appreciate the difficulties that students have in making the transition from arithmetic to algebra. The effect of the Chinese approach is to help smooth the transition from arithmetic to algebra for students.

Concluding Remarks

Teachers in grades K–8 need to have an appreciation of the difficulty students have in making the transition from arithmetic to algebra. They also need to believe that grades K–8 students have the mental capacity to generalize and abstract from their concrete experiences in mathematics classes. Teachers who have a highly developed appreciation of just how difficult the transition is and at the same time believe that students can learn arithmetic and algebraic ideas in tandem become motivated to make adjustments to the way they teach mathematics in grades K–8.

In this article we described some of the difficulties students encounter as they struggle to make the transition from arithmetic to algebra, and we suggested ways to help ease the transition that are in concert with Kieran's (2004) suggested adjustments. We presented examples from curricula used in China and Singapore that make connections between arithmetic and algebra. It is our belief that adaptations of these approaches can be used in the United States to teach mathematics in the earlier grades, thus easing the transition from arithmetic to algebra for U.S. students.

We presented evidence from cross-national studies indicating that U.S. students persist in using concrete, arithmetic-based problem-solving strategies, even when such strategies are inefficient, if not ineffective. We also showed that Chinese students effectively use abstract, algebra-based strategies to solve the same problems that U.S. students approach concretely with arithmetic-based strategies. Research shows that in grades K–8 in the United States, a lack of teachers' expectation for students' use of algebraic problem-solving strategies may explain why their students use such strategies less frequently than their counterparts in China do (Cai 2004b). Despite perceived differences in U.S. and Chinese cultures, a knowledge of Chinese students' success with the use of generalized strategies may prompt U.S. teachers to explore possible ways to encourage their students to move toward the use of abstract strategies in grades K–8, thus easing the transition from arithmetic to algebra.

REFERENCES

Baroody, Arthur J. "How and When Should Place-Value Concepts and Skills Be Taught?" *Journal for Research in Mathematics Education* 21 (July 1990): 281–86.

Beckmann, Sybilla. *Mathematics for Elementary Teachers.* Boston: Pearson Addison Wesley, 2005a.

———. *Activities Manual to Accompany "Mathematics for Elementary Teachers."* Boston: Pearson Addison Wesley, 2005b.

Burrill, Gail. "The NCTM *Standards*: Eight Years Later." *School Science and Mathematics* 97 (October 1997): 335–39.

Cai, Jinfa. "Developing Algebraic Thinking in the Earlier Grades: A Case Study of the Chinese Mathematics Curriculum." *Mathematics Educator* 8 (April 2004a): 107–30.

———. "Why Do U.S. and Chinese Students Think Differently in Mathematical Problem Solving? Exploring the Impact of Early Algebra Learning and Teachers' Beliefs." *Journal of Mathematical Behavior* 23 (June 2004b): 135–67.

Cai, Jinfa, and Stephen Hwang. "Generalized and Generative Thinking in U.S. and Chinese Students' Mathematical Problem Solving and Problem Posing." *Journal of Mathematical Behavior* 21 (March 2002): 401–21.

Cai, Jinfa, and Eric J. Knuth. "The Development of Students' Algebraic Thinking in Earlier Grades from Curricular, Instructional, and Learning Perspectives." *Zentralblatt für Didaktik der Mathematik* [*International Review on Mathematics Education*] 37 (December 2005): 1–4.

Cai, Jinfa, and Frank A. Lester. "Solution and Pedagogical Representations in Chinese and U.S. Mathematics Classrooms." *Journal of Mathematical Behavior* 24 (December 2005): 221–37.

Cai, Jinfa, Hee Chan Lew, Anne Morris, John C. Moyer, Swee Fong Ng, and Jean Schmittau. "The Development of Students' Algebraic Thinking in Earlier Grades: A Cross-Cultural Comparative Perspective." *Zentralblatt für Didaktik der Mathematik* 37 (December 2005): 5–15.

Carpenter, Thomas P., Megan L. Franke, and Linda Levi. *Thinking Mathematically: Integrating Arithmetic and Algebra in Elementary School.* Portsmouth, N.H.: Heinemann, 2003.

Carpenter, Thomas P., Linda Levi, Megan L. Franke, and Julie Koehler Zeringue. "Algebra in Elementary School: Developing Relational Thinking." *Zentralblatt für Didaktik der Mathematik* 37 (December 2005): 53–59.

Curriculum Planning and Development Division (CPDD) of Singapore. *Primary Mathematics.* Singapore: Times Media Private Limited, 2000a.

———. *Primary Mathematics Workbook.* Singapore: Times Media Private Limited, 2000b.

Division of Elementary Mathematics. *Mathematics: Elementary School Textbook (Number 10).* Beijing: People's Education Press, 1999a.

————. *Mathematics: Elementary School Textbook (Number 11)*. Beijing: People's Education Press, 1999b.

Kaput, James. "Teaching and Learning a New Algebra." In *Mathematics Classrooms That Promote Understanding,* edited by Elizabeth Fennema and Thomas Romberg, pp. 133–55. Mahwah, N.J.: Lawrence Erlbaum Associates, 1999.

Kieran, Carolyn. "The Learning and Teaching of School Algebra." In *Handbook of Research on Mathematics Teaching and Learning,* edited by Douglas A. Grouws, pp. 390–419. New York: Macmillan Publishing Co., 1992.

————. "Algebraic Thinking in the Early Grades: What Is It?" *Mathematics Educator* 8 (April 2004): 139–51.

Kilpatrick, Jeremy, Jane Swafford, and Bradford Findell, eds. *Adding It Up*. Washington, D.C.: National Academy Press, 2001.

Lew, Hee Chan. "Developing Algebraic Thinking in the Earlier Grades: A Case Study of the South Korean Elementary School Mathematics Curriculum." *Mathematics Educator* 8 (April 2004): 88–106.

Mathematical Sciences Education Board. *The Nature and Role of Algebra in the K–14 Curriculum: Proceedings of a National Symposium*. Washington, D.C.: National Research Council, 1998.

National Council of Teachers of Mathematics (NCTM). *Principles and Standards for School Mathematics*. Reston, Va.: NCTM, 2000.

Ng, Swee Fong. "Developing Algebraic Thinking: A Case Study of the Singaporean Primary School Curriculum." *Mathematics Educator* 8 (April 2004): 39–59.

Ng, Swee Fong, and Kerry Lee. "Model Method: Singapore Children's Tool for Representing and Solving Algebra Word Problems." Unpublished manuscript, n.d.

Post, Thomas R., Merlyn J. Behr, and Richard Lesh. "Proportionality and the Development of Prealgebra Understandings." In *The Ideas of Algebra, K–12,* 1988 Yearbook of the National Council of Teachers of Mathematics (NCTM), edited by Arthur F. Coxford, pp. 78–90. Reston, Va.: NCTM, 1988.

Schifter, Deborah. "Reasoning about Operations: Early Algebraic Thinking in Grades K–6." In *Developing Mathematical Reasoning in Grades K–12,* 1999 Yearbook of the National Council of Teachers of Mathematics (NCTM), edited by Lee V. Stiff, pp. 62–81. Reston, Va.: NCTM, 1999.

TERC. *The Re-Vision of Investigations in Number, Data, and Space*. Glenview, Ill.: Scott Foresman, forthcoming.

Usiskin, Zalman. "Why Is Algebra Important to Learn?" *American Educator* 19 (spring 1995): 30–37.

Part 4

Algebra in the Classroom

13

Algebra in Elementary School: A Japanese Perspective

Tad Watanabe

*P*RINCIPLES *and Standards for School Mathematics* (National Council of Teachers of Mathematics [NCTM] 2000) differs from the 1989 *Curriculum and Evaluation Standards* in the inclusion of an Algebra Standard for all grades, prekindergarten through grade 12. The introduction of algebra in the pre-K–2 and 3–5 grade bands naturally raises the question "What are the fundamental ideas of algebra that are appropriate for investigation by elementary school students?" The purpose of this article is to suggest possible answers to this question by examining the treatment of algebra in Japanese elementary school curriculum materials.

As many readers may know, Japan has a national curriculum. The Ministry of Education, Culture, Sports, Science, and Technology (hereafter referred to as "the Ministry") publishes the *Course of Study* (*COS*), which specifies what topics are to be taught at what grade levels. The Ministry also publishes the *Elementary School Teaching Guide for the Japanese Course of Study: Arithmetic Grades 1–6* (hereafter referred to as *Teaching Guide*). It should be noted that this document is different from the "teacher's manuals" that each textbook publisher produces to accompany its textbook series. The *COS* and the *Teaching Guide* are studied carefully by authors when writing textbooks, which require the Ministry's approval prior to publication. This paper presents the treatment of algebra both in the *Teaching Guide* for the 1989 *COS* and in the most widely used elementary textbook series.

The 1989 *COS* has been selected instead of the current one, since that is the only *COS* with an available English translation of the *Teaching Guide*. The current elementary school mathematics *COS* contains significantly less content than the 1989 *COS*. However, most of the ideas related to algebra are still discussed in elementary schools, grades 1 through 6. Two major topics related to algebra that were shifted to lower secondary schools are the introduction of letters as variables and the formal study of inverse proportion, both of which are now explored in grade 7.

Where and What Is *Algebra?*

The elementary school mathematics *COS* consists of the following four content strands: Numbers and Calculations, Quantities and Measurements, Geometric Figures, and Quantitative Relations (grades 3–6 only). Some may be surprised to see that there isn't an algebra strand in the *COS*. In fact, there is no algebra strand even in the lower secondary school mathematics *COS*. The Japanese word for "algebra" does not appear in the elementary school *COS* nor in the *Teaching Guide*. The word appears only a few times in the *Lower Secondary School Teaching Guide*, usually in the context of discussing different branches of mathematics. So, where is algebra in the Japanese elementary school mathematics curriculum?

Much of what is considered algebra in elementary schools is found in the Quantitative Relations strand. The *Teaching Guide* states, "The objectives and contents of this domain cover a wide range, but can be divided into three categories: *ideas of functions, writing and interpreting mathematical expressions,* and statistical manipulation" (Takahashi, Watanabe, and Yoshida 2004, p. 36, emphasis added).

Ideas of Functions

Table 13.1 displays a summary of specific ideas of functions that according to the *Teaching Guide* are presented in the Japanese elementary school mathematics curriculum. Although the Quantitative Relations strand does not appear in the grades 1 and 2 *COS*, the *Teaching Guide* identifies one-to-one correspondence and viewing a number as the sum, the difference, or the product of other numbers as foundational ideas related to functions. How are these ideas presented in the textbooks? Two illustrative examples are presented: (1) decomposing and composing numbers, and (2) introducing and developing multiplication.

Table 13.1
Function-Related Topics in COS (Takahashi, Watanabe, and Yoshida 2004, pp. 36–37)

Grade	Topics
1	• One-to-one correspondence • Number as the sum or difference of other numbers
2	• Comparing and ordering numbers • Number as a product of other numbers • How a product increases when the multiplier increases by 1
3	• How a product changes when the multiplier increases or decreases by 1
4	• Dependency relationship of two numbers and its graph
5	• Quantitative relationships represented by formulas such as $A \times B = C$
6	• Ratio and the value of ratio • Proportion and its graph • Inverse proportion • Proportional relationships

Decomposing and Composing Numbers

Figure 13.1 shows a diagram that appears in a grade 1 Japanese textbook near the end of the unit on numbers to 10. Children have yet to study addition formally at this point. The teacher's manual that accompanies this particular textbook (not the *Teaching Guide*) includes the following explanation (Tokyo Shoseki 1998, pp. 56–57, translated by author):

> One of the main objectives of this unit is to help students see a number from multiple perspectives. This is a foundation for functional thinking because, in order to see a number in relationship to another, we must pay attention to any dependency relationship or rule for correspondence. Thus, with decomposition of ten, once you pick "1," then the other number, "9," is determined. Furthermore, if the first number increases 1, 2, 3 ...., the other number will decrease 9, 8, 7, ...
>
> First graders cannot develop such a perspective automatically, and teachers may want to order the written combinations or display the blocks so that a pattern might be more easily noticed visually.

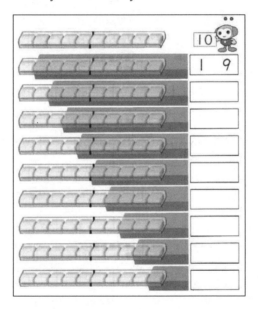

Fig. 13.1. Decomposing 10 (Hironaka and Sugiyama 2006a, p. 25)

Viewing a number as a combination of two other numbers continues to be emphasized throughout grade 1. For example, at the end of the unit that introduces addition (sums to 10), the textbook suggests that students practice addition facts using flash cards. However, the two activities suggested at the bottom of figure 13.2 focus not only on practicing addition facts but also on developing understanding that a number may be viewed as a sum of two other numbers. The picture at the bottom right shows a game in which one student announces a sum and the other students identify expressions that have that sum. Similar activities are suggested as children begin their study of subtraction and of computation with greater numbers.

Fig. 13.2. Flash card activities (Hironaka and Sugiyama 2006a, p. 33)

Introducing and Developing Multiplication

In Japanese elementary schools, multiplication is a major focus of the second-grade curriculum. One of the unique features of the Japanese textbooks' treatment of multiplication is the focus on the relationship that "when the multiplier increases by 1, the product increases by the multiplicand." This is a specific instance of the distributive property. After the idea of multiplication is introduced and students have determined all facts with 2 and 5 as the multiplicand, they begin their study of facts with multiplicands other than 2 and 5 (for a more detailed analysis of the treatment of multiplication, see Watanabe 2003).

Students next determine all the facts with 3 as the multiplicand. In this exploration, the textbook includes questions like these: "To get an answer for 3×5, what do you need to add to the answer of 3×4?" and "Use the answer for 3×5 to find 3×6" (Hironaka and Sugiyama 2006b, p. 23). These questions are often accompanied by a picture of 1 group of 3 being joined to 4 groups of 3, like the one shown in figure 13.3 (a). As students explore all facts with 4 as the multiplicand, questions such as the following are posed: "When the multiplier of 4×3 increases by 1, how much does the answer increase? What happens when the multiplier of 4×4 increases by 1?" (p. 25). For these questions, a diagram similar to that shown in figure 13.3 (b) is presented.

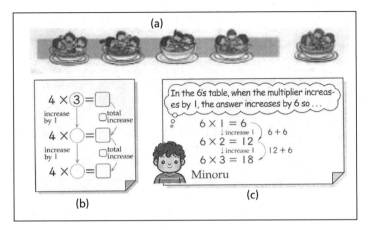

Fig. 13.3. Multiplier-product relationship (Hironaka and Sugiyama 2006b, pp. 23, 25, and 33)

As students begin their exploration of facts with 6 as a multiplier, they are encouraged to use what they already know about multiplication to find all those facts. The textbook presents illustrations of grade 2 students' reasoning. As can be seen in figure 13.3 (c), the child is reasoning that "in the 6's table, when the multiplier increases by 1, the answer increases by 6. So, …" (Hironaka and Sugiyama 2006b, p. 33).

Although the focus of these investigations is on the development of multiplication facts, students are also analyzing what happens to the dependent variable (product) when the independent variable (multiplier) is changed. Although the curriculum does not use such language, it encourages students to pay attention to how two quantities change simultaneously and to identify any pattern in the way the change takes place.

Ideas of Functions in Grades 4–6

In the upper elementary school, the major idea related to functions is covariation, or how two quantities change in relation to each other. The study culminates in grade 6 with the introduction of direct and indirect proportions. As can be seen in the treatment of addition and multiplication described earlier, students have already experienced situations where two quantities covary, even though that was not the main focus of those explorations.

In grade 4, the curriculum actually makes covariation the focus of students' investigations. The diagram in figure 13.4 accompanies the opening problem in the covariation unit. In this problem, a 1-liter measuring cup, with ten equally spaced marks on both sides, is half-filled; the initial water level is at 5 on both the left and right scales. The problem is to determine what happens to the water level when the measuring cup is tilted. Students investigate what is changing (the numbers on the left and the right scales) as well as what remains the same (the sum of those two numbers).

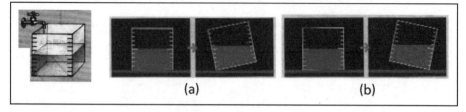

Fig. 13.4. Grade 4 covariation example (Hironaka and Sugiyama 2006d, pp. 54, 55)

In grade 5, the exploration of covariation again is implicit as students explore the effect a change in one measurement has on another. For example, after students have developed the formula for the circumference of a circle, they are directed to investigate "how the circumferences of circles change as their diameters change" (Hironaka and Sugiyama 2006e, p. 82).

In grade 6, as students begin their formal exploration of proportion, it is very common for textbooks to begin the unit with different situations in which two quantities covary. Those situations may include the ages of two siblings on January 1 of every year, the length of a coil spring and the weight attached to it, the number of pages in a book that have already been read and those yet to be read, and the length and the width of rectangles whose area is 24 square centimeters (see fig. 13.5). Students group situations that vary in the same way. In some situations, two quantities change in the same direction; that is, if one quantity increases, the other also increases. In others, the changes in the quantities are in opposite directions, with one quantity increasing and the other quantity decreasing. After grouping like situations, students are encouraged to create other situations where two quantities are changing in one way or the other. Note that this initial analysis does not distinguish proportional from nonproportional situations. This distinction is made later when students are asked to investigate each class of covariation, focusing on not only what changes but also on what remains unchanged. Through such investigations, students come to the conclusion that there are (at least) two cases for the increase-increase situations: (1) where the difference of the two quantities stays the same, and (2) where the quotient of the two quantities stays constant. Then, using tables, graphs, and equations, students explore proportional situations where the quotients stay constant.

Students also analyze increase-decrease situations and discover that there are again (at least) two cases: constant sum and constant product. Neither of these situations results in a proportional relationship. In fact, the constant product situations result in inversely proportional relationships. The constant sum and constant difference situations result in linear but nonproportional relationships. These are investigated much more in depth in grade 7.

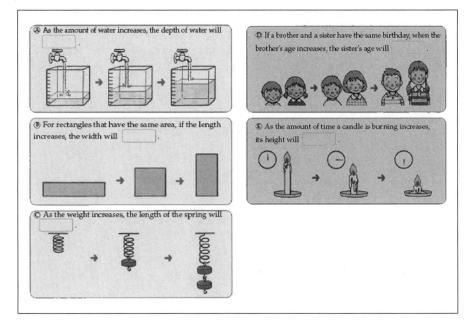

Fig. 13.5. Grade 6 covariation situations (Hironaka and Sugiyama 2006e, pp. 70, 71)

Mathematical Expressions

The Japanese elementary school mathematics curriculum pays close attention to ideas related to "mathematical expressions" (*shiki* in Japanese). The word *shiki* refers to more than simply expressions like $x + 5$; it also refers to equations and inequalities. The phrase *mathematical expressions* is used in the sense of "expressing ideas and relationships using mathematical notations." The main emphases of the Japanese elementary school mathematics curriculum with respect to mathematical expressions are as follows:

- Writing and interpreting mathematical expressions involving addition, subtraction, multiplication, and division
- Comparing numbers and quantities and expressing their relationships
- Writing and interpreting mathematical expressions involving parentheses
- Using $\square$, $\triangle$, a, and x in mathematical expressions, and evaluating such expressions by substituting specific values

The emphasis on writing mathematical expressions begins in grade 1 with the study of simple addition. For example, figure 13.6 shows a pair of situations that require grade 1 students to represent the situations using mathematical expressions. Later in grade 1, the unit on sums greater than 10 opens with the following problem:

"There are 9 persimmons on the front tree and 4 persimmons on the back tree. How many are there altogether?" (Hironaka and Sugiyama 2006a, p. 62). The first subquestion asks students to write a mathematical expression. The second subquestion asks students to think about the ways to carry out the computation indicated by the mathematical expression.

Fig. 13.6. Grade 1 addition problem (Hironaka and Sugiyama 2006a, p. 28).

It is clear that the Japanese curriculum emphasizes mathematical expressions as a way to describe quantitative relationships in different phenomena, not just computational problems to be solved. This is clearly stated in the *Teaching Guide* (Takahashi, Watanabe, and Yoshida 2004, p. 29):

> Teaching about writing and interpreting mathematical expressions already started at the stage of learning addition in first grade…. But, since concrete numbers are used in lower grades and calculation immediately leads to one number, children rarely become aware of the fact that 3 + 4 represents a concrete phenomenon. Therefore, it is important to teach children to focus on the meaning of mathematical expressions instead of paying attention solely to getting results.

Because mathematical expressions describe different phenomena, interpreting mathematical expressions is an important point of emphasis. This emphasis can be observed in the grade 4 problem shown in figure 13.7. In this problem, students are expected to record their reasoning processes using mathematical expressions. Their mathematical expressions are then shared publicly so that other students may be able to understand how their peers thought about the problem. Through such experience, Japanese textbooks try to help students understand the usefulness of mathematical expressions not only as a way to represent their own thinking concisely but also as a tool for communicating their thinking processes.

Because mathematical expressions are an important tool for communication, Japanese textbooks also carefully develop students' abilities to use this tool. In particular, students learn to write compound mathematical expressions, that is, mathematical expressions with more than one operation. This occurs with a problem like the following: "Makoto had a 1000-yen note. He bought a 140-yen notebook and a 460-yen pair of scissors. How much change did he get back?" (Hironaka and Sugiyama 2006c, p. 70). This problem is accompanied by two hypothetical students' solutions:

Naoko's solution: 1000 – 140 = 860, 860 – 460 = 400

Makoto's solution: 140 + 460 = 600, 1000 – 600 = 400

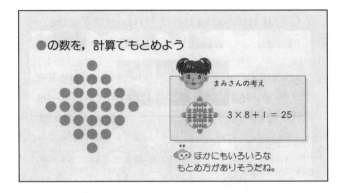

Fig. 13.7. Ways to calculate a number of dots (Sugiyama, Iitaka, and Itoh 2002, p. 41)

Students are asked to think about how each of these mathematical expressions may be combined into one.

To assist students' thinking, Japanese textbooks often use mathematical expressions with words. For example, for this problem, the textbook shows: [Money Paid] – [Total Price] = [Change]. Since the total price can be expressed as 460 + 140, Makoto's solution may be summarized by the mathematical expression

$$1000 – (460 + 140) = 400.$$

Mathematical expressions with words are also used in formulas that are studied in the upper elementary grades. For example, the formula for the area of a parallelogram is given as: [Area of Parallelogram] = [Base] × [Height] instead of $A = b \times h$. Although the use of letters in mathematical expressions is not formally studied until grade 5, beginning as early as grade 3, students learn about expressions in which symbols, such as $\square$, $\bigcirc$, and $\triangle$, are used in place of numbers. They are asked to solve problems like the following (Hironaka and Sugiyama 2006d, p. 77):

The following math sentence shows the relationship between one side of an equilateral triangle and its perimeter. What do $\square$ and $\bigcirc$ indicate?

$$\square \times 3 = \bigcirc$$

After expressing relationships among quantities using symbols to stand for individual quantities, students evaluate the mathematical expressions by substituting specific values for the quantities represented by symbols.

These examples illustrate how the Japanese curriculum materials lay the foundation for the formal study of algebra in later grades by gradually and systematically developing the important ideas related to mathematical expressions with letters.

Conclusions and Implications

Since the publication of *Principles and Standards for School Mathematics* (NCTM 2000), many elementary school mathematics curricula have incorporated ideas related to patterns as a way to introduce algebra to young students. However, *Principles and Standards* clearly suggests that patterns are only one component of algebra in schools (p. 37):

> Instructional programs from prekindergarten through grade 12 should enable all students to—

- understand patterns, relations, and functions;
- represent and analyze mathematical situations and structures using algebraic symbols;
- use mathematical models to represent and understand quantitative relationships;
- analyze change in various contexts.

The analysis of the Japanese curriculum materials presented here may give insight into how all four bullets in the *Principles and Standards* citation above may be addressed more effectively in elementary schools.

Finally, it is important to keep in mind that the ideas related to algebra are included in the *Quantitative Relations* strand. The *Teaching Guide* (Takahashi, Watanabe, and Yoshida 2004, p. 36) states,

> The contents of this domain include items which are useful in examining or manipulating contents in other domains. An important aim of this domain is to understand the contents of other domains using the ideas and methods discussed in this domain.

It is through the study of ideas related to functions and mathematical expressions that students may gain deeper understandings of arithmetic operations and develop ways to investigate changing quantities. As illustrated by the Japanese curriculum, the study of algebra in elementary schools aims not only to develop algebraic competence but also to foster a deeper understanding of other content areas in mathematics. As such, algebra is as much a process standard as a content standard.

REFERENCES

Hironaka, Heisuke, and Yoshishige Sugiyama. *Mathematics for Elementary School 1.* Tokyo: Tokyo Shoseki, 2006. [English translation of *New Mathematics for Elementary School 1,* by Hironaka and Sugiyama.]

_____. *Mathematics for Elementary School 2B.* Tokyo: Tokyo Shoseki, 2006b. [English translation of *New Mathematics for Elementary School 2, Vol. 2,* by Hironaka and Sugiyama.]

_____. *Mathematics for Elementary School 4A.* Tokyo: Tokyo Shoseki, 2006c. [English translation of *New Mathematics for Elementary School 4, Vol. 1,* by Hironaka and Sugiyama.]

_____. *Mathematics for Elementary School 4B.* Tokyo: Tokyo Shoseki, 2006d. [English translation of *New Mathematics for Elementary School 4, Vol. 2,* by Hironaka and Sugiyama.]

_____. *Mathematics for Elementary School 6A.* Tokyo: Tokyo Shoseki, 2006e. [English translation of *New Mathematics for Elementary School 6, Vol. 1,* by Hironaka and Sugiyama.]

National Council of Teachers of Mathematics (NCTM). *Principles and Standards for School Mathematics.* Reston, Va.: NCTM, 2000.

Sugiyama, Yoshishige, Shigeru Iitaka, and Setsuro Itoh. *New Elementary Mathematics 4, Vol. 2* [in Japanese]. Tokyo: Tokyo Shoseki, 2002.

Takahashi, Akihiko, Tad Watanabe, and Makoto Yoshida. *Elementary School Teaching Guide for the Japanese Course of Study: Arithmetic (Grades 1–6).* Madison, N.J.: Global Education Resources, 2004.

Tokyo Shoseki. *New Elementary Mathematics: Teacher's Instruction Manual.* Tokyo: Tokyo Shoseki, 1998.

Watanabe, Tad. "Teaching Multiplication: An Analysis of Elementary School Mathematics Teachers' Manuals from Japan and the United States." *Elementary School Journal* 104 (2003): 111–25.

14

Using a Model Approach to Enhance Algebraic Thinking in the Elementary School Mathematics Classroom

Beverly J. Ferrucci
Berinderjeet Kaur
Jack A. Carter
BanHar Yeap

THE DEFINITION of algebraic thinking has a more expansive and diverse connotation than that usually associated with "algebra." Kieran (1996) describes algebraic thinking as "an approach to quantitative situations that emphasizes the general relational aspects with tools that are not necessarily letter-symbolic" (p. 275), whereas Driscoll (1999) defines algebraic thinking as having the capacity to portray quantitative conditions in a manner that allows the relationships among variables to become apparent. Steele (2005) notes that algebraic thinking includes "the ability to analyze and recognize patterns, to represent the quantitative relationships between the patterns, and to generalize these quantitative relationships" (p. 142).

As well as adopting an expanded notion of algebraic thinking, mathematics educators have increasingly recognized the importance of enhancing students' potential to develop structural knowledge as a means of enriching their abilities to think algebraically. Algebraic structural knowledge is knowledge about how to identify, elaborate, plan, and execute within the context of algebra (Marshall 1995). When students use only procedures and algorithms to solve mathematical problems, it is not always evident that they are accessing structural knowledge. One approach that accentuates students' abilities to develop such knowledge is the model method as it is exemplified and extensively taught in Singapore's elementary schools (Ferrucci, Yeap, and Carter 2002, 2003).

As an essential component of the Singapore elementary school curriculum, the model method is taught to all elementary school students as a problem-solving tool along with other more well known heuristics, such as draw a picture, guess and check, and make a table. The model method basically involves the use of diagrams to represent quantities and relationships between and among quantities and unknowns. The model method also provides teachers with convenient and productive ways to assess the depth of students' structural knowledge and mathematical understanding.

Singapore's model method uses a structured process whereby students in elementary school are taught to visualize abstract mathematical relationships and their varying problem structures through pictorial representations. These representations are frequently presented as rectangles, and this configuration makes it relatively easy for the figures to be partitioned into smaller units when necessary. Clearly, there are multiple ways that students could represent each problem with rectangles. These multiple methods accentuate the uniqueness of individual students' contributions and also provide genuine opportunities for students to express their creativity in mathematical problem solving.

Using the model method, teachers are able to present to students problems that demonstrate how concrete problem situations and accompanying algebraic ideas can emerge from real-world contexts without the use of formal algebraic notation. This approach helps promote several important aspects of algebraic thinking, such as the organization of commonalities among problem situations, the viewing of how change in one relationship affects change in another, and the overall ability to make important mathematical generalizations.

The model method is also very useful in solving challenging word problems that can otherwise require the use of formal algebraic methods. In the discussion that follows, we present word problems with different structures and show how the model method provides students with opportunities to access algebraic thinking.

The following example illustrates how the model method can help a student with no formal study of algebra to solve a problem that may otherwise require knowledge of simultaneous equations. This example serves as a precursor for the formal algebraic techniques involved in solving simultaneous equations with two unknowns. The example also helps to make pivotal connections among logical reasoning, visual models, and structural knowledge.

Example 1

> Mrs. Wu and Mr. Washington went to the Hillside Market to buy some fruit. Mrs. Wu bought 7 oranges and 4 apples for $4.80, and Mr. Washington bought 5 oranges and 2 apples for $3.00. What was the price of each fruit?

Although in formal courses in algebra, letters are used to represent unknown quantities, in the model method rectangles or portions of rectangles are often used to represent the unknowns. To make problems that involve two unknown quantities easier to comprehend, students can use different colors or shading for the rectangles. In one possible approach, students could begin by using rectangles of different colors or shading to represent (by using identification and elaboration knowledge) the price of each fruit and proceed to draw the model for Mrs. Wu's purchase and Mr. Washington's purchase (see Step 1). This is essentially the same as writing the two equations $7x + 4y = \$4.80$ and $5x + 2y = \$3.00$ where x is the price of an orange and y is the price of an apple.

Students can use the visual representation to look for a relationship among the

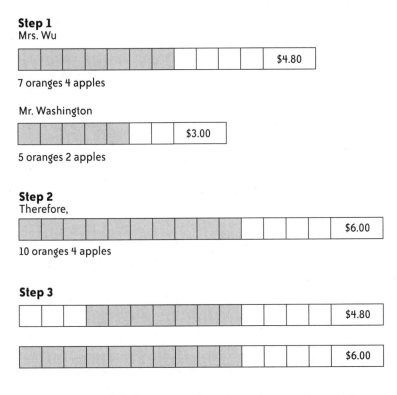

Fig. 14.1. Models illustrating a three-step solution to Example 1

quantities. The students can use simple proportional reasoning that if 5 oranges and 2 apples cost $3.00, then 2×5, or 10 oranges and 2×2, or 4 apples, cost $2 \times \$3.00$, or $6.00 (see Step 2).

By comparing the Step 1 diagram with the Step 2 diagram, the students can easily see that 3 extra oranges in the last diagram cost $6.00 – $4.80, or $1.20 more (see Step 3). Hence, if 3 oranges cost $1.20, then each orange costs $0.40.

Knowing that each orange costs 40 cents, the lower diagram in Step 3 depicts the total cost of the oranges as 10×40 cents, or $4.00. By using subtraction, the students can then determine that 4 apples cost $6.00 – $4.00, or $2.00. Hence, each apple costs $2.00 ÷ 4, or $0.50.

A comparison of the model method solution with the method of solving simultaneous equations can also be instructive and be a motivating introduction to algebraic solutions and the knowledge of structure for older or more able students. Steps in the model method also illustrate details of the algebraic solution.

Let the price of an orange be x and the price of an apple be y.

$$7x + 4y = \$4.80\ldots\ldots\ldots(1)$$ This is Step 1 in the model method

$$5x + 2y = \$3.00\ldots\ldots\ldots(2)$$ and an illustration of identification and elaboration knowledge.

$(2) \times 2:$ $$10x + 4y = \$6.00\ldots\ldots\ldots(3)$$ This is Step 2 in the model method and an illustration of knowledge of planning.

$(3) - (1)$ $10x + 4y = \$6.00$ This is Step 3 in the model method and
$- (7x + 4y) = \$4.80$ an illustration of execution.

$\overline{\qquad\quad 3x = \$1.20}$

Therefore, $x = \$0.40$.
Substitute $x = \$0.40$ into (2) to obtain:

$$\$2.00 + 2y = \$3.00$$
$$2y = \$1.00$$
$$y = \$0.50.$$

Hence, the price of an orange is $0.40 and the price of an apple is $0.50.

The Model Method in Singapore

Tek-Hong Kho, a former project director for primary mathematics at the Curriculum Development Institute of Singapore's Ministry of Education, was instrumental in introducing the model method to elementary students in Singapore in a deliberate and structured manner (Kho 1987). Today, students in Singapore elementary schools are introduced to three kinds of mathematical models within the context of the model method. These mathematical models are the part-whole model (fig. 14.2), the comparison model, and the change model. The following sections illustrate how the model method may be applied to these mathematical models.

A. Part-whole model

A part-whole model illustrates the situation when a whole is composed of a number of parts.

The whole may have two or more parts. When the parts are given, the students can determine the whole. Sometimes the whole and some parts are given and other

Whole

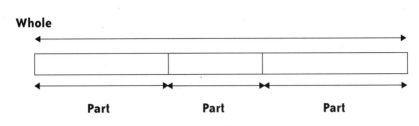

Fig. 14.2. A part-whole model

parts are unknown. The model method's concrete representation of an unknown part provides an excellent foundation for algebraic thinking, and the use of the model method allows students to make better sense of the situations. The usefulness of the method is evident in simple algebraic word problems, such as shown in Example A1.

Example A1

$\frac{3}{7}$ of the children at a basketball game are girls.

48 of the children are boys. How many girls are at the basketball game?

Instead of writing an algebraic equation such as $\frac{4}{7}x = 48$, where x is the number of children at the basketball game, one possible approach could be for students to identify and elaborate a model such as that in figure 14.3. They could draw seven rectangles to represent all the children at the game and select 3 out of 7 of them to represent the girls. They can then calculate the value for ⬜ ,which is 48 ÷ 4, or 12, and can conclude that there are 3 × 12, or 36 girls, at the game.

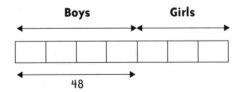

Fig. 14.3. A model illustrating a solution to Example A1

B. The comparison model

The comparison model demonstrates the relationship between two or more quantities when they are compared, contrasted, or described by differences. As in the part-whole model, the comparison model provides an excellent springboard for students to use in making transitions between arithmetic and algebraic thinking skills. Examples B1 and B2 illustrate the use of this model in algebraic word problems that involve multiplicative comparison and additive comparison, respectively.

Example B1

There are 3 baskets labeled Basket A, Basket B, and Basket C.

Basket A contains 4 times as many bananas as Basket C.

Basket B contains 16 fewer bananas than Basket A.

Basket C contains half as many bananas as Basket B.

Find the number of bananas in each basket.

In this problem, students can draw three rectangles to represent the three different baskets (see fig. 14.4). Basket A contains 4 times as many bananas as Basket C, so Basket A's model contains 4 small rectangles and Basket C's model contains one small rectangle. The model for Basket B is then constructed using the fact that Basket C contains half as many bananas as Basket B. Since Basket B contains 16 fewer bananas than Basket A, a double-headed arrow with the value of 16 inside is drawn next to Basket B's model to indicate the difference between it and Basket A's model.

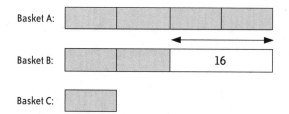

Fig. 14.4. A model illustrating a solution to Example B1

A typical sequence of reasoning to plan and execute a solution is shown below.

2 small rectangles depict 16 bananas

1 small rectangle depicts 16 ÷ 2, or 8, bananas

Basket A: 4 small rectangles depict 4 × 8, or 32, bananas

Basket B: 2 small rectangles depict 2 × 8, or 16, bananas

Basket C: 1 small rectangle depicts 1 × 8, or 8, bananas

Hence,

Basket A has 32 bananas;

Basket B has 16 bananas;

Basket C has 8 bananas.

Example B2

A local restaurant owner bought three crates of melons at a farmers' market. The total weight of the three crates was 16 kg. Crate 1 was 0.4 kg heavier than crate 2 and crate 1 was 0.16 kg heavier than crate 3.

    (a) How much heavier was crate 3 than crate 2?

    (b) Find the weight of each crate.

One approach to planning the solution is to compare two quantities at a time. Students may compare the weights of crate 1 and crate 2. Since crate 1 is 0.4 kg heavier than crate 2, a double-headed arrow with the value 0.4 inside is drawn first next to the model for crate 2 to indicate this difference. Then a vertical dotted line is drawn to emphasize the difference (see Step 1, fig. 14.5)).

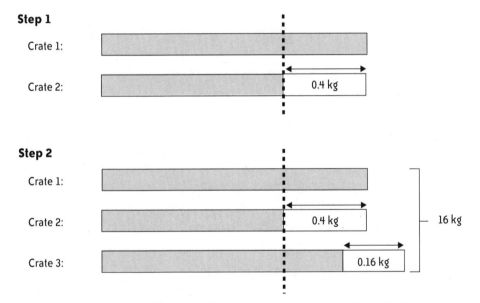

Fig. 14.5. Models illustrating Steps 1 and 2 in a solution to Example B2

Students may do likewise for crate 1 and crate 3. Teachers may want to draw students' attention to the relative value between 0.16 and 0.4. In particular, students who possess number sense are able to reflect the notion of 0.16 as being less than half of 0.4 in their model. The value of 16 (kg) can then be indicated within a sidebar, since it is the sum of the weights of all three crates (see Step 2, fig. 14.5).

In a next step students can easily elaborate the difference in weights between crate 3 and crate 2 by subtraction. The relationship is clear because of the visual representation that the model method allows.

(a) 0.4 kg – 0.16 kg = 0.24 kg

Hence, crate 3 is 0.24 kg heavier than crate 2. By substituting these values into the models, students can illustrate the relationship as in Step 3 (see fig. 14.6). To determine the weights of the individual crates, the students may notice that the models of all three crates contain rectangles to the left of the dotted line that are equal in area. This means that 16 kg, the sum of all three crates, minus 0.64 kg (the sum of the outer rectangles of 0.4 kg and 0.24 kg) is 15.36 kg. Hence, one rectangle to the left of the dotted line stands for 15.36 kg ÷ 3, or 5.12 kg. By substituting the value of 5.12 kg in the respective rectangles, the students use addition to determine the weights of each crate (see Step 4, fig. 14.6).

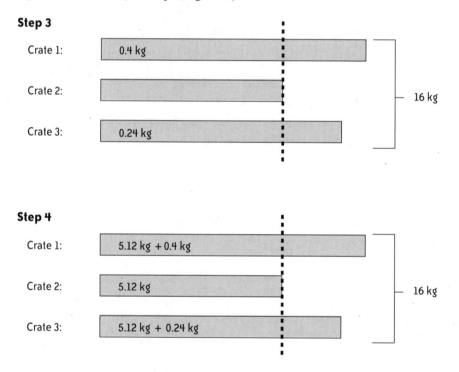

Fig. 14.6. Models illustrating Steps 3 and 4 in a solution to Example B2

(b) Crate 1 = 5.12 kg + 0.4 kg = 5.52 kg

   Crate 2 = 5.12 kg

   Crate 3 = 5.12 kg + 0.24 kg = 5.36 kg

The transition from this model-based thinking to a more traditional algebraic approach is constructively enhanced by students' practice with a variety of problems using the model approach. That is, continued practice with the model method aids students in building the foundation for symbolic representation and helps them to make the connection between algebraic thinking using the model and the traditional, symbolic way of completing problems. Students may also gain insights by comparing model-based thinking with results of solving systems of equations.

$$(x + 0.4) + x + (x + 0.24) = 16$$
$$3x + 0.64 = 16$$
$$3x = 16 - 0.64$$
$$3x = 15.36$$
$$x = 15.36 \div 3 = 5.12$$

C. The Change Model

The change model provides representations of the relationship between the new value of a quantity and its original value in a before-and-after situation, often before and after an increase or a decrease. Examples C1 and C2 illustrate the change model in before-and-after situations. Reinforcing the concept of change is important because it is a basis for many important applications of algebraic thinking. As a result, change models generalize robustly and elegantly as students progress through the gamut of algebraic endeavours.

Example C1

John and Pedro have equal amounts of money. If John spends $18 and Pedro spends $25, then John will have twice as much money left as Pedro. How much money do they each have at the beginning?

Using the model, a student could identify and elaborate the solution by drawing two rectangles with the same area to illustrate that John and Pedro have equal amounts of money (see Step 1, fig. 14.7). One may proceed by putting in the amounts that each person spends, while keeping in mind that John will have twice as much left as Pedro. This means that a student may record $18 in the model for John's money and then divide the remaining portion of the model into two smaller rectangles to illustrate twice the amount. The amount of $25 is then recorded in the rectangle for Pedro's money with one smaller rectangle left over compared to the two smaller rectangles in the model for John's money (see Step 2, fig. 14.7). The difference between the two labelled rectangles can then be determined to be $25 − $18, or $7. This means that one small rectangle has a value of $7. Since John will have twice as much money left as Pedro and one small rectangle represents $7, it follows that John has 2 × $7, or $14, left (see Step 3, fig. 14.7). When these values are placed within the models, the amount of money that John and Pedro had at the beginning is easily determined.

John has $32 [($7 × 2) + $18 = $32].

Pedro has $32 [$7 + $25 = $32].

Hence, John and Pedro each had $32 at the beginning.

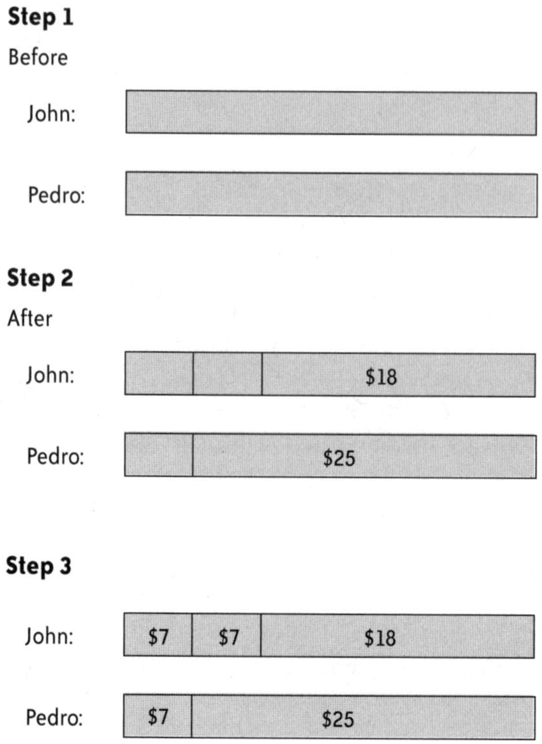

Step 1

Before

John:

Pedro:

Step 2

After

John: $18

Pedro: $25

Step 3

John: $7 $7 $18

Pedro: $7 $25

Fig. 14.7. Models illustrating a three-step solution to Example C1

The model method also has application to simple algebraic problems that involve fractional parts or percentages. This is illustrated in Example C2.

Example C2

In Mariam's aquarium, there are swordtails and guppies.

25% of the fish are swordtails.

Mariam then buys more swordtails and puts them into the aquarium to double their number.

a) What percentage of the fish are guppies after she doubles the number of swordtails?

One way students may begin to solve this problem is by drawing the "before" picture with four rectangles and with one of the four representing the number of sword-tails (see Step 1, fig, 14.8). To model the situation of Mariam's doubling the number of swordtails, another rectangle representing the number of swordtails is appended to the model. This additional rectangle now increases the number of rectangles to five and changes the percent represented by each rectangle from 25 to 20 percent. From the "after" picture, a student can conclude that now 60 percent of the fish are guppies (see Step 2, fig, 14.8).

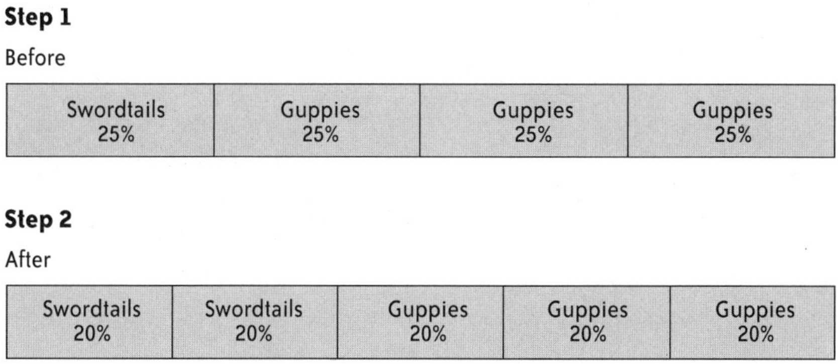

Step 1

Before

Swordtails 25%	Guppies 25%	Guppies 25%	Guppies 25%

Step 2

After

Swordtails 20%	Swordtails 20%	Guppies 20%	Guppies 20%	Guppies 20%

Fig. 14.8. Models illustrating a two-step solution to Example C2

Example C3 illustrates how the change model can be modified to accommodate word problems with varied mathematical structures.

Example C3

Yesterday, Sara had $\frac{4}{7}$ as many marbles as Eiko had.

Today Sara received 36 marbles from Eiko. Now they each have the same number of marbles.

(a) How many more marbles did Eiko have than Sara yesterday?

(b) How many marbles did they have altogether yesterday?

To begin to solve this problem, students draw two rectangles using the information from yesterday to construct a "Before" model (see Step 1, fig. 14. 9). The rectangle representing Eiko's marbles depicts one whole ($\frac{7}{7}$). The model for Sara's marbles represents $\frac{4}{7}$ of Eiko's marbles. Next, the model needs to reflect the action of Eiko giving 36 marbles to Sara. This action results in both girls having an equal number of marbles. To elaborate this with the model, students can color or shade the 3 additional rectangles in the model for Eiko's marbles that need to be shared with Sara to result in each girl having an equal number of marbles (see Step 2, fig, 14.9).

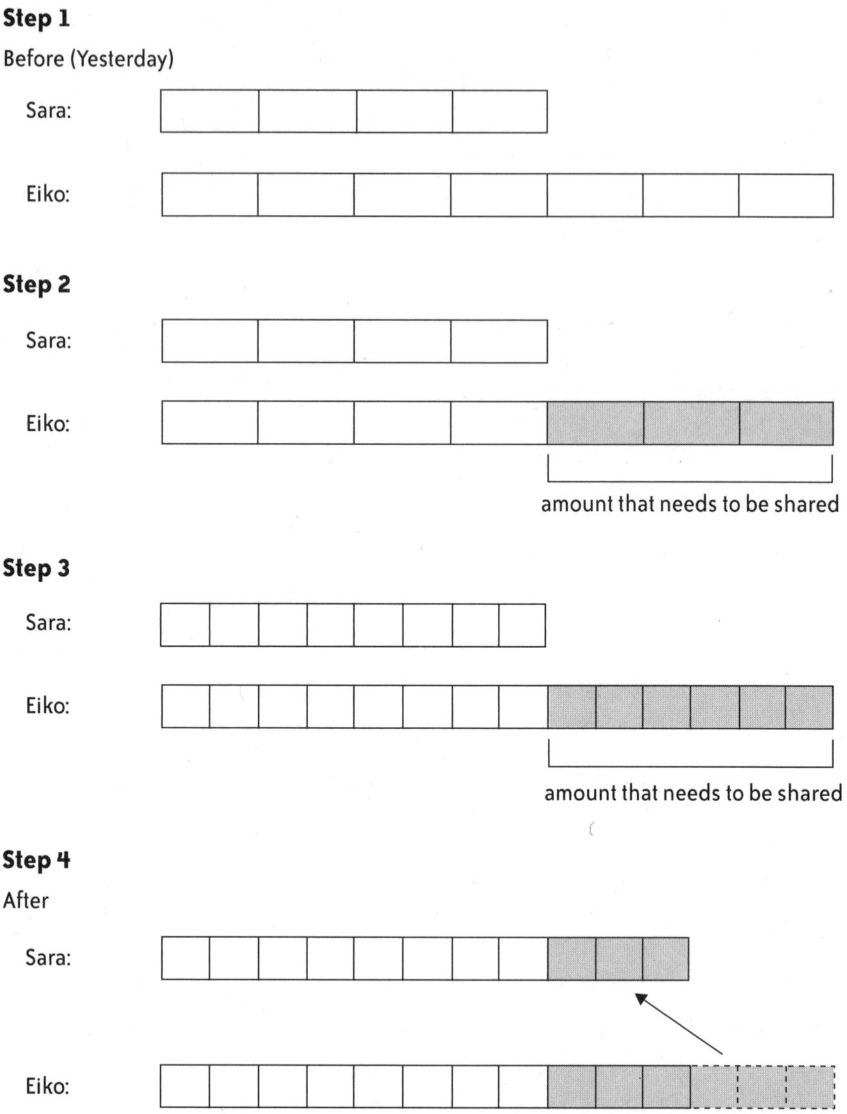

Step 1

Before (Yesterday)

Sara:

Eiko:

Step 2

Sara:

Eiko:

amount that needs to be shared

Step 3

Sara:

Eiko:

amount that needs to be shared

Step 4

After

Sara:

Eiko:

Fig. 14.9. Models illustrating Steps 1, 2, 3, and 4 in a solution to Example C3

Once this sharing is completed, both models will show an equal number of marbles. However, sharing these three rectangles can be problematic for some students. Thus students must carefully plan and execute the sharing activity. Partitioning the three rectangles into halves results in the three original rectangles being represented as six smaller rectangles (see Step 3, fig. 14.9). Now the students can visualize that 3 of these 6 rectangles must be given to Sara for both of the models to represent equal amounts (see Step 4, fig. 14.9).

Students can also note that 3 of the smaller rectangles actually represent the 36 marbles that Eiko gave to Sara. Since 3 smaller rectangles represent 36 marbles, then one small rectangle represents 12 marbles (see Step 5, fig, 14.10). By returning to the first (before) diagram and substituting the value of 12 for each smaller rectangle, students can find the solutions to the original questions (see Step 6, fig, 14.10).

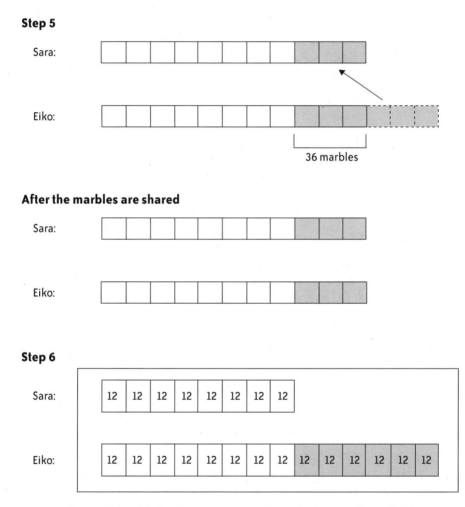

Fig. 14.10. Models illustrating Steps 5 and 6 in a solution to Example C3

That is, yesterday Sara had 12 × 8, or 96, marbles and Eiko had 12 × 14, or 168, marbles. It follows that Eiko had 168 – 92, or 72, more marbles than Sara yesterday. Yesterday they had a total of 96 + 168, or 264, marbles.

Concluding Remarks

The preceding examples illustrate a range of problem-solving situations for which Singapore's model method can aid in the development of algebraic thinking. The dual benefits of the model method in enabling students to create mathematical expressions grounded in contextual diagrams and in developing structural knowledge for more advanced problem solving has the potential to induce the development of mathematical problem-solving competence in elementary and middle school students. As a result, the model method provides a viable methodology for elementary school teachers as they struggle with the challenge of promoting mathematical problem solving. Moreover, this methodology can be applied to the range of problem types typically found in school curricula and can be one approach for enhancing mathematical problem-solving outcomes for students at multiple achievement levels.

As students develop effective problem-solving techniques, the model method also directs students' attention to the persistence of particularly successful representations in solving problems. As students work across structurally related problems, the model method enables a representational view of the connections among the problems. By finding, generalizing, and articulating these connections, students are encouraged to think algebraically by considering representational and notational shortcuts. The model method also has the potential to encourage students to construct algebraic notation in a meaningful way through their generalizations in drawing diagrams from the models and then analyzing these diagrams as instances of mathematical structures.

The model method provides a powerful resource for students to access knowledge of their problem-solving structures. Students who connect generalizations to the physical action of drawing diagrams in the model method are essentially building a sequence of individual experiences and as a result, knowledge of mathematical structures can arise from these experiences. As students create their own detailed problem-solving structures by designing a sequence of solution-oriented episodes, they are performing as active learners in the course of transitioning to formal algebraic thinking. Accordingly, Singapore's model method is one practical approach to preparing students for learning formal algebra. Students across the achievement continuum are apt to benefit from the transitions afforded by this structurally configured model method as they individually develop their own methods for solving problems.

REFERENCES

Driscoll, Mark. *Fostering Algebraic Thinking: A Guide for Teachers Grades 6–10.* Portsmouth, N.H.: Heinemann, 1999.

Ferrucci, Beverly, BanHar Yeap, and Jack Carter. "A Modeling Approach for Enhancing

Problem Solving in the Middle Grades." *Mathematics Teaching in the Middle School* 8 (May 2003): 470–75.

———. "Developing Algebraic Thinking." *Mathematics Teaching* 178 (March 2002): 39–41.

Kieran, Carolyn. "The Changing Face of School Algebra." In *8th International Congress of Mathematical Education: Selected Lectures,* edited by Claudi Alsina, José Alvarez, Bernard Hodgson, Colette Laborde, and António Perez, pp. 271–90. Seville, Spain: Sociedad Andaluza de Educación Mathemática (SAEM). Thales, 1996.

Kho, Tek-Hong. "Mathematical Models for Solving Arithmetic Problems." In *Proceedings of Fourth Southeast Asian Conference on Mathematical Education,* pp. 345–51. Singapore: Institute of Education, 1987.

Marshall, Sandra P. *Schemas in Problem Solving.* Cambridge: Cambridge University Press, 1995.

Steele, Diana. "Using Writing to Access Students' Schema Knowledge for Algebraic Thinking." *School Science and Mathematics* 105 (March 2005): 142–54.

15

Uncovering Variables in the Context of Modeling Activities

A. Susan Gay
Alyson R. Jones

IMPORTANT learning goals in algebra for middle-grades students articulated by the National Council of Teachers of Mathematics (NCTM) (1989, 2000) include understanding the concept of variable, developing competence with equivalent forms of algebraic expressions, and becoming skillful in representing situations algebraically. The representation of mathematical relationships using variables is a powerful but difficult process for students to learn (Kieran 1992). Research has documented that learners struggle to understand the nature and use of variables (e.g., Booth 1988; Philipp 1992; Stacey and MacGregor 1997; Usiskin 1988); this obviously affects students' work with algebraic expressions.

Mathematical modeling is a process that is useful when working with real-world phenomena and when solving real-world problems (Swetz and Hartzler 1991). The first stage in the process of mathematical modeling is representation (Abrams 2001). This stage involves identifying the variables relevant to a situation and creating models (e.g., expressions, equations, tables, graphs) to represent relationships among the variables (Abrams 2001; NCTM 2000). Additional stages involve manipulating the model to derive results and interpreting those results with respect to the original setting. Sometimes this can be a cyclical process that involves refining the model (Abrams 2001; Swetz and Hartzler 1991).

The activities that follow spark students' interest in working with variables. Students identify variables of interest and importance to themselves, use their variables in a real-world problem setting (an amusement park), and then apply thinking skills to justify a decision that is guided by the variables they choose as important.

The authors would like to thank the teachers who used these activities, shared their ideas and students' comments, and provided examples of their students' work.

Thus, they become personally involved in problems that involve algebraic expressions. Since its introduction in a professional development workshop in 2000, this set of activities has been used successfully in more than a dozen classrooms.

The activities do not provide an introduction to variables and algebraic expressions; rather, they require an application of a knowledge of variables. Some of the tasks are difficult and will challenge students. Throughout the description of the activities, sample responses from seventh-, eighth-, and ninth-grade students—and their teachers—are presented.

Introduction to the Activity

The teacher can introduce this activity with a reference to an amusement park and then by asking the students if they like to ride roller coasters or which type of roller coaster is their favorite. In order to connect the amusement park with the study of algebra, the teacher can prompt the class to brainstorm variables or quantities associated with an amusement park. Students' responses commonly include the price of food, the price of parking, the price of tickets, the height you have to be to take a ride, the speed of a ride, the number of people in the park, and the cost to play the games. Variables should be grouped into categories such as costs for those attending (e.g., the price of food, the price of tickets, cost for parking), the number of people in the park (e.g., those visiting and those working), and other quantities (e.g., the number of rides, the speed of a ride, the height required to take some rides). The list of variables and categories may be constructed by small groups of students or by students in a large-group setting working with the teacher.

During the activity, students will work with some variables that are likely to be on their initial lists and with others they may not yet have considered. They will also have experiences creating algebraic expressions using these variables. Lastly, they will apply their work with variables and expressions as they explore the constraints and considerations related to adding another roller coaster in the amusement park.

People at the Amusement Park

The first set of tasks, shown in figure 15.1, emphasizes operations with variables. Students are expected to create algebraic expressions using the listed variables. For example, item 2 in figure 15.1—the total number of people in the park on a given day—is the sum of the number of employees and the number of visitors to the park on that day. Since most students wrote this as either $F + E + M + W + Y$ or $M + W + Y + F + E$, the teacher could use this as an opportunity to reinforce the use of the commutative property in creating and recognizing equivalent expressions.

Item 3 requests an expression for the amount of money collected for all tickets on a given day. A common response from students was $(A)(W + M) + YT$, which could be read as the product of the adult ticket price and the total number of adult

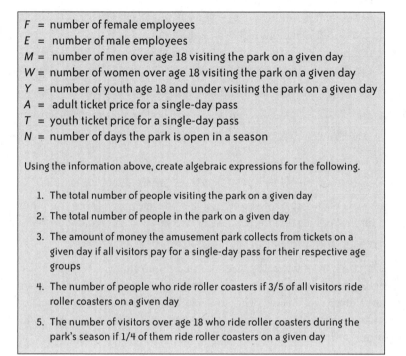

F = number of female employees
E = number of male employees
M = number of men over age 18 visiting the park on a given day
W = number of women over age 18 visiting the park on a given day
Y = number of youth age 18 and under visiting the park on a given day
A = adult ticket price for a single-day pass
T = youth ticket price for a single-day pass
N = number of days the park is open in a season

Using the information above, create algebraic expressions for the following.

1. The total number of people visiting the park on a given day

2. The total number of people in the park on a given day

3. The amount of money the amusement park collects from tickets on a given day if all visitors pay for a single-day pass for their respective age groups

4. The number of people who ride roller coasters if 3/5 of all visitors ride roller coasters on a given day

5. The number of visitors over age 18 who ride roller coasters during the park's season if 1/4 of them ride roller coasters on a given day

Fig. 15.1. People at the amusement park

men and women visitors plus the product of the youth ticket price and the number of youth visitors. A few students wrote $(WA) + (MA) + (YT)$, read as the number of women visitors times the adult ticket price plus the number of men visitors times the adult ticket price plus the number of youth visitors times the youth ticket price. Several teachers used the comparison of these two expressions to ask students to identify the property that insures that the expressions are equivalent. Students responded by identifying the distributive property, and as a class, they discussed the meaning of each of the expressions to see why they are equivalent. Other expressions offered by students, such as $YT + (M + W)A$ and $MA + WA + YT$, gave teachers an opportunity to reinforce the use of the commutative property.

One common type of error made by students involved confusing addition or subtraction with multiplication. On item 3, some students said "M times W times A and Y times T." In response, one teacher supplied some easy-to-work-with values for the variables as a strategy for students to use to test the reasonableness of their expression. Her suggestion was to consider that 10 men, 10 women, and 10 youth attended the park paying $20 as the adult price ($A$) and $5 as the youth price ($T$). Students quickly computed the sum of the two products and realized that they had a value that was too large. When reconsidering, they found their error and wrote a correct expression. As well as testing the value of the expression, the teacher pointed out that in this setting, where M and W represent numbers of people, it does not make sense to find the product of M and W.

The fifth item was difficult for many students. Some saw only part of the information in the item and wrote an expression for the number of visitors over age 18 who ride roller coasters on a given day. Some students wrote $(1/4)(M + W)$, and others wrote $\dfrac{(M + W)}{4}$. One teacher focused on both of these expressions and asked the class if these were equivalent expressions. Continuing to reinforce equivalent expressions, the teacher asked if $\dfrac{M}{4} + \dfrac{W}{4}$ is the same. On the fifth item, some students incorrectly wrote $M + W(1/4)$, whereas others wrote $(M + W) \div \dfrac{1}{4}$. When students correctly wrote expressions for the fifth item that showed the number of adults riding roller coasters for the season, the three most common responses were $\dfrac{1}{4}(M + W) \cdot N$, $[(M + W)N]\dfrac{1}{4}$, and $[(M + W) \cdot N] \div 4$.

During this set of tasks, the teacher often asked students whether two or more expressions were equivalent. At other times, the students themselves noticed that expressions were equivalent. The students frequently recognized the use of the distributive property, the commutative property, or both. For example, both $A(W + M) + TY$ and $AM + TY + WA$ were acknowledged as correct expressions for item 3 by different students; the class agreed that these were both correct because of the use of the distributive and the commutative properties. With other expressions, the relationship between multiplication and division was used to justify equivalent expressions; these included $(1/4)(M + W)$ and $\dfrac{(M + W)}{4}$. Still other expressions were identified as equivalent because there are different ways to write division, such as $(M + W) \div 4$ and $\dfrac{(M + W)}{4}$.

Passengers on the Roller Coasters

The second task, shown in figure 15.2, focuses on the roller coasters in the park. Although the primary emphasis of the roller coaster tasks is once again on constructing algebraic expressions, students must also use their knowledge of ratios, rates, and dimensional analysis. The first three items focus on simple expressions, and they should be attempted and discussed before the more complicated ones that follow.

Item 4 is challenging because it requires a time conversion; students have to use the rate of 3600 seconds per hour. Students have to focus attention on the units in the variable descriptions as well as on the units stated in the written phrase. Other items with a similar focus are 5 and 6.

For the fourth item, many students gave a correct expression in the form of $\left[\dfrac{3600}{(D + U)}\right]$. One student wrote $60 \div [(D + U) \div 60]P$, which is also correct. Some

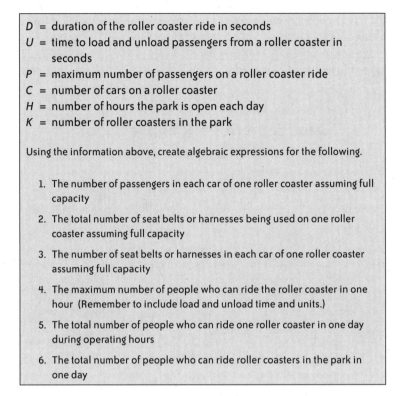

D = duration of the roller coaster ride in seconds

U = time to load and unload passengers from a roller coaster in seconds

P = maximum number of passengers on a roller coaster ride

C = number of cars on a roller coaster

H = number of hours the park is open each day

K = number of roller coasters in the park

Using the information above, create algebraic expressions for the following.

1. The number of passengers in each car of one roller coaster assuming full capacity

2. The total number of seat belts or harnesses being used on one roller coaster assuming full capacity

3. The number of seat belts or harnesses in each car of one roller coaster assuming full capacity

4. The maximum number of people who can ride the roller coaster in one hour (Remember to include load and unload time and units.)

5. The total number of people who can ride one roller coaster in one day during operating hours

6. The total number of people who can ride roller coasters in the park in one day

Fig. 15.2. Passengers on roller coasters

students ignored the time conversion and wrote $(D + U)(P)$. Others who wrote $(D + U)P \cdot 60$, or $(D + U)P \cdot 60^2$ knew that time had to be part of the expression but were uncertain how to include it. In one class, a student commented that in the expression $(D + U)P \cdot 60^2$, "you are multiplying by people" to convince her peers that multiplying a measure of time by a number of people did not make sense.

For items 4 through 6, many students were very careful in their use of grouping symbols, creating rather elaborate expressions with some combination of parentheses, brackets, and the fraction bar. One correct response to item 5 was $H[3600 \div (D + U)]P$. One student incorrectly wrote $3600 \div [(U + D) \cdot P] \cdot H$, providing an excellent opportunity for the teacher to discuss errors involving grouping symbols and order of operations.

When students noticed the commonality among items 4, 5, and 6, as many of them did, they used the expression created for number 4, whether correct or not, and wrote that expression multiplied by H as the response for item 5. Likewise, the response to item 5 was multiplied by K to become the response for item 6.

When students were not in agreement about how an expression should be written, it was helpful for them to see all the student-created expressions recorded on the board. This enabled them to make comparisons more easily. They were able to identify expressions that were meaningless when they verbally communicated the meaning of each expression. For example, describing *PC* as the product of the number of people times the number of cars helped students recognize that this expression is meaningless.

Amusement Park Expressions

With experience gained from the previous two sets of tasks, students are prepared to explore the tasks described in figure 15.3. Some teachers chose to revise the list of variables presented on the worksheet so that important student-generated variables, including some from the initial brainstorming session, were included.

Data concerning the amusement park and the roller coaster rides are listed below. A capital letter is used to represent each item of data; a typical numerical value is also presented.

F = number of female employees	1000 employees/day
E = number of male employees	1000 employees/day
M = number of men over age 18 visiting the park	3000 men/day
W = number of women over age 18 visiting the park	3000 women/day
Y = number of youth age 18 and under visiting the park	9000 youth/day
A = adult ticket price for a single-day pass	$30/day
T = youth ticket price for a single-day pass	$7/day
P = maximum number of passengers on a roller coaster ride	36 passengers/ride
C = number of cars per train	9 cars/train
S = number of days scheduled to be open in one season	190 days/season
Q = fraction of a season closed due to inclement weather	1/22 of a season
H = number of hours open each day	12 hours/day
Z = number of miles traveled per roller coaster ride	1.6 miles/roller coaster ride
D = duration of the roller coaster ride	180 seconds/ride
U = time to load and unload passengers from a roller coaster	60 seconds/ride
K = number of roller coasters in the park	2 roller coasters/park

If the given letters are used, it is possible to write many different algebraic expressions. Some of these expressions are meaningless, but some do make sense. Using the data above, create as many meaningful expressions as you can. For each expression, write the meaning in words, then evaluate the expression using the numerical values of the variables.

Fig. 15.3. Amusement park expressions

In these tasks, capital letters are used to represent the variables. For each variable, a typical numerical value is presented. The job for students is to use the variables to write expressions that make sense. Once again, students are alerted to the fact that some expressions may be meaningless. For example, *FC* represents the number of female employees times the number of cars per train, which does not make sense.

A sample of the expressions created by middle-grades students is presented in figure 15.4. For each expression created, students also wrote the meaning in words. Some of the incorrect expressions show errors in the choice of arithmetic operation or inaccurate work with units. The correct expressions show variety in the use of arithmetic operations and understanding of the process of creating meaningful expressions. One group of students posed the question, "If all youth visiting the park in one day rode one roller coaster without any adults, how many cars would it take to accommodate them?" They answered the question with the expression $Y/(P \div C)$.

Correct Expressions	Meaning
SH	Number of hours open in a season
$(M + W + Y)(S - SQ)$	The number of visitors in the park in a season
$D + U$	Time from the start of a ride to the start of the next ride
KZ	Miles traveled by all roller coasters in the park during one ride
$A - T$	Difference in adult and youth ticket prices
CK	Total number of cars on all roller coasters
Incorrect Expressions	**Meaning**
$A + T + M + W + Y$	The number of tickets sold in one day
$(D + U)/60$	The number of times you can ride one roller coaster in one day
Y/K	Youth per roller coaster
$(S - Q)H$	Total number of hours the park is open per season
FE	The number of employees per day
$S \cdot M \cdot W$	The number of adults in the park in one year

Fig. 15.4. Student-created amusement park expressions

Attention to the units in an expression helps students sort out meaningless expressions from those that are meaningful. Students usually started the task in figure 15.3 by creating expressions using two variables, and for many students, the units for these expressions were relatively easy to determine. For example, *HS* represents the number of hours per day times the number of days scheduled to be open in one season, resulting in an expression that indicates the number of hours scheduled to be open in one season. The units in expressions created with addition or subtraction were easier for students to determine. However, some expressions were created that mixed the units inappropriately; for example, in figure 15.4, the first incorrect expression, $A + T + M + W + Y$, is a sum of numbers of people and prices of tickets. The incorrect expressions in figure 15.4 also show that some students failed to understand the result of multiplication on the units in the expression. A fundamental step in deciding the meaning of an expression and at the same time judging that the expression is valid must involve an analysis of the units associated with the variables in that expression.

Results of this activity can give the teacher a clear picture of students' understanding of the meaning of an expression. Teachers should expect students to explain, in writing, the meaning of a given expression within the context. Students will also benefit from both small-group and large-group discussions. Discussions help students validate correct expressions and reveal the need to revise incorrect ones.

During the creation of expressions in one teacher's classroom, there was an opportunity to explore the use of the distributive property. One group of students proposed $(S - SQ)$ as the number of days the park was open during the season and $(S - SQ)H$ as the number of hours the park was open in the season. The teacher asked the students if $S(1 - Q)H$ was equivalent to $(S - SQ)H$. The students responded that it was and that the distributive property had been used.

Although students commented that there were "many things to consider," most of them were not deterred from creating expressions. Some students noted that it was interesting to make lots of different expressions with the variables. One class created an expression they called "total profit of the day." They wrote $[A(M + W) + YT] - (F + E)X \cdot H$, in which H is the number of hours the park is open each day and X represents the amount each employee is paid per hour, assuming that all employees are paid at the same rate.

Is Another Roller Coaster Needed?

In order to encourage more thinking about the variables and expressions associated with the amusement park, the students were challenged with the task of determining if the amusement park needed another roller coaster. The problem was posed as shown in figure 13.5. From the list of variables and expressions created for previous tasks, students had to identify those that were important to consider in the decision-making process. A justification was expected for each choice.

In the work we analyzed, several students identified only the variables and other issues that needed to be considered and neglected to state a decision about the construction of a new roller coaster. The variables selected were the same as those identified by students who did provide a final decision. The students noted that it was important to consider the total number of visitors on a given day, the total number of roller coaster rides possible on a given day, the number of times people like to ride the roller coasters, the cost of construction, the amount of space necessary for

> The owners of an amusement park are considering whether to build an additional roller coaster. Use the list of variables and your expressions from the previous pages as information. Select the most important variables and expressions the park owners should consider as they decide whether to add another roller coaster. If there are items that need to be considered that are not in your list, you may add them, either as words or variables. Support your choices with appropriate explanations.

Fig. 15.5. Is another roller coaster needed?

an additional coaster, the number of employees needed to run the new coaster, the level of customer satisfaction, and the cost of the electricity for each ride.

Some students believed that it was not necessary to build another roller coaster. They supported their decision with the information from the worksheets for the first three tasks (figs. 15.1–3). Students concluded that on a given day if 3/5 of the visitors ride the roller coasters, then 9,000 of the 15,000 visitors ride the roller coasters. The students compared 9,000 with the total number of roller coaster rides possible on a given day, or 12,960, and concluded that visitors who wanted to ride a roller coaster were guaranteed a ride. Thus, an additional coaster was not needed.

Some students made the decision to build another roller coaster and supported their decision with data about the number of rides possible on the roller coasters (12,960) and the number of people present at the amusement park (15,000) on any given day. According to these students, not all visitors could ride the roller coasters even once. A few students, who acknowledged that only 9,000 of the 15,000 visitors on a given day would ride the roller coasters, were still of the opinion that an additional coaster was needed because they believed that most people like to ride roller coasters more than one time in a day. Other reasons students gave for building an additional coaster included shorter lines and increased revenue from ticket sales.

Students' work on the question of another roller coaster gave them an introduction to the process of optimization. They identified some variables as more important and others as less important. They considered ways to balance the many variables that would affect their decision. Informally, they explored the profit function. Students commented that they learned that there were many components to consider about a roller coaster and that was interesting to them.

The Importance of Context

During their development of algebraic thinking, students work with variables in both expressions and equations. Much of that work is with variables and expressions without context, so that there is no real-world meaning attached to the variable or expression. By placing work with algebraic expressions in a real-world setting, teachers can help students not only to develop skill and proficiency with manipulating the expressions but also to determine if such expressions make sense.

Context is essential to the mathematical modeling process. The context frames the problem and supplies information that identifies the variables along with the relationships to be modeled as expressions, equations, or inequalities. The context is also the setting in which conclusions are evaluated for reasonableness. Amit and Klass-Tsirulnikov (2005) noted that an unappealing problem context affects students' willingness to engage in a problem. Comments from many students doing the amusement park activities indicated that they found these tasks to be "interesting," "challenging," "fun," and "cool."

Conclusion

The amusement park setting was purposefully chosen because students in middle schools are genuinely interested in amusement parks. The amusement park activities reinforce basic skills and the order of operations. They also give students experience using variables to represent real-world situations. Within these activities, the teacher can either introduce or give students continued practice with the mathematical modeling process.

The amusement park activities offer numerous opportunities for students to work with, and discuss the use of, the distributive property, the commutative property, and other properties that can be used to create equivalent algebraic expressions. Students' understanding that there can be different ways to express a relationship among variable quantities is reinforced.

Students are active participants throughout these activities. At the start, they select the variables they want to use to create meaningful algebraic expressions. Later, they identify the variables that play an important role in their decision-making process regarding the new roller coaster. The open-endedness and extendibility of the activities allow the teacher to modify the activities appropriately to meet and challenge the intellectual needs of all students. These same qualities helped spark our students' interest and gave them a sense of satisfaction in completing the tasks and doing them well.

REFERENCES

Abrams, Joshua Paul. "Teaching Mathematical Modeling and the Skills of Representation." In *The Roles of Representation in School Mathematics,* 2001 Yearbook of the National Council of Teachers of Mathematics (NCTM), edited by Albert A. Cuoco, pp. 269–82. Reston, Va.: NCTM, 2001.

Amit, Miriam, and Bella Klass-Tsirulnikov. "Paving a Way to Algebraic Word Problems Using a Nonalgebraic Route." *Mathematics Teaching in the Middle School* 10 (February 2005): 271–76.

Booth, Lesley R. "Children's Difficulties in Beginning Algebra." In *The Ideas of Algebra, K–12,* 1988 Yearbook of the National Council of Teachers of Mathematics (NCTM), edited by Arthur F. Coxford, pp. 20–32. Reston, Va.: NCTM, 1988.

Kieran, Carolyn. "The Learning and Teaching of School Algebra." In *Handbook of Research on Mathematics Teaching and Learning,* edited by Douglas A. Grouws, pp. 390–419. New York: Macmillan Publishing Co., 1992.

National Council of Teachers of Mathematics (NCTM). *Curriculum and Evaluation Standards for School Mathematics.* Reston, Va.: NCTM, 1989.

———. *Principles and Standards for School Mathematics.* Reston, Va.: NCTM, 2000.

Philipp, Randolph A. "The Many Uses of Algebraic Variables." *Mathematics Teacher* 85 (October 1992): 557–61.

Stacey, Kaye, and Mollie MacGregor. "Ideas about Symbolism That Students Bring to Algebra." *Mathematics Teacher* 90 (February 1997): 110–13.

Swetz, Frank, and Jefferson S. Hartzler, eds. *Mathematical Modeling in the Secondary School Curriculum: A Resource Guide of Classroom Exercises.* Reston, Va.: National Council of Teachers of Mathematics, 1991.

Usiskin, Zalman. "Conceptions of School Algebra and Uses of Variables." In *The Ideas of Algebra, K–12,* 1988 Yearbook of the National Council of Teachers of Mathematics (NCTM), edited by Arthur F. Coxford, pp. 8–19. Reston, Va.: NCTM, 1988.

16

The Role of Context in Learning Beginning Algebra

Michal Tabach
Alex Friedlander

ALGEBRA has been traditionally described as "generalized arithmetic." As a consequence, instruction has focused primarily on its symbolic aspect (e.g., the manipulation of symbolic expressions, the solution of algebraic equations, and the investigation of symbolically presented functions). Once these manipulations were mastered, the use of algebraic objects and concepts in real-life, fictitious, or mathematical contexts was considered later—if at all—as applications of the learned concepts.

By contrast with this "manipulations first and then apply instructions" approach, in context-based learning of mathematics, real-life situations or situations involving mathematical problems constitute both the starting point and the main process for understanding concepts and the performance of operations. Bickmore-Brand (cited by Wiest 2001) points out that "context is paramount to the construction of meaning the whole way through. It is the backdrop against which the parts have to make sense" (p. 75).

According to Gravemeijer and Doorman (1999), a pure mathematical problem can also be a context problem. In any instance, a contextual task should be experientially real for the student and should serve as a basis on which a mathematical concept can be built.

A context-based approach has both immediate and more general advantages. Such an approach—

- facilitates learning processes by providing real or concrete meaning to an otherwise abstract concept or algorithm (Heid et al. 1995);

- provides points of reference that students can review at a more advanced stage of learning when work is performed at a more abstract level;

- raises students' motivation and willingness to become engaged in the learning activity; and

- emphasizes the potential of using algebraic models and skills in other fields.

The value of a context-based approach is described by Mason and his colleagues (1985): "In order to have clear, confident and automatic mastery of any skill, it is necessary to practise but the wish to practise will arise naturally from stimulating contexts" (p. 36).

In this article, we will show how a context-based approach can facilitate the learning of four big algebraic ideas: the role of variables and expressions as representatives of meaningful phenomena of changes, the difference between changing and constant quantities, the lack of closure of algebraic expressions, and the equivalence of algebraic expressions.

The Role of Variables and Expressions as Representatives of Meaningful Phenomena of Changes

In many instances students—and educators—refer to a symbol as an unknown quantity or a "placeholder" (Usiskin 1988). In this regard, the expression $2 + 3x$ is interpreted as "the sum of two and a multiplication of a number by three." This is a limited view of symbols and expressions. The same expression can represent a range of possible numbers, all of which have a common characteristic—they are all the result of 3 plus the product of 2 and some number. Usiskin (1988) noted that students are expected to understand a wide variety of meanings attributed to a letter in algebra (e.g., as a varying quantity, a fixed solution of an equation, a generalized number, a function, or a set). An awareness of different interpretations enhances understanding of the concept of variable. How context can be used to address the idea of the symbol as a variable and expressions as representations of changing phenomena is addressed later in this article.

The Difference between Changing and Constant Quantities

Another obstacle to understanding symbolic expressions is the need to distinguish between constants and variables (Schoenfeld and Arcavi 1988). As Usiskin notes (1988), at the stage of beginning algebra, students are required to use letters mainly as generalized numbers, and therefore the distinction between these letters and constants is important. Usiskin also mentions the use of letters and numbers in generalizing patterns. A discussion of the potential of visual context for clarifying the different roles of constants and variables will be presented.

The Lack of Closure of Algebraic Expressions

Teachers and researchers (Matz 1982) have indicated that students studying algebra tend to add up unlike terms, as, for example, thinking that $2 + 3x = 5x$. This tendency is usually attributed to students' eagerness to bring an algebraic expression to a "closed result," in a way similar to the final results obtained in arithmetical exercises. Tirosh, Even, and Robinson (1998) analyzed teachers' approaches to students' tendencies to "close" algebraic expressions. They identified four approaches for dealing with the algebraic lack of closure.

1. Identify and collect like terms. For example, in the expression $2 + 3y + 4x + 8y$, the terms $2x$ and $4x$ are alike, and hence can be added to form one term, $6x$. In the same manner the terms $3y$ and $8y$ can be added to form $11y$. However, the terms $6x$ and $11y$ are not alike, and hence cannot be added.

2. Associate unlike terms with different objects. For example, $2a + 3b$ may represent 2 apples and 3 bananas that cannot be added or subtracted (but for some miraculous, unexplained reason they can be multiplied). Note that here the use of apples and bananas is a limited illustration of the symbols, rather than a comprehensive context. Some students even may perceive the a as a short symbol for apple and the b as a short symbol for banana.

3. Emphasize the order of operations. For example, in an expression like $2 + 3x$, the multiplication of 3 and x precedes the addition, but it cannot be performed. As a result, the expression cannot be simplified.

4. Substitute numbers for variables in two expressions that are considered equivalent. For example, suppose that $x = 4$ in both expressions $2 + 3x$ and $5x$ and compare the results: $2 + 3 \times 4 = 14$ and $5 \times 4 = 20$, $14 \neq 20$, so $2 + 3x \neq 5x$.

None of these approaches considers the potential of meaningful contexts as a means of overcoming this difficulty. Later in this article we will demonstrate the potential of a contextual approach to clarify this issue.

The equivalence of algebraic expressions

Traditionally, the concept of the equivalence of expressions is introduced when students are required to simplify expressions. The expressions produced in a process of algebraic simplification are considered equivalent. The equivalence of expressions is defined in one or both of the following ways:

- Definition 1: If one expression can be transformed into the other by performing a sequence of valid algebraic operations for a common domain of numbers, then the two expressions are equivalent.

- Definition 2: If the substitution of all numbers in two expressions produces equal results for their common domain, then the two expressions are equivalent.

The application of the first definition is problematic due to the large variety and sometimes arbitrary nature of the simplification rules as perceived by beginning algebra students (Matz 1982). The second definition of equivalence cannot be applied in an operative manner, since the defined domain of many expressions is an infinite set of numbers.

In the discussion that follows, the Toothpick Towers problem is used to illustrate how a context-based problem approach can help to overcome or prevent the reported difficulties.

The Toothpick Towers Problem

Toothpick Towers is one of a sequence of activities that constitute the core of the beginning algebra course in the Compu-Math materials for thirteen-year-old students (Hershkowitz et al. 2002). The main task in this activity is to analyze the patterns of two sequences of "toothpick towers" (fig. 16.1). The first stages of the activity are aimed at acquainting students with the given sequences and the numerical patterns behind them.

This figure presents two sequences of growing toothpick towers.

First sequence of towers:

Second sequence of towers:

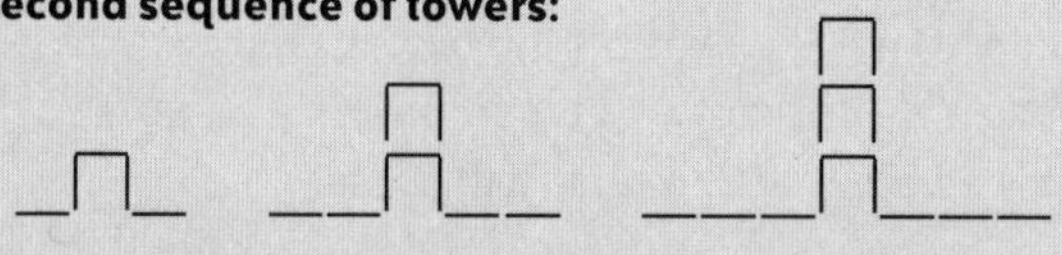

- Find the number of toothpicks for the fourth, fifth, and tenth "tower" in each sequence.
- Generalize: How many toothpicks are in the nth "tower" of each sequence?
- Find the place of the "tower" made of 40 toothpicks in each sequence.

Fig. 16.1. The Toothpick Towers problem

Understanding Algebraic Concepts in Context

In this section, we describe how the context of the Toothpick Tower problem helps to clarify the four basic algebraic concepts that were identified in the introductory section of the article.

The Role of Variables and Expressions as Representatives of Phenomena of Changes

In the context of Toothpick Towers, the variable represents the place index (e.g., Tower 1, Tower 2, Tower 3) for the two tower sequences, and the corresponding algebraic expressions describe the number of toothpicks in these towers (If n represents the position of the tower, then for sequence 1, the number of toothpicks is $3n + 2$). Thus, students relate to these algebraic expressions as descriptors of complete sequences, as opposed to a visual representation presented by a figure that describes only a few particular instances (e.g., the first three towers in fig. 16.1).

The Difference between Changing and Constant Quantities

In Toothpick Towers and other similar activities, students are involved in generalization processes, and as a result they must consider the meaning, the notation, and the difference between a variable and a constant quantity. The obvious difference between the two sequences of toothpicks is in the towers' constant base in the first sequence (two toothpicks, one on each side of the structure for all towers), as opposed to the changing base in the second (two toothpicks in Tower 1 with one on each side of the structure; four in Tower 2, with two on each side of the structure; six in Tower 3, with three on each side of the structure). Thus, the context of the problem provides a visual representation of a varying quantity, such as the number of toothpicks in the vertical walls and horizontal ceilings, as well as a constant—the two toothpicks in the base for the towers in the first sequence. Because these quantities are different, they must be represented in different ways—the first as an expression $(3n)$ and the second as a number (2). The visual representation here makes the difference between varying and constant quantities concrete and hence more understandable to students.

Simon (1995) recommends basing some student tasks on the conceptual difficulties previously observed among students working on a similar task. Accordingly, the issue of constants versus variables was further addressed in the question presented in figure 16.2. This question requires students to consider an episode, on the basis of an error observed in one of the project's experimental classes, and to reflect on the meaning of constant and variable.

> Daniel found that the number of toothpicks in the second tower of the first sequence is $3 \cdot 2 + 2$.
>
> He thought, "Three 2s and another 2 are the same as $4 \cdot 2$, and therefore, the number of toothpicks for the nth tower should be $4 \cdot 4 \cdot n$."
>
> Do you think that Daniel is right? Explain your answer.

Fig. 16.2. A reflective item dealing with variables and constants

The importance of this question lies in the opportunity it provides for teachers to discuss this issue with their students. Many students' immediate reactions to this item were that Daniel "made a mistake. He added the numbers correctly. However, he based his symbolic expression on a particular numerical instance (the second tower) and that was his mistake." In such a discussion, terms such as *static and dynamic*, or *fixed* and *changing* are used frequently by students and can be naturally rephrased by the teacher as *constant* and *variable*, respectively.

The Lack of Closure in Algebraic Expressions

Our classroom observations revealed that attaching a visual or other concrete meaning to algebraic terms, and generalizing or modeling authentic problems, are effective in preventing the closure of unlike terms. As mentioned before in the Toothpick Towers problem, each algebraic term has a visual counterpart. This allows students to consider whether each term represents a changing or a constant quantity. Work in the context of the activity also provides meaning to each algebraic operation performed by the students. For example, the addends of $3n + n + n$ derive their meaning from the number of toothpicks in the different components of the towers that change in the same way; hence, they can be added. Conversely, the terms $3n$ and 2 represent a changing and a constant quantity, correspondingly, and as a consequence, the expression $3n + 2$ cannot be simplified. Because the addition of similar terms or the lack of closure for unlike terms is given a visual interpretation, understanding is enhanced.

The reflective question presented in figure 16.3 relates to the issue of the lack of closure. As in the example of the previous reflective item (fig. 16.2), this question is based on a classroom episode observed during the development of the curriculum. Again, this question provides an opportunity for classroom discussion.

Rachel found that the number of toothpicks in the nth tower is

$2 + 3 \cdot n$ for the first sequence, and
$5 \cdot n$ for the second sequence.

She wondered, "How can I get two equivalent expressions for two different sequences?"

How would you solve Rachel's problem?

Fig. 16.3. A reflective item regarding the lack of closure for algebraic expressions

On a more general level, we claim that a contextual approach enables students to identify unlike terms that cannot be added, since their sum does not display the same pattern of change as its addends. Thus, a context can provide a specific meaning to syntactic rules of manipulation that are usually considered arbitrary by students. Various syntactic rules can be addressed by using different contextual problems.

The Equivalence of Algebraic Expressions

As mentioned before, a context-based algebraic activity provides opportunities for students to assign a meaning actively to each component of an algebraic expression. Furthermore, comparisons of different expressions based on meaningful interpretations enable a better understanding of the concept of algebraic equivalence. In many context-based activities, expressions both describe a pattern and reflect a method of modeling.

By working in a contextual situation, the concept of equivalence is raised by an authentic need to compare different models that were designed by students to describe the same situation, and not by an arbitrary requirement to simplify abstract expressions presented by the teacher.

In the second sequence in figure 16.4, both $n + 3n + n$ and $n + n + n + n + n$ represent the number of toothpicks for the nth tower, and we can establish their equivalence by following the modeling process that underlies each model. These two expressions represent different ways of looking at the same situation. The first expression, $n + 3n + n$ represents a counting method that considers the tower's two base lines and its wall structure separately. By contrast, the second expression $(n + n + n + n + n)$ counts each straight line and the set of ceilings separately. Thus, the equivalence of these expressions can be established by validating the counting methods for the two models. Our students actually used their counting methods to determine the equivalence of expressions. Moreover, they were able to look at a given expression and describe the counting method that underlies the expression.

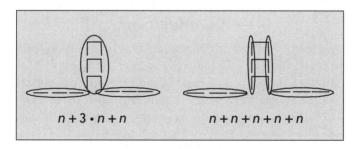

$$n + 3 \cdot n + n \qquad n + n + n + n + n$$

Fig. 16.4. A visual interpretation of equivalent expressions

The potential of equivalent expressions to reflect different ways of viewing the same situation is also illustrated by the problems presented in figure 16.5. The expressions shown in figure 16.5 were generated by our students while working on the Toothpick Tower problem.

Find expressions that describe the number of toothpicks in the nth tower in the first sequence; mark them by (1).

Find expressions that describe the number of toothpicks in the nth tower in the second sequence; mark them by (2).

$2 \cdot (2 \cdot n) + n$	$2 + 3 \cdot n$
$n + 2 \cdot (n + 1)$	$3 \cdot n + 2 \cdot n$
$5 \cdot n$	$n + 3 \cdot n + n$
$5 + 3\,(n - 1)$	$4 \cdot n + n$

Fig. 16.5. Identifying equivalent expressions

In a more general view, in a context-based approach, the expressions produced by students during an activity may represent different ways of modeling the same phenomenon. As a result, equivalent expressions can be viewed by students as different descriptors of the same phenomenon. This approach enables teachers and curriculum developers to introduce the concept of equivalence at early stages in the learning of algebra when students' skills of manipulation are very limited.

At a more advanced stage in the study of algebra, the situations and their corresponding expressions become more complex. Consequently, validating the equivalence of models by visual inspection or by reasoning becomes more difficult. By then, we hope, most students have acquired enough experience with modeling so that an intuitive understanding of equivalence is achieved, and they can resort to the other two, more abstract definitions of algebraic equivalence—performing a sequence of valid algebraic operations or getting equal results when substituting any number from a common domain.

Conclusion

Learning algebra at an almost exclusively abstract, symbolic level can cause many cognitive and affective difficulties (Sutherland and Rojano 1993; Tall 2004). We claim that the provision of contextual meanings to algebraic objects, concepts, and operations must occur at the initial stages and accompany the whole learning process, as opposed to presenting these meanings only at more advanced stages, as possible applications. Our experience with developing a context-based algebra curriculum shows that this approach provides an important bridge between arithmetic and algebra, and between concrete and abstract objects, enabling students to learn algebraic concepts in a more comprehensible way.

We used the Toothpick Towers problem to illustrate our claim that context facilitates the learning of algebraic concepts throughout the stages of initial exposure and provides opportunities to reinforce learning by meaningful applications and personal reflection. The context exemplified here was based on a visual sequence.

Other context-based situations can and should be used as, for example, a change in the amount of allowance money or sequences of growing rectangles (Friedlander and Tabach 2001; Tabach and Friedlander 2004) to provide support for newly learned abstract entities.

We include three cautionary notes:

1. A context-based approach cannot be employed exclusively. For varied reasons, mathematics teaching in general, and algebra teaching in particular, should be accompanied by abstract, symbolic tasks. Gravemeijer (1998) and his colleagues at the Freudenthal Institute claim that besides the process of converting a contextual problem into a mathematical problem (in their terms, horizontal mathematization) considered in this article, there also has to be room for the mathematization of concepts, notations, and problem-solving procedures (vertical mathematization).

2. In spite of its potential to promote a deeper understanding of mathematical concepts, a context-based approach is prone to cause some cognitive difficulties. For example, for some students, a "familiar" context tends to be "familiar" in different ways. As a result, students might understand a mathematical concept in unintended ways, or follow "unproductive" paths of solution. This phenomenon is described by Sutherland, Robertson, and John (2004) as construction of idiosyncratic knowledge that is at odds with intended learning.

3. Teaching in a context-based approach is very challenging. Many teaching strategies (e.g., predicting or reacting to students' "productive" or "unproductive" answers) require skills that can be acquired gradually by experience, participation in teachers' workshops, and supportive teamwork.

Thus, there is a need to strike a careful balance between the contextual and mathematical abstract approaches in teaching algebra. However, in view of the traditional emphasis on the abstract, symbolic aspects of algebra, we would like to recommend to teachers, curriculum developers, and researchers that they focus on the issues of teaching beginning algebra using a context-based approach.

REFERENCES

Friedlander, Alex, and Michal Tabach. "Promoting Multiple Representations in Algebra." In *The Roles of Representation in School Mathematics,* 2001 Yearbook of the National Council of Teachers of Mathematics (NCTM), edited by Albert A. Cuoco, pp. 173–85. Reston, Va.: NCTM, 2001.

Gravemeijer, Koeno. "From a Different Perspective: Building on Students' Informal Knowledge." In *Designing Learning Environments for Developing Understanding of Geometry and Space,* edited by Richard Lehrer and Daniel Chazan, pp. 45–66. Mahwah, N.J.: Lawrence Erlbaum Associates, 1998.

Gravemeijer, Koeno, and Michiel Doorman. "Context Problems in Realistic Mathematics Education: A Calculus Course as an Example." *Educational Studies in Mathematics* 39 (1999): 111–29.

Heid, M. Kathleen, Jonathan Choate, Charlene Sheets, and Rose Mary Zbiek. *Algebra in a Technological World. Curriculum and Evaluation Standards for School Mathematics* Addenda Series. Reston, Va.: National Council of Teachers of Mathematics, 1995.

Hershkowitz, Rina, Tommy Dreyfus, Dani Ben-Zvi, Alex Friedlander, Nurit Hadas, Tzippora Resnick, and Michal Tabach. "Mathematics Curriculum Development for Computerized Environments: A Designer-Researcher-Teacher-Learner Activity." In *Handbook of International Research in Mathematics Education*, edited by Lyn English, pp. 657–94. Mahwah, N.J.: Lawrence Erlbaum Associates, 2002.

Mason, John, Alan Graham, David Pimm, and Norman Gowar. *Routes to/Roots of Algebra*. Milton Keynes, England: Open University, 1985.

Matz, Marilyn. "Towards a Process Model for School Algebra Errors." In *Intelligent Tutoring Systems*, edited by Derek Sleeman and John Seely Brown, pp. 25–50. London: Academic Press, 1982.

Schoenfeld, Alan, and Abraham Arcavi. "On the Meaning of Variable." *Mathematics Teacher* 81 (1988): 420–27.

Simon, Martin A. "Reconstructing Mathematics Pedagogy from a Constructivist Perspective." *Journal for Research in Mathematics Education* 26 (March 1995): 114–45.

Sutherland, Rosamund, and Teresa Rojano. "A Spreadsheet Approach to Solving Algebra Problems." *Journal of Mathematical Behavior* 12 (1993): 353–83.

Sutherland, Rosamund, Susan Robertson, and Peter John. "Interactive Education: Teaching and Learning in the Information Age." *Journal of Computer Assisted Learning* 20 (2004): 410–12.

Tabach, Michal, and Alex Friedlander. "Levels of Student Responses in a Spreadsheet-Based Environment." In *Proceedings of the 28th Conference of the International Group for the Psychology of Mathematics Education* (PME), edited by Marit Johnsen Hoines and Anne Berit Fuglestadt, vol. 2, pp. 423–30. Bergen, Norway: PME, 2004.

Tall, David. "Thinking through Three Worlds of Mathematics." In *Proceedings of the 28th Conference of the International Group for the Psychology of Mathematics Education* (PME), edited by Marit Johnsen Hoines and Anne Berit Fuglestadt, vol. 4, pp. 281–88. Bergen, Norway: PME, 2004.

Tirosh, Dina, Ruhama Even, and Neomi Robinson. "Simplifying Algebraic Expressions: Teacher Awareness and Teaching Approaches." *Educational Studies in Mathematics* 35 (1998): 51–64.

Usiskin, Zalman. "Conceptions of School Algebra and Uses of Variables." In *The Ideas of Algebra K–12*, 1988 Yearbook of the National Council of Teachers of Mathematics (NCTM), edited by Arthur F. Coxford, pp. 8–19. Reston, Va.: NCTM, 1988.

Wiest, Lynda. "The Role of Fantasy Contexts in Word Problems." *Mathematics Education Research Journal* 13 (2001): 74–90.

17

Walk the Line: Making Sense of $y = mx + b$

Nancy Canavan Anderson

LINEAR relationships are the most basic functions that students encounter in the study of algebra (Lappan et al. 2002). The equation of a line in slope-intercept form, $y = mx + b$, is a focal point in the study of linear functions in first-year algebra courses (National Council of Teachers of Mathematics [NCTM] 2006; Usiskin 1999b). The prerequisite skills and knowledge that lay the foundation for understanding and applying the equation are developed in students' elementary and early middle school experiences. Since $y = mx + b$ has many real-world applications, it is important that students learn to do more than manipulate the equation. Students must develop proficiency using the equation to represent relationships among variables described in a mathematics problem.

I used the following problem from *Moving Straight Ahead* (Lappan et al. 2002, p. 21) to introduce students to the equation of a line in slope-intercept form:

> Emile and Henri are brothers. Emile, the older brother, has a walking rate of 2.5 meters per second. His younger brother, Henri, has a walking rate of 1 meter per second.
>
> - Henri has challenged Emile to a walking race. Since he has a faster walking rate, Emile gives Henri a 45-meter head start.
>
> - Emile wants Henri to win the race, but he does not want to make it obvious that he let his little brother win.
>
> - How long might the race be so that Henri will win but in a close race?

I chose this problem because it is accessible, meaningful, and realistic. It is accessible because students can use their prior experience with making tables and graphs to help them solve the problem. Students can link new learning of the slope-intercept form to these solution methods, thereby rooting their initial experiences with $y = mx + b$ in understanding (Greenes and Findell 1999). It is meaningful because students gain essential understanding about the equation of a line that they will be able to apply to problems across many different contexts. The problem is realistic because representing and extending the linear relationship between distance and time is a sensible and effective way to solve the problem (Usiskin 1999a). The context and constraints of the problem are personally relevant and motivating to students and inherently promote the use of a variety of algebraic methods.

Classroom Implementation

Before beginning the investigation, I set the following six goals that students will do:

1. Represent the walking rates described in the problem using tables and graphs and use them to find a length for the walking race that upholds the constraints of the problem.

2. Justify why the points on each boy's graph lie in a straight line.

3. Connect the data for distance and time as seen in the table with the data as displayed in the graph.

4. Use their tables and graphs to write equations relating each boy's distance to the amount of time transpired.

5. Justify why their equations are equivalent to ones in the form $y = mx + b$.

6. Identify the given value of m, the coefficient of x, as the walking rate of each boy, and identify b as the point at which the line crosses the y-axis.

Interpreting the Problem and Constructing Tables

After students had read the problem, we discussed its constraints. I then asked two questions that I thought would frame their work on the problem without revealing too much information: "What are the two variables in this problem? What tools have we used in the past to keep track of variables as they change?" Many students suggested using tables and graphs. I asked the students to describe the headings of the table. After some discussion, students concluded that the table would need three columns, since we were tracking both boys' distances over time. I also asked them to identify the x-axis and y-axis labels for the graph. Students determined that time would be plotted along the x-axis and distance along the y-axis. We agreed as a class that we could plot both sets of data on one graph.

Students worked in pairs to solve this problem. Most students who chose to make a table used one-second intervals. This led me to believe that students were thinking about the function iteratively, filling in each entry according to the previous one (see fig. 17.1). Students were satisfied with this approach because it was an effective way to solve the problem, requiring only about thirty entries. However, I was concerned that thinking about the pattern iteratively would prevent students from writing an equation for each function. Only a few students included zero seconds in the table. Some students who did not include zero seconds made errors recording Henri's distances (see fig. 17.2). Since this did not prevent them from solving the problem, I did not correct this error immediately. While they worked with their partners, students needed to focus on using the table to solve the problem. Later, in the whole-class discussion, the focus would shift to writing an equation that represented the data in the table. Since we would use the table to help us write the equation, this would be the appropriate time to reflect on the data in the table, namely, the entry for zero seconds and its relationship to both the equation and the graph.

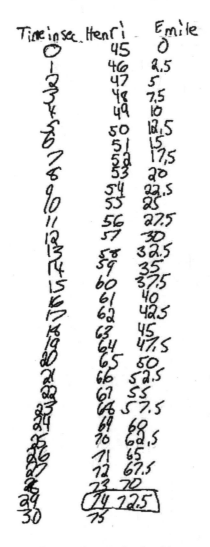

Fig. 17.1. One student's table

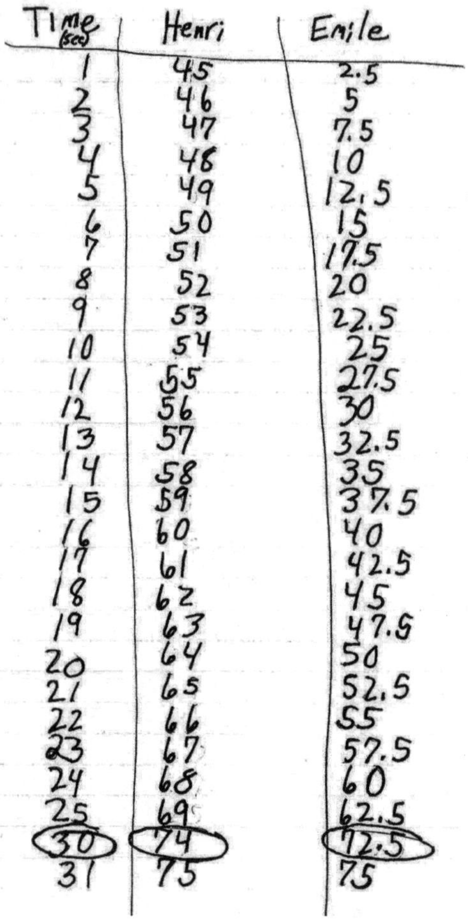

Time (sec)	Henri	Emile
1	45	2.5
2	46	5
3	47	7.5
4	48	10
5	49	12.5
6	50	15
7	51	17.5
8	52	20
9	53	22.5
10	54	25
11	55	27.5
12	56	30
13	57	32.5
14	58	35
15	59	37.5
16	60	40
17	61	42.5
18	62	45
19	63	47.5
20	64	50
21	65	52.5
22	66	55
23	67	57.5
24	68	60
25	69	62.5
⟨30⟩	⟨74⟩	⟨72.5⟩
31	75	75

Fig. 17.2. A table with incorrect data

Interpreting the Problem and Constructing Graphs

Some students chose to make a graph without making a table. Others made the table first and then used the table values to plot the points on the graph. Students who chose to make a graph first had difficulty choosing the scales for the x- and y-axes. Since students determined that the scale on the y-axis had to extend to at least 45 meters, many chose a factor of 45, such as 3 or 5. If students chose a y-axis scale such as 2 or 3 meters, their graphs did not show the point of intersection of the two lines (see fig. 17.3). Instead of telling students to re-create the graph to show the point of intersection, I encouraged them to reflect on their graphs:

- Choose one point on one line. Explain what that point reveals about the walking race.

- Describe the appearance of the two lines in relation to each other. Justify this appearance on the basis of the context of the problem.

- Choose one point on one line. Determine the time when each boy would reach that distance.

- Choose another point on one line. Determine the distance each boy had walked at that time.

- Recall the constraints of the problem, namely, Emile's wish for a close finish.

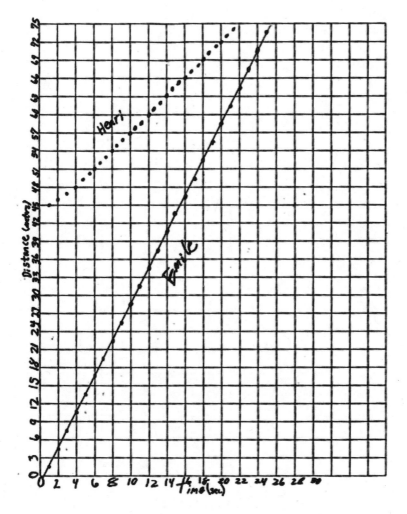

Fig. 17.3. A graph without the point of intersection

At this time most students realized that they needed to extend their graphs or create new graphs that showed data about the boys as they got closer in distance. Interestingly, even when students created such graphs, some continued to plot individual points on each boy's line, including points between the gridlines (see fig. 17.4). These students preferred working with the walking rate in its unit-rate form to scaling up the unit rate to plot only points that fell on the gridlines. I questioned students about this decision, asking them which points were easy and which were difficult to plot on the graph. When students told me that the points that fell on the gridlines were easiest, I asked them how they could use these points to create the rest of the graph. Many students were able to use a ruler to connect these points to create the line. Some of them then used the line to plot each of the individual data points on the graph. This led me to believe that students' understanding of the linearity in the graph, and the problem itself, was quite tenuous. I wondered if they were thinking of the line as a series of discrete data points rather than as a pictorial image of the linear relationship between each boy's distance and time.

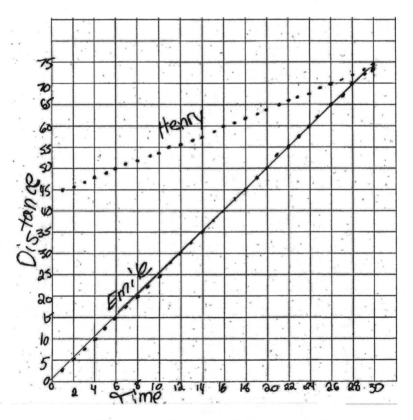

Fig. 17.4. A graph with points plotted between grid lines

Many students misplaced the point on Henri's line that represented his distance at zero seconds, namely, his head start. These students placed a point at (1, 45), not (0, 45). Some students placed a point at (0, 0) as well. My students' decisions to place the first point at the origin and represent the constant only after this point reminded me that they were unfamiliar with linear functions with a positive y-intercept. It seemed that their prior experiences with graphing made them uncomfortable plotting a point on the y-axis above the origin. Instead of correcting the error with individual students, I chose to wait until the whole-class discussion to talk about the location of the first point on Henri's line. Since I knew that the first point was important in interpreting the value of b in the equation $y = mx + b$, I wanted to give students the opportunity to discuss this idea among themselves. Doing so would require them to reason about the constraints of the problem and would lead to deeper understanding of the concept of the y-intercept in the different representations of the function.

Talking about Tabular and Graphic Representations

Before beginning the whole-class discussion, I asked one pair of students to record their table on the board and another pair to record their graph on a piece of poster-sized graph paper (see fig. 17.5). My goal for the first part of the discussion was to emphasize the observations students made about their tables and graphs that would assist them in developing equations for the lines. I began by asking the students how long the race should be. Students' answers varied, but most agreed that the race should be a little less than 75 meters, since both boys reached 75 meters at the same time, but that in one more second Emile would be ahead. I asked the students who had suggested a race length to use the table or graph to justify their answers. I asked students who did not volunteer to rephrase what their classmates had said. This technique helps to ensure that those who were unable to find a solution to the problem could make sense of the solution by participating in the discussion (Chapin, O'Connor, and Anderson 2003).

Our discussion then focused on the graph of the lines. I asked students to justify the placement of Henri's first point. Specifically, I asked whether the point should be at (0, 45) or (0, 0). After some discussion, students agreed that the point should be at (0, 45), since Henri is 45 meters ahead of his brother before the race even starts. After one second, Henri walks one meter and is now 46 meters from the start. To focus students' attention on the concept of the y-intercept, I pushed on the misconception further. I asked students if they thought that plotting (0, 0) and (1, 46) on Henri's graph would also accurately represent the head start. To dispute this statement, some students said that this would show that Henri walked 46 meters in the first second of the race—a feat that was not only impossible but

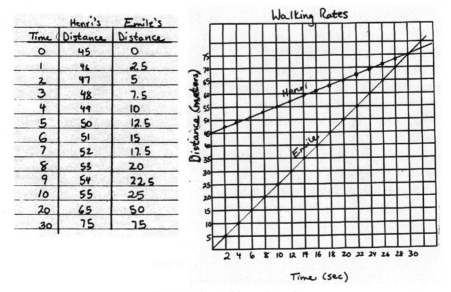

Time	Henri's Distance	Emile's Distance
0	45	0
1	46	2.5
2	47	5
3	48	7.5
4	49	10
5	50	12.5
6	51	15
7	52	17.5
8	53	20
9	54	22.5
10	55	25
20	65	50
30	75	75

Fig. 17.5. Class table and graph

also inaccurate according to his walking rate. I gave students an opportunity to debate the placement of the first point with partners and correct any errors they had on their individual graphs before finally affirming that we needed to show that Henri's distance was 45 meters from the start, at zero seconds into the race. I asked students why the points on each boy's graph lie in a line. Students responded that this was because each boy is walking at a constant rate; every second he walks the same number of meters.

Next we discussed students' tables. My decision to post a table that did not increase the time by a constant interval of one second encouraged students to think explicitly about the linearity of the problem. I asked students to check their tables against this one to give them an opportunity to fix their errors. When I stated that some students suggested that Henri was 66 meters from the start at 20 seconds instead of 65 meters, students justified that the distance was 65 meters in a variety of ways. Some generated all times and distances from 10 through 20 seconds; others isolated the 45-meter head start and then added on one meter for each of the 20 seconds. Pushing those who had included entries from 1 through 30 seconds to consider this idea, I asked three questions:

- How many meters did Henri walk during the first 20 seconds of the race?
- How many meters was Henri's head start?
- What was Henri's total distance?

These questions helped students differentiate between Henri's walking rate and the constant of his head start.

It was important that students link the features of the linear graph with certain characteristics of the table. I asked if we could have predicted that each boy's graph would form a line just by looking at the table. Students agreed that indeed we could have predicted this, since every time the time changes by one, each boy's distance increases by the same amount. I asked why this constant change in the table created a line graph. Several students explained that on the graph, every time they went over 1 on the x-axis, they always went up the same amount on the y-axis. They explained that this created a straight line of points. Reminding students that Henri's line started above the origin, I asked if we could have predicted this by looking at the table. Some students responded that the first row of the table revealed that Henri's first point would be at (0, 45), but Emile's would be at (0, 0), or the origin. Recalling that some students had omitted zero seconds from the table, I asked students to talk with their partners about why it made sense to begin the table at zero seconds. This allowed students to think about using zero seconds as the first row in a table to determine where each boy's graph begins on the y-axis. It also gave students an opportunity to reflect on and improve the tables that they had made earlier. When I asked if we could have used the table to determine whether Emile's line would be steeper than Henri's, students looked at successive differences in distance for each boy and then compared them. They found that since Emile's distances changed at a greater rate than Henri's, his line would "go up" faster.

Generalizing Relationships Symbolically

Students were now ready to generalize the linear relationship between each boy's distance and time in the form of an equation. Students worked on writing a rule that we could use to determine Henri's distance at any time. Students were familiar with using rules from work they had done in prior units on patterns and functions. So that we could have a discussion about our rules, we agreed to use the letter D to represent distance (in meters) and the letter t to represent time (in seconds). Students worked in pairs to generate the rules. Some students were able to write only iterative rules. For example, some students stated that Emile's rule would be to "add 2.5 meters each time." I asked these students to explain how to use time to determine Emile's distance. "How can you figure out that Emile's distance at 20 seconds is 50 meters without having to fill in entries for 11 through 19 seconds? How far does Emile walk during each of those 20 seconds?" When students responded 2.5 seconds, I demonstrated repeating this for several seconds on my fingers. I said, "So that's 2.5 meters for the first second, another 2.5 meters in the next second, another 2.5 meters during the third second, and so on for 20 seconds. What number sentence can you use to figure out the total distance walked?" I asked variations of these questions until students were ready to generalize about using any time t to describe the distance walked. After further discussion, the class determined that $D = t + 45$ and $D = 2.5t$ could be used for Henri's and Emile's walking distances, respectively.

I wanted my students to rewrite Henri's rule with 1 as the coefficient of *t,* since doing so would help them make sense of the equation when it was written in slope-intercept form. When asked to identify the coefficient of time in Henri's equation, students had a variety of answers (including zero). Most students were not using the identity property of multiplication to recognize 1 as the coefficient of the variable in Henri's rule. Rather than clarify this myself, I asked the students what 2.5 in Emile's rule meant in the context of the problem. Students had no difficulty identifying this as Emile's walking rate. I then asked, "Where do you see Henri's walking rate in his equation?" After students talked about this with their partners, several pairs of students were able to explain that Henri's walking rate could be seen in the rule if the number 1 was recorded as the coefficient of *t*. We discussed this comment as a class, and again I asked students who were initially unable to identify the coefficient to explain their classmates' reasoning.

Connecting *D = rt* to Graphs and Tables

Students needed to see each equation as a description of the line. I asked them, "Where do you see 2.5 in the graph?" This question puzzled most students, since their *y*-axis scales did not show intervals of 2.5 meters. Students first talked about this question with their partners. When we reconvened moments later as a whole class, some students explained that their graphs did show points that "went up" by 2.5 (see fig. 17.4). I asked many students to explain what was meant by "went up by 2.5," so that they could develop an understanding that 2.5 expressed the rate of change from one point on the line to the next when *t* changed by one second.

Pointing to the class graph (see fig. 17.5), I asked students to explain where they saw 2.5 on this graph. To exaggerate the point, I stated emphatically that I did not see 2.5 *anywhere* on this graph. Students were eager to dispute my statement. To do so, they pointed to a specific point on the graph, such as (2, 5), and explained that this meant Emile traveled 5 meters in 2 seconds so in each second he traveled 2.5 meters. I stubbornly insisted on arguing the point further. I pointed to the graph shown in figure 17.4 and said, "On this graph, the points go up by 2.5. Every time we move over one on the *x*-axis, we move up 2.5 on the *y*-axis. But on [our class] graph, it's different. This shows that every time we go up 2 seconds, the distance goes up 5 meters. Isn't that a different rate of change?" Again, students were eager to prove me wrong. They explained that 5 meters in 2 seconds really means "2.5 meters plus 2.5 meters." I gave more students an opportunity to respond before facilitating a similar discussion about the rate of change of the points on Henri's line. We next discussed which line was steeper. Many of my students used the technique of placing a pencil on top of one line, then moving that pencil to the other line, adjusting its angle so that they could compare the steepness of each. When students agreed that Emile's line was steeper, I asked, "How can you tell that Emile's line is steeper by examining the equations?" Again, I asked student pairs to discuss this before we talked as a whole class. Students explained that because Emile's equation multiplies *time* by 2.5, his graph would be steeper because his points will "go up faster."

Connecting $D = rt$ with $y = mx + b$

The class was now ready to connect the table, graph, and rules with the slope-intercept form of the equation of a line. After writing $y = mx + b$ on the board, I explained to students that mathematicians use this form to write the equation of any set of points that fall in a line. I asked the students if they thought their lines for Emile and Henri could be represented with an equation in this form. The answer was a resounding no! The students did not see the connection between the rules they had written and the slope-intercept form of the equation. I wrote $y = mx + b$ directly beneath the students' rule for Henri. I asked the students to talk with their partners about how the two equations, $D = 1t + 45$ and $y = mx + b$, were similar and different. Students talked mostly about the differences, such as the fact that the second equation had four variables and Henri's rule had only two. Students were familiar with using x and y to represent the independent and dependent variables, respectively, in a function. I asked the students what letters we used in our rules to represent these variables, and students correctly identified D for the dependent variable and t for the independent variable. I asked students if we could replace D with y and t with x. When they agreed, I showed them what this would look like (see fig. 17.6). Now we had $y = 1x + 45$, and I again asked students if they thought this equation fit the form $y = mx + b$. Students explained that the second equation had "m and b," whereas the first had numbers in their places. After asking the students to recall the meaning of 1 in the term $1x$, I explained that m describes the rate of change between the two variables in a problem. Since Henri's distance changed at a rate of 1 meter per second, his value for m was 1. I asked the students to recall how "+ 45" affected the look of the graph. After students stated that Henri's line started at $y = 45$ on the y-axis, I confirmed that in the equation $y = mx + b$, b reveals the y-value of the point that falls on the y-axis. In order to push students' thinking on this matter, I explained that many people predict that Henri's line will be steeper because his equation includes "+ 45." As students discussed this question with their partners, I could hear that some did believe that the value of this term affected the steepness of the line. Some of the other students who disagreed were having difficulty articulating the difference between how steep the line was and where it touched the y-axis. I knew that I would need to continue to address this conceptual obstacle in future instruction.

We then tried to connect our rule for Emile's distance and time, $D = 2.5t$, with $y = mx + b$. Students translated D and t to y and x, respectively, to create the equation $y = 2.5x$ (see fig. 17.6). But they were confused about the variable b. I asked the students where Emile's line crossed the y-axis and how that differed from Henri's line. Students observed that Emile's line began at (0, 0). Several students made a

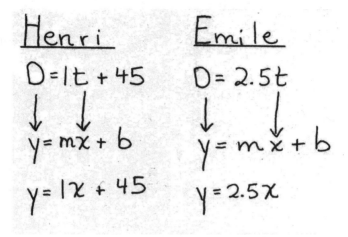

Fig. 17.6. Linear equations

conjecture that the value of b for Emile's equation was 0. After some discussion about this topic, I asked the students, once again, if they thought Emile's equation fit the form $y = mx + b$. Students agreed that it did. Since Emile's equation began at $(0, 0)$, b was equal to zero and so "there was nothing to add." I wrote Emile's equation as $y = 2.5x + 0$ so that students could see that this equation was equivalent to $y = 2.5x$. I summarized important findings by pointing to each term in each equation, and I repeatedly asked the same question, "What does this tell us about the graph?" I called on students to answer this question about each term so that many had the opportunity to articulate what they had learned.

I chose not to introduce the terms *slope* and *y-intercept* during this investigation but instead continued to use more informal terms such as *steepness* and *where the line touches the y-axis*. My students had begun to develop essential knowledge of the meaning of these terms. The vocabulary terms *slope, y-intercept*, and *slope-intercept form* would be a focal point in upcoming investigations.

Conclusion

The National Council of Teachers of Mathematics (2000) advocates an increase in real-world problems in the instruction of algebra. Students need to explore a topic, such as slope-intercept form, in a variety of contexts in order to develop strong understanding of the concepts and skills associated with that topic (Burns 2000). So, following the investigation described here, my students solved similar problems about constant rates of change using other applications problems, such as telephone charges and payment plans. Some of the problems included negative slopes and negative *y*-intercepts. During the course of this unit, my students came to rely on the use of tables to help them write linear equations about narrative problems. As seen in this investigation, students who used tables were better able to solve the problem than those who made graphs. Over time, my students became proficient using tables to determine the values of the parameters m and b in the slope-intercept form of the equation of a line. Specifically, they developed an understanding that beginning a table at $x = 0$ revealed the value of b in the linear equation. They also reasoned that successive changes in the dependent variable compared to unit changes in the independent variable revealed the value of m.

In future lessons, when students were asked to examine a set of linear equations and predict the appearance of the graphs, they often used this problem as a basis for their conjectures. Since students linked the idea of a greater coefficient of x with a faster walking rate, they used this idea to argue that the greater the coefficient of x, the steeper the slope of the line. This problem also helped students think about using a table to identify the y-intercept of a linear function, since Henri's head start could be detected in the first row of the table (0, 45). We later revisited this problem when we studied systems of equations. Students explored how to set the two equations equal in distance and solve for time. Since completing this investigation, I have learned how important it is to maintain the idea of slope as a *ratio* of two quantities. As seen in the equations in this problem, slope can appear as a whole-number value for m in slope-intercept form. As a result, the meaning of slope can be misconstrued as a specific number. When asked where they see the slope of a line or the value of m in a table, students often look for a specific entry containing that number instead of identifying it as the rate of change. Throughout a unit on linear functions, I am mindful to ask my students questions that encourage them to think of m (in $y = mx + b$) in three ways—as the slope of the line, the rate of change between the variables, and the coefficient of x. I also insist that students be explicit when they read an equation tied to a particular narrative. For example, if my students read $y = 2.5x$ as "y equals $2.5x$," I encourage them to elaborate further and articulate that "y equals 2.5 meters per second times the number of seconds."

I have also learned that exploring $y = mx + b$ in many different contexts helps my students identify the slope of a line that is not anchored to a particular context. Like many, my students often reverse the measures within the ratio, expressing slope as horizontal change to vertical change. This error could be caused by the fact that a point is identified and plotted first by its x-coordinate and then by its y-coordinate (e.g., over, up). I have found that my students are much less inclined to make this reversal when exploring slope in the context of a particular problem. Whether the context is dollars per pound, cents per minute, or meters per second, students tend to use the context to identify the rate of change (the slope of the line) as a ratio of the change in the dependent variable to unit change in the independent variable. Through discussions where we link the dependent variable to the y-axis and the independent variable to the x-axis, my students have been able to transfer this idea to identify the slope of an arbitrary line drawn on a coordinate grid.

The use of context is also beneficial with other skills related to slope-intercept form. For example, my students typically struggle with the skills of writing the equation of a line if given the slope and one point on the line or two points on the line. I plan to reuse the Emile and Henri problem to help students develop these two skills. For example, I could ask students how to use only two points on Emile's graph to determine the equation of his line. Or, I could ask them to use one specific point and Henri's walking rate to determine the equation of his line. I plan to recycle several of the problems, or ones similar in constraints, that students solved earlier in our explorations of slope-intercept form to acquire these skills. This will connect students' understanding of these new skills to previous knowledge, allowing them to develop confidence and proficiency with these skills.

REFERENCES

Burns, Marilyn. *About Teaching Mathematics*. Sausalito, Calif.: Math Solutions Publications, 2000.

Chapin, Suzanne, Catherine O'Connor, and Nancy Canavan Anderson. *Classroom Discussions: Using Math Talk to Help Students Learn*. Sausalito, Calif.: Math Solutions Publications, 2003.

Greenes, Carole, and Carol Findell. "Developing Students' Algebraic Reasoning Abilities." In *Developing Mathematical Reasoning in Grades K–12*, 1999 Yearbook of the National Council of Teachers of Mathematics (NCTM), edited by Lee V. Stiff, pp. 127–37. Reston, Va.: NCTM, 1999.

Lappan, Glenda, James Fey, William Fitzgerald, Susan Friel, and Elizabeth Phillips. *Moving Straight Ahead*. East Lansing, Mich.: Michigan State University, 2002.

National Council of Teachers of Mathematics (NCTM). *Principles and Standards for School Mathematics*. Reston, Va.: NCTM, 2000.

———. *Curriculum Focal Points for Prekindergarten through Grade 8 Mathematics*. Reston, Va.: NCTM, 2006.

Usiskin, Zalman. "What Should Not Be in the Algebra Curriculum of Average College-Bound Students?" In *Algebraic Thinking, Grades K–12,* edited by Barbara Moses, pp. 76–81. Reston, Va.: National Council of Teachers of Mathematics, 1999a.

———. "Why Elementary Algebra Can, Should, and Must Be an Eighth-Grade Course for Average Students." In *Algebraic Thinking, Grades K–12,* edited by Barbara Moses, pp. 40–48. Reston, Va.: National Council of Teachers of Mathematics, 1999b.

18

Digging Deeply into Intermediate Algebra: Using Symbols to Reason and Technology to Connect Symbols and Graphs

Rose Mary Zbiek
M. Kathleen Heid

"TECHNOLOGY is essential in teaching and learning mathematics; it influences the mathematics that is taught and enhances students' learning" (National Council of Teachers of Mathematics [NCTM] 2000a, p. 24). It is crucial to go beyond the statement of NCTM's Technology Principle and to look carefully at examples of good uses of technology in intermediate algebra both to understand the strength of each example and to unearth general principles that indicate how students might benefit from technology use beyond these particular settings. In this article, we describe and reflect on examples of intermediate algebra tasks through which students connect ideas of algebra and shape in ways that turn familiar topics inside out to expose the mathematical heart of the issue. The examples provide evidence of how students with access to mathematics technology intricately connect symbols and graphs and reason symbolically to develop deeper understanding of fundamental ideas in algebra (and geometry) and to discover the power of symbols. Technology involved in the examples includes a blend of computer algebra systems (CAS), dynamical geometry construction environments, and graphing calculators, all of which are used in conjunction with the need to interpret symbols and perhaps the occasion to do some by-hand symbolic manipulation.

The development of the Technology-Intensive Curriculum materials was supported by the National Science Foundation under Grant No. TPE 96-18029 to The Pennsylvania State University with a major subcontract to the University of Iowa, June 1997 through May 2004. Any opinions, findings, and conclusions or recommendations expressed in this article or those materials are those of the authors and do not necessarily reflect the views of the National Science Foundation.

Examples of Tasks

The examples we use in this article are drawn from a multiyear set of materials developed through the Technology-Intensive Mathematics (TIM) Project (Heid et al. 2004; Zbiek et al. 2004, available online through www.ed.psu.edu/casim/). The materials were designed for students who had completed an introductory algebra course that used a technology-intensive functions-based approach and that crossed traditional algebra-geometry boundaries. The materials assume individual student access to graphing calculators, computer algebra systems, and dynamical geometry construction tools. Module topics were chosen as ones for which technology could play a role in deepening understanding of fundamental ideas of transformations, functions, iteration, composition and inverses, geometric constraints, dynamical systems, and symbolic reasoning.

What follows are two scenarios from intermediate algebra lessons that are illustrative of how reasoning with symbols and connecting symbols and graphs can take students deeply into important mathematical ideas. In each example, the lesson generated a graphical or symbolic algebra result that captured students' attention and called for algebraic explanation. Each example begins with a description of what we were hoping to achieve with the activity and the mathematical question that captures students' attention.

Example 1: Logistic Function

Much of the TIM curriculum materials are based on mathematical representations of real-world situations. An example of what students may gain from reasoning with symbols and connecting graphs and symbols arises from an exploration of limited growth (e.g., the number of fish in a stocked pond x months after stocking). In this example, technology does not simply reinforce algebra; it leads to new algebraic calculations.

Lessons involving logistic growth functions engage students in explorations with complex compositions of familiar functions. For example, they interpret a function of the form

$$f(x) = \frac{a}{1 + b(2.7)^{cx}} + d$$

as the composition of a linear function ($g(x) = cx$), an exponential function ($j(x) = 2.7^x$), a second linear function ($h(x) = 1 + bx$, a rational function ($k(x) = a/x$), and a third linear function ($m(x) = x + d$). Lessons engage students in using symbolic representations to analyze changes in graphical output generated by changes in the parameters of functions. Students study the effects of changing the values of the parameters on the shapes of the graph, such as observing and explaining how changing a to $-a$ in $k(x) = a/x$ produces a graph that is the reflection about the x-axis of the graph related to $k(x) = a/x$. In many of these explorations, the change in output is continuous (e.g., as the value of b in $h(x) = 1 + bx$ increases, the slope of the graph of h increases). In a particular lesson, students encounter an unusual result as they investigate the effects of the parameters on the graphs of functions f of the form

$$f(x) = \frac{a}{1 + b(2.7)^{cx}} + d.$$

Students use what we call a "slidergraph," a Cartesian graph of a function that is created in an interactive geometry environment in such a way that changes in its parameter values are controlled by dragging points. As students drag point B to change the value of b from the positive values into the negative values, they see the smooth curve (fig. 18.1a) suddenly "break" into two pieces (fig. 18.1b). This unusual occurrence leads students to wonder: Should this happen? Why does it happen? For what value of x does the "break" happen?

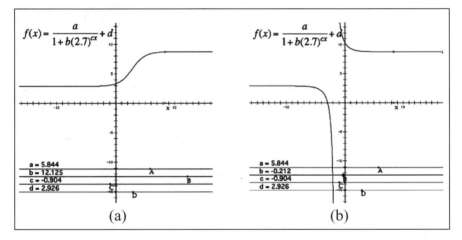

(a)   (b)

Fig. 18.1. Logistic-function family graphs showing smooth curve (a) and "break" (b)

Students with intermediate algebra experience can reason about this graphic event by thinking about an asymptote in relation to a zero denominator. Solving $1 + (-0.212)(2.7)^{-0.904x} = 0$ for x should yield the value of x for which the break occurs in the given graph. We choose to use CAS in order to decrease students' attention to the details of the computation and to keep their attention focused on the big mathematical picture. Many CAS are capable of both exact and approximate calculations. For some CAS, exact and approximate calculations happen in Exact Mode and Approximate Mode, respectively. Using a CAS in Exact Mode to solve $1 - 0.212(2.7)^{0.904x} = 0$ for x yields

$$\frac{-125 \ln\left(\frac{53}{250}\right)}{113 \ln\left(\frac{10}{27}\right)}.$$

In this instance, the CAS produces an exact value for the solution, but this result is both complicated and uninformative when it comes to locating the asymptote as it would appear in the graph shown in figure 18.1b. Using by-hand methods yields a similar result. In Approximate Mode, the CAS result is approximately –1.728. Students can locate the line given by $x = -1.728$, which is close to the location of the asymptote.

With or without access to CAS, students looking at the exact-value expression can be challenged to explain why the value of

$$\frac{-125 \ln\left(\frac{53}{250}\right)}{113 \ln\left(\frac{10}{27}\right)}$$

is close to the approximate value. Students may be drawn into explanations that appeal to properties of natural logarithms, such as the reasoning suggested by the following rough estimation:

$$\frac{-125 \ln\left(\frac{53}{250}\right)}{113 \ln\left(\frac{10}{27}\right)} = \frac{-125}{113} \times \frac{\ln\left(\frac{53}{250}\right)}{\ln\left(\frac{10}{27}\right)} \approx -1 \times \frac{\ln\left(\frac{53}{250}\right)}{\ln\left(\frac{10}{27}\right)} \approx -\frac{\ln\left(\frac{50}{250}\right)}{\ln\left(\frac{10}{30}\right)}$$

$$= -\frac{\ln\left(\frac{1}{5}\right)}{\ln\left(\frac{1}{3}\right)} = -\frac{-\ln(5)}{-\ln(3)} \approx -\frac{2}{1} = -2.$$

Students' attention should be drawn to noting that although this value of the expression may be close to –2, they should question the accuracy of these approximations involving natural logarithms. For example, students can easily conclude that

$$\frac{-125}{113} \times \frac{\ln\left(\frac{53}{250}\right)}{\ln\left(\frac{10}{27}\right)} < -1 \times \frac{\ln\left(\frac{53}{250}\right)}{\ln\left(\frac{10}{27}\right)}$$

because –125/113 is less than –1 and the value of

$$\frac{\ln\left(\frac{53}{250}\right)}{\ln\left(\frac{10}{27}\right)}$$

is positive. However, it is more difficult for them to determine whether

$$-1 \times \frac{\ln\left(\frac{53}{250}\right)}{\ln\left(\frac{10}{27}\right)}$$

is greater than or less than

$$-\frac{\ln\left(\frac{50}{250}\right)}{\ln\left(\frac{10}{30}\right)}.$$

The solution of the equation is the value of x at which the "break" that appears in the graph shown in figure 18.1b occurs. Plotting the point given by $(-1.728, 0)$ and constructing the vertical line through this point (as shown in fig. 18.2), students have visual evidence of the accuracy of the symbolically determined answer.

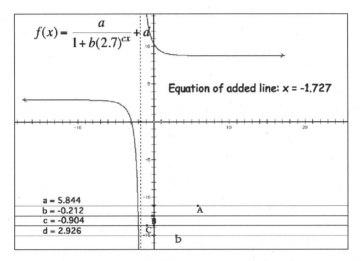

$$f(x) = \frac{a}{1+b(2.7)^{cx}} + d$$

Equation of added line: $x = -1.727$

a = 5.844
b = -0.212
c = -0.904
d = 2.926

Fig. 18.2. Graphing a line to verify that the computed value of x is reasonable

Using the values $a = 5.844$, $c = -0.904$, and $d = 2.926$ and dragging point B, students note there is more than one value for b for which an asymptote is present. Can they identify where the asymptote would be for other values of b? To answer this question requires students to extend their notion of "zero denominator goes with asymptote" to think about for which value of b it is possible for the value of $1 + b(2.7)^{0.904x}$ to be 0 for some value of x. The condition, $1 + b(2.7)^{-0.904x} = 0$, requires the value of b to be negative. This observation arises from the inspection of a symbolic form and noting that 1 and $(2.7)^{0.904x}$ are both positive values. The necessarily negative value of b for an asymptote suggests why the break never happened when the point B was dragged to the right of the vertical axis and suddenly happened after the point B was dragged from the positive values of b into the negative values of b.

For the negative values of b, which yield an asymptote, where does that asymptote appear? When a symbolic calculator is used, it is easy to generate the general result when $1 + b(2.7)^{0.904x} = 0$ is solved for x, as shown in figure 18.3. The first line in figure 18.3 is the CAS command for the solution. The second line, which is right justified on the CAS screen, is the resulting solution in Exact Mode,

$$x = \frac{125 \ln\left(\frac{-1}{b}\right)}{113 \ln\left(\frac{10}{27}\right)},$$

with the condition that

$$\frac{1}{b} \leq 0.$$

The third line is the CAS solution command repeated, but this time the calculation is done in Approximate Mode. The last line in figure 18.3 is the approximate solution, $x = 1.1137102599\ln(-b)$, with the condition that $b < 0$. Interpreting these symbolic results, students confirm their expectation that an asymptote would occur for every negative value of b.

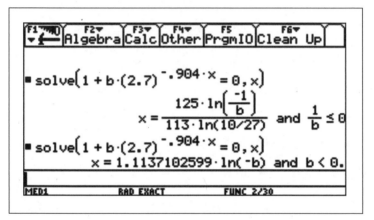

Fig. 18.3. Exact and approximate solutions to $1 + b(2.7)^{0.904x} = 0$

This example shows how tasks that require students to reason symbolically and to connect graphs and symbols in intermediate algebra can extend and enrich students' ideas. First, the important mathematical task is determining where the "break" in the graph occurs. This task extends a naïve sense of "zero denominator goes with asymptote" to a situation that requires thinking about what causes an expression with two variables to take on a value of 0. The example illustrates two general principles about the use of technology that are particularly important in intermediate algebra. First, students should appreciate the role of symbols in mathematics. The "break" in the graph of the logistic function puzzled students. Trying to explain this event using a blend of CAS and slidergraphs helped learners understand the power of and necessity for symbolic work to yield approximate results as well as exact answers and the potential of symbol-graph connections to furnish visual evidence that symbolic calculations are correct. Second, technology use can underscore distinctions between variables and parameters. Dragging point B to change the values of b and seeing the "break" happen in the graph draws students' attention not only to the crucial role that b plays in determining the shape of the graph but also to the relationship of the value of b to the presence and location of the asymptote. Students then may draw on algebraic ideas to reason about why the "break" makes sense and on their symbolic techniques to determine the particular value of b for which the "break" occurs.

Example 2: Parameter Exploration

Facility with algebraic symbols entails the ability to recognize the graphs of certain function families and generate symbolic rules for these graphs. An introductory lesson in the TIM materials engages students in an analysis of a familiar-looking graph that arises in a somewhat surprising setting. The setting is an envelope (i.e., a curve that is tangent to every one of a collection of curves) generated by a family of lines that arises in the course of a linear slidergraph-assisted parameter exploration.

When using slidergraphs for parameter explorations, like that described for the logistic example, it is not unusual for students to drag something other than the one point they need to change the value of the parameter. Although some dragging mishaps may be annoying, some of them yield interesting opportunities to connect graphs and symbols and to reason symbolically. The tasks for this lesson arose from capitalizing on what might have been considered an error in dragging a point to change a parameter value for a slidergraph. While we were developing the curriculum materials, we watched a colleague accidentally drag both points A and B in a slidergraph for the family of functions given by $f(x) = ax + b$. We noticed that this dragging produced a collection of lines that seemingly pass through a single point, as shown in figure 18.4a. Each different pair of initial values for a and b that we tried produced a collection of lines that passed through a single point; moreover, each time the point of concurrence had an x-value of -1. Figures 18.4b and 18.4c show two more examples of what we saw.

Do the lines always pass through a point with x-coordinate -1 regardless of the original values of a and b? When both points A and B are grabbed simultaneously and dragged, they move the same distance. So the difference between the values of a and b is the same no matter how far the pair of points, A and B, is moved. It likely helps students to consider a specific case to start. For instance, suppose the values of the parameters are given by $a = 4$ and $b = 3$, *and* the points A and B are dragged simultaneously some nonzero distance, say, 2 units. The line depicted in the slidergraph prior to dragging is that of $f(x) = 4x + 3$. After dragging points A and B simultaneously 2 units to the right, $a = 6$, $b = 5$, and the line appearing in the slidergraph is given by $g(x) = 6x + 5$. Point A is still 1 unit to the right of point B, and $a = b + 1$. If points A and B are dragged 2 more units to the right, $a = 8$, $b = 7$, and the line is represented by $h(x) = 8x + 7$, with $a = b + 1$. All three of these lines intersect at $(-1, -1)$.

For the general case, students can use a and b to be the initial values of the slope

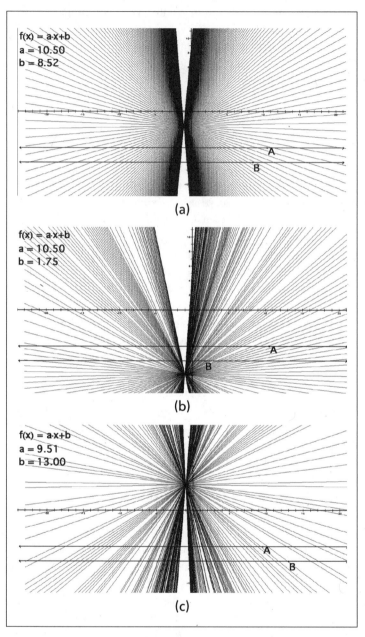

Fig. 18.4. Simultaneously dragging points *A* and *B* changes both the slope and the intercept in $f(x) = ax + b$.

and intercept, respectively, with point *A* *k* units from point *B*. Point *A* is to the right of point *B* if $k > 0$, and to the left if $k < 0$. The equation of the original line is $f(x) = ax + b$, and the equation of the line after points *A* and *B* are moved is $g(x) = (a + k)x +$

($b + k$). The intersection point of these two lines can be found by solving $f(x) = g(x)$ or $ax + b = (a + k) x + (b + k)$, as described in detail in the e-Standards of *Principles and Standards* (NCTM 2000b). The graphs of f and g intersect at $(-1, -a + b)$.

The slidergraph representing $f(x) = ax + b$ (with sliders for a and b) worked well when we wanted to talk about slope and intercept. However, we wanted students to see more general parameter effects. When we asked students to explore a family of functions of the form $f(x) = a \cdot p(d(x - b)) + c$, with parameters a, b, c, and d and function p where $p(x) = x$, we supplied a different slidergraph to represent linear functions. We asked students to start with a simplified situation and use a d-value of 1, resulting in the family of linear functions given by $f(x) = a(x - b) + c$. Again, each position of parameters generated the graph of a line, but this time when points A and B were dragged at the same time, a very different image resulted, as shown in figure 18.5.

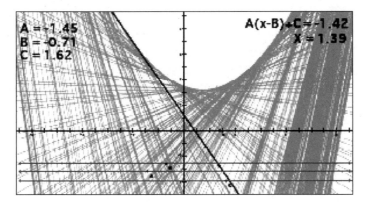

Fig. 18.5. The envelope of lines generated when points A
and B are dragged simultaneously for $f(x) = a (x - b) + c$

Students with intermediate algebra experience notice that the envelope generated by the lines looks like a parabola. Is the shape a parabola? Reasoning with symbols (as shown in the following discussion) leads to the conclusion that the boundary is a parabola.

The slidergraph shows the line for each member of the family given by $f(x) = a(x - b) + c$. For each initial position of points A and B, when points A and B are dragged concurrently, they each move the same distance and the distance between them does not change. For a specific example, suppose we start with $c = 3$, $a = 5$, and $b = 7$. No matter how far the points are dragged (ideally speaking and paying attention to the limits of the computer screen), the distance between points A and B will always be 2. Dragging points A and B in this instance generates the envelope for the collection of all lines for which $c = 3$ and $b = a + 2$. We can analyze the envelope for this collection as follows.

Investigating the envelope for the collection of lines given by $c = 3$ and $b = 2 + a$:

1. Find a function rule for the collection of lines designated by this case.

How can we describe all the lines that fit these conditions on the parameters? Suppose that the value of c is 3 and that b is 2 more than a as A and B are dragged simultaneously. Then we are looking at the collection of functions $f(x) = a(x - b) + 3$ in which $b = a + 2$. So, in this case, we are looking at the collection of lines given by the rule $f(x) = a(x - (a + 2)) + 3$, which is equivalent to $f(x) = -a^2 + ax - 2a + 3$ as well as to $f(x) = ax + (-a^2 - 2a + 3)$.

2. Determine a relationship between the collection of lines graphed and the envelope formed.

How is each of these lines related to the boundary? We can see from the function rule, $f(x) = ax + (-a^2 - 2a + 3)$, that this is a collection of linear functions in x, so the graph of each member of the family is a line. We are interested in the boundary formed by these lines. From the graph and related information shown in figure 18.6, students notice that each point of the boundary seems to be a point on a unique line in the collection. Consider any one of the boundary points. Its first coordinate is some real number x. Its second coordinate is the maximum value of all the linear functions evaluated for the given x-value.

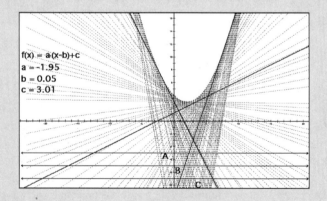

$f(x) = a(x-b)+c$
$a = -1.95$
$b = 0.05$
$c = 3.01$

Fig. 18.6. Noting three lines in the collection of lines for $c = 3$ and $b = 2 + a$

3. Look at a specific value of x for insight about this maximum value.

How can we look more closely at how a line is related to a corresponding point on the boundary? We can find out more about the nature of these boundary points by examining what happens for a particular value of x. As an example, let's look at what happens when $x = 1$. If $x = 1$, the set of values of possible values for f is given by $f(1) = -a^2 + a - 2a + 3 = -a^2 + -a + 3$, and the maximum of $-a^2 + -a + 3$ is 3.25, which is the value of the quadratic expression when a is

$$\frac{-(-1)}{2(-1)} = -0.5.$$

Students see that they can substitute any fixed value of x into the expression, $f(x) = -a^2 + ax - 2a + 3$, and then find the maximum value of the resulting quadratic function in a.

The important idea from the specific case given by $c = 3$ and $b = 2 + a$ or $f(x) = a(x - -a) + 3$ or $f(x) = -a^2 + a(x - 2) + 3$ is that for each x-value, the maximum value of the linear functions is a function of a, and each x-value is associated with a different function of a. The challenge is to find a function rule to describe those maximum values. To do so, students need to think about $f(x) = a(x - b) + c$.

In this general case, let's suppose that c is an arbitrary value and $b = a + h$. If point B is to the right of point A, $h > 0$; if point B is to the left of point A, $h < 0$. The envelope is the boundary formed by the set of lines given by $f(x) = a(x - a - h) + c$ or $f(x) = -a^2 + a(x - h) + c$. During the dragging, the value of a changes, but the values of h and c are constant. For each value of x, the point on the boundary is the point with that x-value that has the greatest output value; that is, for each x, the point on the boundary is the point with the maximum value of a quadratic function in a given by $m(a) = -a^2 + a(x - h) + c$. For each different value of x, the values of x, h, and c are fixed and $m(a)$ is a quadratic expression in a. For a fixed x, the maximum value of $m(a)$ occurs when a is $\frac{x - h}{2}$. Using this value for a in $m(a)$ yields the function rule for the graph of the boundary:

$$g(x) = -\left(\frac{x-h}{2}\right)^2 + \left(\frac{x-h}{2}\right)(x-h) + c \ \text{ or } \ g(x) = \tfrac{1}{4}(x-h)^2 + c.$$

Since the envelope is the graph of this quadratic function, students conclude that the envelope in figure 18.5 must be a parabola.

The important mathematical task in the Parameter Exploration example is to find the symbolic rule for a graphical figure. Like the Logistic Function example, this example underscores the principle that students should appreciate the role of symbols in mathematics. The symbolic rule generated in the reasoning process,

$$g(x) = \tfrac{1}{4}(x - h)^2 + c,$$

is a tool for predicting exactly which parabola would be the boundary generated by any initial choice of values for a, $b = a + h$, and c. As in the first example, symbols aid in reaching a definitive conclusion about the general case as well as allowing one to predict the mathematical details for any given case.

This second example also embodies the principle that the use of technology can underscore distinctions between variables and parameters. However, this second example also addresses a third principle: Technology use can help students understand that functions are not merely symbolic rules; thinking about functions requires acknowledging input variables and domains. This is particularly true when students are faced with an expression that involves two or more letters as variables or parameters. In developing the function rule for the envelope, students need to distinguish between functions with different input variables (e.g., x or a). This task challenges students to move beyond assumptions that x is always the input variable and to think about how a change in variable from a to x necessitates talking about two different functions. The expression $-a^2 + a(x - h) + c$ was used in the symbolic representations of both a quadratic function in a and a linear function in x.

Conclusion

When we first tried to use CAS, as well as graphing calculators and geometry-construction environments in intermediate algebra, we typically used the technology to do the routine things that most people expected students to be able to do by hand, such as producing graphs and manipulating symbols. We learned that we needed to change our perspective from one that simply delegated part of the usual work to the technology to one that asked what students can learn about algebra when they have access to these technological tools. The examples described in this article illustrate our general principles of using technology to help students appreciate the power of symbols in mathematical reasoning and prediction, distinguish variables from parameters, and work with functions as more than symbolic rules. The tasks embody a synergistic relationship among what students do with CAS and other tools, what they do with paper and pencil, and what they think about mathematical ideas and symbols.

Unlike beginning algebra students, intermediate algebra students, including those students who often are not considered as successful in mathematics as their peers, have a repertoire of mathematical means for reasoning with symbols in ways that connect graphic and symbolic representations of algebraic and geometric ideas. Students can see and learn to look for patterns, even if they struggle to produce the necessary reasoning, graphs, and symbolic results. Students can learn to see familiar shapes, such as points or parabolas, and have a sense that symbols might be used to describe and predict things about those shapes. CAS and slidergraphs help students who struggle with producing graphs and manipulating symbols. These tools also help students who embrace intriguing mathematical questions to delve into the mathematics they enjoy.

Using technology to connect graphs and symbols and to reason with the symbols creates a setting in which students can dig deeply into intermediate algebra ideas as they encounter multiple roles and the power of symbols. Tasks that engage students in using technology to connect graphic and symbolic representations and then reason about the phenomena they encounter are settings in which students can challenge limited conceptions, deepen emerging ideas, and employ the power of symbols.

References

Heid, M. Kathleen, et al. *Technology-Intensive Mathematics Module IX: Symbolic Reasoning.* University Park, Pa.: Pennsylvania State University, CAS-Intensive Mathematics Project, 2004. www.ed.psu.edu/casim (accessed August 19, 2006).

National Council of Teachers of Mathematics (NCTM). *Principles and Standards for School Mathematics.* Reston, Va.: NCTM, 2000a.

―――. "Exploring Linear Functions: Representational Relationships." *Principles and Standards for School Mathematics: Electronic Examples.* Reston, Va.: NCTM, 2000b. my.nctm.org/standards/document/eexamples/chap7/7.5/index.htm (accessed August 19, 2006).

Zbiek, Rose Mary, et al. *Technology-Intensive Mathematics Module IV: Families of Functions.* University Park, Pa.: Pennsylvania State University, CAS-Intensive Mathematics Project, 2004. www.ed.psu.edu/casim/ (accessed August 19, 2006).

Part 5

Educating Teachers

19

Algebra in the Grades K–5 Classroom: Learning Opportunities for Students and Teachers

Deborah Schifter
Virginia Bastable
Susan Jo Russell
Lisa Seyferth
Margaret Riddle

FOR MOST Americans, the identifying feature of algebra is the formal equation consisting of variables and signs for the operations and equality. However, beneath the high abstraction of equations like $a(b + c) = ab + ac$ lie ways of reasoning about how quantities can be decomposed and recombined under different operations—ways of reasoning, unlike the conventions of the notation itself, fully accessible to elementary-school-aged students.

For the last decade, a number of groups have been studying how early algebraic thinking can be introduced into the grades K–5 classroom (Ball and Bass 2003; Bastable and Schifter 2007; Carpenter, Franke, and Levi 2003; Carraher, Brizuela, and Schliemann 2000; Kaput and Blanton 1999; Kaput 1999; Schifter 1999, in preparation; Schifter et al. 2007; Smith 2003). During this time, the first three named authors of this paper have directed projects with groups of teacher-collaborators to investigate what early algebra can mean to their students. Our data consist of cases, written by these teachers, intended to capture their students' thinking as it finds expression in classroom process. The teachers' own reflections—insights, questions—are equally revealing and valued as such. Together we have found that as children learn about the four basic operations—understanding the kinds of situations the operations can model, sorting out different means of representing them, and figuring out how to compute efficiently—they observe and comment on regularities in the number system. For example, they may notice that the calculations $72 - 38$ and $74 - 40$ produce the same result, or that successive answers to a series of problems ($8 + 1 = ?, 8 + 2 = ?, 8 + 3 = ?, \ldots$) increase by 1. In our view, such regularities, emerging naturally from children's work, become the foundation not only for exploration of generalizations about number and operations but also of the practices of formulating, testing, and proving such generalizations—and it is these practices that are at the heart of what we mean by "early algebra."

Through our work with teachers, we have found evidence that students' engagement with early algebra can translate into greater computational fluency. Indeed, our collaborators report that these algebraic practices—stating generalizations about the number system and proving them—support *all* students, challenging those who tend to be ahead of their classmates, even as these same practices help struggling students gain access to basic arithmetic principles.

Our collaborators' cases also form the core of a professional development seminar designed to help teachers develop the knowledge and skills needed to support early algebraic reasoning in their classrooms (Schifter, Bastable, and Russell 2008a, 2008b). By studying such cases, teachers come to understand the importance of generalization and the central role visual representations of the operations play in developing arguments for infinite classes of numbers. Furthermore, we have found that when teachers study how elementary school students think algebraically, they are themselves provided a context that endows the formal notation with meaning, hence utility. Starting with an *idea*, a generalization, instantiated with particular numbers or expressed in natural language, teachers can learn the conventions of algebraic notation to express that generalization concisely. This contrasts with the experience of many elementary school teachers who learned the syntax of algebraic notation in high school, but without meaning.

In this paper, we present two classroom cases—one drawn from kindergarten; the other, from fourth grade—to illustrate how early algebraic thinking can arise quite naturally in the context of instruction on number and operations. Then we present scenes from a professional development seminar to illustrate some of what teachers can learn from studying such cases.

Kindergartners as Algebraic Thinkers: Adding the Same Amount to Unequal Amounts[1]

Kindergarten teacher Lisa Seyferth had set up her students to play double compare[2], a card game similar to war. Each card bears a numeral from 1 to 6 and a picture of that number of objects. Players lay down the top two cards from their piles,

---

1. This case is drawn from one that appears in Schifter, Bastable, and Russell (2008a), pp. 31–33.

2. The game Double Compare is taken from How Many in All?, a kindergarten unit of Investigations in Number, Data, and Space (TERC 1998).

and the player with the higher total when the numbers on the cards are combined says "me." For example, when Wei[3] turns over a 2 and a 6, and Marta turns over a 3 and a 4, they count up the totals and Wei says "me."

No sooner was the game in question under way when Seyferth realized that there were several pairs of children saying "me" or "you" before they could possibly have had time to find the sum of their numbers—but they were always right! For example, when Martina had 6 and 2 and Karen had 6 and 1, Karen quickly said, "You." When Seyferth asked how she knew, Karen pointed to the 2 and said, "This is big. Even though these are the same [the sixes], this [the 6 and 2] must be more."

Paul and his partner had similar sets of hands. Paul had 6 and 3 and his partner had 6 and 1. Paul said, "I had 6 and he had 6, and then I had a higher number." When Seyferth asked what their cards added to, each counted up all the little objects pictured on the cards to get their totals. But as they continued to play, they frequently did *not* count to accurately determine who got to say "me." On a later turn, Paul had 4 and 3 and his partner had 4 and 5. Paul commented, "I have 3 and he has 5." He knew he could ignore the two fours.

Seyferth had set up a task with the intention of giving her kindergartners an opportunity to practice counting up to find totals. But it seemed that her students were subverting her goals for the exercise: They could play many rounds correctly without doing any totaling.

However, Seyferth went beyond noticing what her students *weren't* doing to figure out what they *were* doing. Implicit in their moves was a general principle: If each child has a card of equal value, compare the other two cards; the child with the card of greater value has the greater total. When it was time to put the cards away, Seyferth brought the students together to discuss this idea. She later wrote,

> We talked for a while about how all the pairs "ignored" cards when each partner had the same value, and only paid attention to the cards that were different. Martina said that 6 and 3 is more than 6 and 1 because the 3 is bigger than the 1. I asked, "What about the sixes?" and she said, "They're the same." Paul added, "They don't matter. You don't have to pay attention to the sixes." I put out a few more sets of cards, varying the number that was the same. ("Does this only work for 6?" "No.") They said it always works, and Paul reiterated that you don't have to pay attention to the numbers that are the same. (Schifter, Bastable, and Russell 2008a, p. 32)

As young children begin to learn about numbers and operations, they begin to see regularities in our number system and think about what stays the same among things that are changing. The regularity, or generalization, illustrated above—if one number is greater than another, and the same number is added to each, the first total will be greater than the second—is one example. This statement is true for *any* three

---

3. Students' names are pseudonyms.

numbers. For example, since $54 > 36$, $54 + 98 > 36 + 98$. This idea can be expressed with algebraic notation: *For any numbers, a, b, and c, if a > b, then a + c > b + c.*

However, it is important not to attribute too much to these kindergartners. The children are playing a card game that involves the numbers 1 through 6. They determine who gets to say "me" by combining the number of pictured objects when they each turn over two cards. We do not know if the children have a conception of numbers greater than 6, whether they think about the operation of addition, or whether the ideas they are discussing apply to contexts outside of the card game.

Yet as this vignette illustrates, teachers can invite even young children to talk about the general ideas implicit in their actions. Consider Seyferth's moves: First, she noticed that some of the children were playing the game in a way that indicated they may have been acting on a general principle or rule they had noticed but had not articulated. Next, she decided to bring this to the attention of the whole class during discussion. Then she asked her students to explain their rule and why it worked by suggesting additional examples for them to consider. Finally, she posed the question, "Does this rule work for just a few examples or does it apply more generally?"

This discussion provided the students, who had been acting on an unstated rule, the opportunity to express their thinking in words and to begin to see what kinds of examples the rule applies to and why it works. Furthermore, students who had not noticed the regularity were given a demonstration that this kind of thinking—looking across examples for general principles—is part of mathematics class routine. By posing the question "Does this work only for 6?" the teacher brought into her classroom the practice of asking, "Will it always work?"

As the year progressed, Seyferth continued to look for opportunities to encourage her students to think about general principles. For example[4], when she laid out a set of 8 checkers for a counting exercise—3 red and 5 black—she asked, "Does it matter if we count the red checkers first and then the black, or start with the black and then count the red?" When her students agreed that it didn't matter in what order you counted, as long as you didn't take any away or add any more in, she pushed the class to be clear about the claim they were making, asking, "Is this true only about checkers, or does it work if we have 3 yellow teddies and 5 blue teddies? Is this something special about the number 8, or would it work with other numbers?" Even though children are still learning to count, discussions like these lay the foundation for understanding the logic of the operations. Thus, the children will soon be working with the operation of addition. Just as the insights from double compare can be called on as students compare sums, the corresponding question about counting checkers might be "Does it matter if we add the red checkers first and then the black, or if we start with black and then red?" That is, they are laying the foundation for articulating the commutative property of addition, $a + b = b + a$.

---

4. This example is drawn from a case that appears in Schifter, Bastable, and Russell (2008a, pp. 54–56).

Fourth Graders as Algebraic Thinkers: Subtracting Less Results in More[5]

As part of her morning routine, Margie Riddle had given her fourth-grade students some subtraction problems. Included among them were 145 – 100 and 145 – 98. As the children began to consider the latter problem, Riddle realized that here was an opening that held much potential for learning, and so she deferred further discussion until the math lesson later in the day.

What Riddle had seen was this: Many of the children realized there was a connection between the two problems. However, after calculating 145 – 100 = 45 but *before* actually solving 145 – 98 = ?, they weren't sure if the answer to the second problem would turn out to be 2 more or 2 less than 45. Once they did solve it and knew the answer was 47, they wondered why it was 2 *more*. After all, when they changed 100 to 98, they *subtracted* 2, so why *add* 2 to get the right result? Their puzzlement, Riddle believed, could lead her students to a deeper appreciation of the meaning of the operation of subtraction.

When the class returned to this question later that day, Riddle's students began, as was their habit, by sharing a variety of ways to calculate 145 – 98. But at a certain point in their discussion, Brian insisted on explaining his thinking to his classmates. He struggled to find the words. "It goes with the problem before," he declared. "It's like you've got this big thing to take away, and then you have a littler thing to take away, so you have more. Can I draw a picture?" He went up to the chalkboard, thought for a while, and then drew a blob (see fig. 19.1).

The Whole Thing

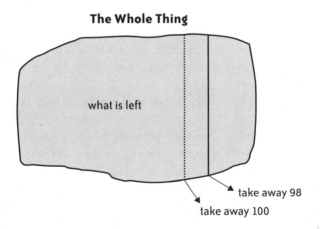

Fig. 19.1. Brian's diagram comparing 145 – 100 and 145 – 98

---

5. This case is drawn from one that appears in Schifter, Bastable, and Russell (2008a, pp. 45–47).

Riddle described what happened next. "Brian's classmates were watching and listening fairly intently, and suddenly, inspired by his presentation, Rebecca said excitedly, 'Yeah, it's like you have this big hunk of bread and you can take a tiny bite or a bigger bite. If you take away smaller you end up with bigger.'" Riddle asked if she thought this would always be true, and Rebecca said, "I think so." Up to this point Max had been quiet. But now, inspired in turn by Brian's picture and Rebecca's explanation, he carried the unfolding line of thinking even further.

"Yeah," he said, "the less you subtract, the more you end up with. And," he continued with great emphasis, "the thing you end up with is exactly as much larger as the amount less that you subtracted."

Max's insight, translated into algebraic notation, would be $a - (b - x) = (a - b) + x$, where a, b, and x are positive numbers and $a > b > x$. Referring back to the diagram, when the strip between the dotted line and the solid line (x) is subtracted from the region to the right of the dotted line (b), it is joined to the region to the left of the dotted line ($a - b$). However, it is not the notation, but the *generalization*, that is, the *idea* expressed by this equation, that qualifies this fourth-grade discussion as algebraic.

Consider how the teacher moves through this episode. By posing the related problems ($145 - 100 = ?$ and $145 - 98 = ?$), Riddle had created a situation in which her students, while working on a subtraction exercise, could notice a deep feature of the operation of subtraction itself. As she listened to her students' expressions of puzzlement, she decided to center her next mathematics lesson on their confusion.

Already established in this classroom was the practice of representing a mathematical situation with such aids to thinking as diagrams, story contexts, or manipulatives. So when Brian offered a diagram of the problem situation, other students were ready to seize on it to articulate their own thoughts. Riddle picked up on their thinking to get at a general principle and asked, "Rebecca, do you think this is always true?"

The work of generalizing and justifying in the elementary school classroom has the potential for enhancing the learning of *all* students. Teachers with whom we have collaborated have realized this potential in their classrooms (Schweitzer 2006). They report to us that students who tend to have difficulty in mathematics become stronger mathematical thinkers through this work. As one teacher wrote, "When I began to work on generalizations with my students, I noticed a shift in my less capable learners. Things seemed more accessible to them." When generalizations are made explicit—in natural language or through spatial representations used to justify them—they become accessible to more students and can become the foundation for greater computational fluency. Furthermore, the disposition to create a representation when a mathematical question arises supports students in reasoning through their confusions. Brian, who Riddle later explained was a tentative learner in mathematics, created the representation that illuminated an important idea for the whole class.

At the same time, students who generally outperform their peers in mathematics find this content challenging and stimulating. For them, the study of number and operations can extend beyond efficient computation to the excitement of making and proving conjectures about mathematical relationships that apply to infinite classes of numbers. As one teacher explained, "Students develop a habit of mind of looking beyond the activity to search for something more, some broader mathematical context to fit the experience into." Max, one of the most mathematically successful students in Riddle's class, listened carefully to his classmates and then enjoyed the challenge of formulating a precise statement of the generalization.

Teachers as Algebraic Thinkers: Algebra as an Expression of Ideas

To encourage algebraic thinking among their students, teachers must recognize the importance of discussing mathematical generalizations. And so, self-evidently, must they be capable of noticing when students' actions and observations broach such. Furthermore, they must have a sense of the kinds of problems or questions likely to stretch students' thinking, and they must be able to steer students' discussion in productive directions. Studying cases that describe classroom episodes—like those written by Lisa Seyferth and Margie Riddle, from which the examples presented above were drawn—can be one mechanism by which teachers can begin to develop these skills.

But it is also important for elementary school teachers to understand more deeply the mathematics content their students will encounter as they pass *beyond* the elementary grades. What may not be as obvious is that these cases of elementary school classrooms can provide rich contexts for such understanding: Rather than (re-)encountering algebraic manipulation as syntax devoid of meaning, teachers here learn to use algebraic notation to represent *ideas*.

In our work with elementary school teachers, we frequently ask them about their prior experience with algebra. Generally, their responses fall into one of two categories: some (1) never understood the purpose of algebraic notation and generally felt hopelessly lost, and these report that the mere sight of algebraic notation makes their stomachs clench; for others (2), their study of algebra was pleasurable because it felt like a puzzle to them, and they were adept at finding solutions. But in neither instance do these teachers say they looked for meaning in the algebra problems they worked on. Thus, for all of them, to begin with an idea that may be expressed in natural language or for which they can offer examples, and then *represent it using algebraic notation,* is a large and novel step.

Teachers Discuss the Kindergarten Case

The following scene[6] is drawn from a teachers' seminar in which participants were working from Lisa Seyferth's case. The session began with attempts to state in English the rule underlying her kindergartners' actions in the double compare exercise.

> Antonia started the group off with the suggestion, "If two cards are the same and two cards are different, then the one with the larger of the different numbers says 'me.'"
>
> Taking a moment to think, Madelyn expressed doubt about Antonia's generalization. "I don't know if this is too picky or not—but what if one person has the two numbers that are the same? Like, what if one person has 5 and 5, and the other person has 6 and 2? It satisfies the conditions, but it's wrong. The person who has 6 doesn't win."
>
> M'Leah suggested rewording Antonia's statement: "If each person has two cards, and one of the cards each person has is the same, then the person with the higher different card says 'me.'" Madelyn said this wording worked for her, and others nodded.
>
> Lorraine offered a different version. "A number plus a big number is more than a number plus a small number." The group then talked about some of the assumptions in this statement. Lorraine says "a number" twice, but it must be the same number. And when she says "a big number" and "a small number," she means in relation to one another. For example, if you have the cards 5, 3 and 5, 1, then 3 is the big number, even though it isn't the biggest number in the two hands. In this instance, it's called the big number because it's compared to 1. And if you have the cards 2, 3 and 2, 6, then 3 is the small number, even though it isn't the smallest number in the two hands. Here, the 3 is small because it's compared to 6.

The teachers were struck by how difficult it was to state the generalization in English without ambiguity. But rather than push for a less ambiguous version, the facilitator chose to compare the two statements that had been offered.

- If each person has two cards, and one of the cards each person has is the same, then the person with the higher different card says, "Me."

- A number plus a big number is more than a number plus a small number.

6. This vignette, drawn from a component of the facilitator's guide of *Reasoning Algebraically about Operations* (Schifter, Bastable, and Russell 2008b, pp. 54–58), is a composite derived from field notes taken while piloting. Teachers' names are pseudonyms.

As the teachers discussed the differences between the two statements, two major points emerged: (1) one statement was about cards, the other about numbers; (2) only one statement was about the operation of addition.

This is a very important issue to keep in mind when working with children. It might *seem* that students grasp a generalization, but when confronted with the same mathematical idea in a different context, they fail to recognize it. Thus, the generalization the kindergartners are working on might not extend beyond the card game.

In this session, one teacher observed, "The same thing comes up in older grades, too. You work on an idea in one context, and you think the idea is really solid for the kids, but when you change the context, you realize the idea has disappeared."

The facilitator now objected that the idea might still be present. "Rather," she said, "the idea they had in the first place was not as general as you thought. But the idea they had, confined to the original context, is likely to still be there, and it's something you can draw on as you work to help them understand the more general idea. Indeed, this is precisely why it's important to have discussions about these ideas. By articulating them, making them part of the shared knowledge of the class, you can refer to them in future discussions. You can ask, 'Do you remember when we talked about such-and-such? Is that anything like what we are discussing now?'" Having considered the *idea* the kindergartners were working on, the teachers were ready to represent it with algebraic notation. Grace presented her version first:

$$a + (> b) > a + (< b).$$

She explained, "I wasn't really sure how to write it, but I decided to take a stab at it. If you add to a some number larger than b, the sum will be more than if you add to a some number smaller than b. That's what I was trying to write." Similar to children who invent their own spelling as they learn to write, so, too, did Grace invent her own notation in her attempt to express the idea under discussion. Now she and her classmates had the opportunity to see which aspects of her statement did not observe the generally accepted conventions, and to write a statement that did.

The facilitator explained to Grace, "Even though I can see what you mean, mathematicians don't write '$> b$' to mean some number greater than b. They might write '$x > b$,' which means that x is some number greater than b."

Then another teacher, Mishal, offered two ways to state the generalization. "You've got three numbers, a, b, and c. You can write, 'If $a > b$, then $a + c > b + c$.' And you can write, 'If $a > b$, then $c + a > c + b$.'"

Risa said that the second line looks just like the second of our statements: "A number plus a big number is more than a number plus a small number." Denise pointed out that it's much easier to read the algebraic notation. "You don't have to go through all the talk we did about what 'a number' and 'big number' and 'small number' mean." Leeann said that algebraic notation is easier only if you already know how to read it. "Right now, I still need the English to help me."

Although the algebraic statements that were now before the seminar were correct, the facilitator recognized that there was more for the teachers to think about. She asked participants to go in the other direction, to look at the algebraic notation with particular numbers in mind. "What if we had these cards: 4, 2 and 4, 3? What are the values of a, b, and c?" June answered, "c is 4, b is 2, a is 3." The seminar group worked through several possible sets of cards without difficulty until they came to 3, 3 and 5, 3. At this point, there was some confusion—there were too many 3s! Denise, who was already quite fluent with algebraic notation, pointed out that this didn't matter; a is 5, and b and c can both be 3. The facilitator had the group go back to the English language versions of the generalization to see if they covered this instance. Once the group was satisfied they did, the teachers returned to the algebraic notation. The facilitator explained that when c appears twice, it must refer to the same number in both places. But if different letters are used, the numbers they stand for do not need to be different.

Finally, the facilitator asked about 4, 2 and 6, 3. Everyone was pretty clear that this example wasn't covered by the generalization they were working with because all four numbers are different. But Madelyn pointed out that they could write a statement that covered this instance: If $a > b$ and $c > d$, then $a + c > b + d$.

Teachers Discuss the Fourth-Grade Case[7]

Although the teachers found it a challenge to articulate precisely the generalization implicit in the kindergartners' work, they began with a strong sense of the nature of the idea. However, when they read Margie Riddle's case, they needed to work hard to get hold of the idea those fourth graders were working on.

> Kaneesha said, "I can look at Brian's picture, but at first I wasn't sure I got it. It really took Rebecca's comment about the bread to help me see it. If you have a hunk of bread and take a small bite, you end up with more than if you take a large bite."
>
> Jorge agreed that it was Rebecca's image that helped him. "When she puts it like that," Jorge said, "it's so clear what's happening with the numbers. Whenever you see a subtraction problem, you can think about breaking off a hunk of bread. If you take less, you leave more. Wow."
>
> Risa said that it was easier for her to see the relationship on the number line than in Brian's blob (see fig. 19.2).

---

7. This vignette, drawn from a component of the facilitator's guide of Reasoning Algebraically about Operations (Schifter, Bastable, and Russell 2008b, pp. 64–66), is a composite derived from field notes taken while piloting.

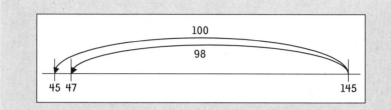

Fig. 19.2. Risa's number line representing subtraction as movement to the left

Risa explained, "If you start at 145 and go back 100, you end up farther to the left than if you go back 98."
Charlotte said she saw subtraction as distance between two numbers. "When you look at the number line, you can see the distance between 98 and 145 is greater than the distance between 100 and 145. So 145 – 98 is more than 145 – 100" (see fig. 19.3).

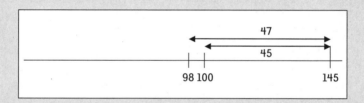

Fig. 19.3. Charlotte's number line representing subtraction as distance between two points

Next the facilitator asked the class which of the two representations they preferred, Risa's or Charlotte's, and it seemed that everyone had a preference. Then she challenged the teachers to spend a few minutes making sense of the representation they had not favored.

The facilitator asked both Risa and Charlotte if they could change their representations to illustrate the generalization. Risa said, "Sure, all I have to do is erase the numbers. I can start at any place—that's the number I'm subtracting from. If I jump back more, I end up further to the left than if I jump back less."

Charlotte looked at her number line for a while and then said it works for hers, too. "Like Risa did, fix the number you're subtracting from. If you start at a smaller number, you have to go farther to reach your destination than if you start at a larger one."

Each participant changed her representation: "a" replaced 145, "b" replaced 100, and "$b - x$" replaced 98 (see fig. 19.4).

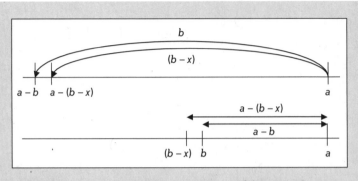

Fig. 19.4. Two number-line representations of the generalization,
$a - (b - x) = (a - b) + x$

When the facilitator asked for a representation of the statement with algebraic notation, Mishal suggested, "If $a - b = c$, then $a - (b - x) = c + x$." Since the teachers had explained that once an algebraic statement was made it helped to translate it back into specific numbers, the facilitator gave them two sets of numbers to test. "What if $a = 75$, $b = 25$, and $x = 3$? If $a = 149$, $b = 18$, and $x = 10$?"

Once the teachers were confident that they understood Mishal's statement, the facilitator suggested another way to represent the same idea. "Mishal's way of writing out the idea is correct, but it's also possible to write it as a single equation: $a - (b - x) = (a - b) + x$."

Then she explained, "I understand that algebraic notation can become pretty terse. When we see the idea written out this way, what we need to understand is that the expression $(a - b)$ represents at once the operation of subtraction, $a - b$, and the single number that results from the act of subtraction. Mishal used 'c' to represent that single number."

This was not the first time that the facilitator introduced the idea of the duality in the notation. Earlier, when working on a case where students discussed what happens to a sum when 1 is added to one addend, the teachers represented this idea as, If $a + b = c$, then $(a + 1) + b = c + 1$. The facilitator suggested this same idea can be written as $(a + 1) + b = (a + b) + 1$, and explained that $(a + b)$ at once represents the operation of addition, $a + b$, and the resulting sum.

Grace commented, "You know, in kindergarten, children think of $4 + 2$ as simply $4 + 2$; we need to teach them that when we think about the total, we say that it's 6: $4 + 2 = 6$. It feels like there's something connected here with the algebraic notation, but it's backwards. We don't need to specify the total with a single symbol. It's enough to leave it as $a + b$."

Returning to discussion of the Riddle's case, Denise came to the board to explain her way of thinking about the equation. As she wrote, she said, "When I took algebra in high school, I learned to distribute the subtraction sign, like this: $a - (b - x) = a - b - (-x)$."

Denise continued, "We also learned $-(-x) = x$. So you get this equation: $a - (b - x) = a - b - (-x) = a - b + x$."

She concluded, pointing to where the facilitator had written $a - (b - x) = (a - b) + x$, "And that's how you get to this. The thing is, now I'm looking at that same equation with a completely different sense of what it means. I don't have to think about distributing the subtraction sign, and I don't need to think about $- (-x)$. It feels really different to think, the less you subtract, the greater the result. *That's* what the equation says."

The facilitator specified more precisely, "That's what the equation says as long as x is a positive number. We'll soon extend the domain of number to integers, and then we'll need to look back at this statement."

This seminar session was designed to achieve a number of purposes and to that end the two cases were being considered together.[8] First, teachers worked to understand the ideas of the students in the terms the students themselves use. Next, they analyzed the idea implicit in the kindergartners' card-game strategy and considered different levels of generality of that idea—from a claim that applied only to this particular card game to a claim about the operation of addition itself. In order to understand more deeply the idea the fourth graders were working on, the teachers carefully read the students' discussion and then represented the same ideas on a number line. Finally, the teachers worked to express these ideas in the language of algebra. This provided them with the opportunity to experience the power, precision, and economy of algebraic notation while, at the same time, becoming familiar with its conventions. After thinking through the *ideas*, they express them as algebraic identities or inequalities. In sum, the teachers have learned to use the notation meaningfully, and the conventions governing its syntax make sense.

Conclusion

Alarmed by the difficulty many secondary school students have learning algebra, policymakers have been led to consider introducing "early algebra" into the elementary grades. In the last decade, some researchers have taken on the challenge of investigating what early algebraic thinking might look like and how young students might engage in it. The authors of this paper, together with a group of elementary school teachers, have identified generalizations that arise quite naturally from students' work on number and operations and explored what happens when teachers make explicit these generalizations for their students to consider. They challenged

---

8. Omitted from the seminar vignettes presented in this paper are discussions of pedagogy.

their students with the questions "Will this work for all numbers?" and "How can we decide?" The kindergarten and fourth-grade cases presented in this article provide examples of how this work can be situated in elementary school classroom contexts. Teachers have found that consideration of such generalizations, especially when grounded in visual representations students can use to explain them, support the work of all their students, those who tend to struggle as well as those who tend to excel.

To realize such practices in the classroom will require teachers to learn much. To that end, we argue that, rather than enrolling elementary school teachers in a conventional high school or college algebra course, they should learn about algebra and its connections to arithmetic by working with mathematical ideas based in the grades K–5 classroom. This approach, which the authors have been developing over the past several years, allows teachers to internalize images of what it means to engage their students with algebraic ideas, identify those ideas that lead to fruitful exploration at different grades, and consider the kinds of tasks and questions likely to elicit them. At the same time, as this paper shows, teachers can learn how these ideas are expressed in algebraic notation. Working with grades K–5 cases supports teachers' attempts to learn algebra with meaning and to see algebra as a seamless strand that begins in kindergarten and extends into secondary school and beyond.

However, even strong teaching in elementary school will not by itself eliminate the difficulties secondary school students encounter in learning algebra. If secondary school teachers are to mine their students' deep understanding of the number system developed through exploration of early algebraic ideas in the elementary grades, they, too, will need to learn to teach algebra not only syntactically but also as an expression of ways of reasoning about how quantities can be decomposed and recombined under different operations.

REFERENCES

Ball, Deborah Loewenberg, and Hyman Bass. "Making Mathematics Reasonable in School." In *A Research Companion to "Principles and Standards for School Mathematics,"* edited by Jeremy Kilpatrick, W. Gary Martin, and Deborah Schifter, pp. 27–44. Reston, Va.: National Council of Teachers of Mathematics, 2003.

Bastable, Virginia, and Deborah Schifter. "Classroom Stories: Examples of Elementary Students Engaged in Early Algebra." In *Algebra in the Early Grades,* edited by James Kaput, Maria Blanton, and David Carraher. Mahwah, N.J.: Lawrence Erlbaum Associates, 2007.

Carpenter, Thomas P., Megan Franke, and Linda Levi. *Thinking Mathematically.* Portsmouth, N.H.: Heinemann Educational Books, 2003.

Carraher, David, Barbara Brizuela, and Analucia Schliemann. "Bringing Out the Algebraic Character of Arithmetic: Instantiating Variables in Addition and Subtraction." In

Proceedings of the 24th Conference of the International Group for the Psychology of Mathematics Education, vol. 2, edited by Te Nakahara and Me Koyama, pp. 145–51. Hiroshima, Japan: Hiroshima University, 2000.

Kaput, James. "Teaching and Learning a New Algebra." In *Mathematics Classrooms That Promote Understanding,* edited by Elizabeth Fennema and Thomas A. Romberg, pp. 133–55. Mahwah, N.J.: Lawrence Erlbaum Associates, 1999.

Kaput, James, and Maria Blanton. "Algebraic Reasoning in the Context of Elementary Mathematics: Making It Implementable on a Massive Scale." Paper given at the annual meeting of the American Educational Research Association, Montreal, April 1999.

Schifter, Deborah. "Proof in the Elementary Grades." In *The Teaching and Learning of Proof across the Grades,* edited by Despina A. Stylianou, Maria Blanton, and Eric Knuth, in preparation.

———. "Reasoning about Operations: Early Algebraic Thinking, Grades K through 6." In *Mathematical Reasoning, Grades K–12,* 1999 Yearbook of the National Council of Teachers of Mathematics (NCTM), edited by Lee V. Stiff, pp. 62–81. Reston, Va.: NCTM, 1999.

Schifter, Deborah, Virginia Bastable, and Susan Jo Russell. *Reasoning Algebraically about Operations Casebook.* Parsippany, N.J.: Pearson Learning Group, 2008a.

———. *Reasoning Algebraically about Operations Facilitator's Guide.* Parsippany, N.J.: Pearson Learning Group, 2008b.

Schifter, Deborah, Stephen Monk, Susan Jo Russell, and Virginia Bastable. "Early Algebra: What Does Understanding the Laws of Arithmetic Mean in the Elementary Grades?" In *Algebra in the Early Grades,* edited by James Kaput, Maria Blanton, and David Carraher, pp. 413–47. Mahwah, N.J.: Lawrence Erlbaum Associates, 2007.

Schweitzer, Karen. "Teacher as Researcher: Research as a Partnership." In *Teachers Engaged in Research: Inquiry into Mathematics Practice, Grades Pre-K–2,* edited by Stephanie Z. Smith and Marvin Smith, pp. 69–94. Greenwich, Conn.: Information Age Publishing, 2006.

Smith, Erick. "Stasis and Change: Integrating Patterns, Functions, and Algebra throughout the K–12 Curriculum." In *A Research Companion to "Principles and Standards for School Mathematics,"* edited by Jeremy Kilpatrick, W. Gary Martin, and Deborah Schifter, pp. 136–50. Reston, Va.: National Council of Teachers of Mathematics, 2003.

TERC. *Investigations in Number, Data, and Space.* Chicago: Scott Foresman, 1998.

20

Exploring Generalization through Pictorial Growth Patterns

Esther Marie Huntzinger Billings

WHEN asking prospective and practicing elementary school teachers to describe algebraic thinking at the beginning of a university course or professional development workshop, both give similar, yet limited descriptions. They equate algebraic thinking with algebra, viewing it as a subject that requires solving equations, using variables, and learning or memorizing rules for manipulating expressions. This viewpoint is a "traditional image of algebra" (Kaput 1999). As Smith (2003) observes, the term *algebra* is typically equated with a study of symbol systems, whereas *algebraic thinking* is a broader term, used "to indicate the kinds of generalizing that precede or accompany the use of algebra" (p. 138).

The study of algebra as conceptualized by *Principles and Standards for School Mathematics* (National Council of Teachers of Mathematics 2000) focuses on algebraic thinking and "emphasizes relationships among quantities, including functions, ways of representing mathematical relationships, and the analysis of change" (p. 37). In thinking about algebra in the elementary grades, it is essential to focus on aspects of algebraic thinking, reflecting on how generalizing (Kaput 1999) and analyzing change (Smith 2003) lie at the heart of algebraic thinking.

Fostering algebraic thinking in elementary school classrooms establishes a firm foundation for students to draw on as they begin a formalized study of algebra in the later grades. Since elementary school teachers often believe they do not have time to explore algebraic thinking in their classrooms, my goal in professional development is to help teachers see how algebraic thinking can be infused into the curriculum without becoming a separate topic. Teachers require a personal understanding of what it means to think algebraically before they can promote algebraic understanding in their classrooms. They need multiple experiences analyzing change and identifying, representing, and generalizing relationships among variables.

In this article, four tasks will be described that involve pictorial growth patterns used with both prospective and practicing teachers to challenge them to think algebraically. Three tools to help teachers grow in their abilities to generalize relationships will be examined, and suggestions for promoting flexibility in the use of these tools will be given.

What Is a Pictorial Growth Pattern?

The swimming pool problem (Ferrini-Mundy, Lappan, and Phillips 1997) and the V-pattern, from the Mathematics in Context curriculum (National Center for Research in Mathematical Sciences and Freudenthal Institute 1998, p. 6), shown in figure 20.1, are examples of pictorial growth patterns, also called geometric patterns (NCTM 2000). A pictorial growth pattern is a sequence of figures in which the objects in the figure change from one term to the next, usually in a predictable way. A pictorial growth pattern typically involves two variables; some quantifiable aspect of this pictorial pattern of objects (the dependent variable) is coordinated with an indexing or counting system (the independent variable) that provides an identification of the position of the figure in the pattern. For example, in figure 20.1, the independent variable for both patterns is a counting sequence. Often, the dependent variable is the total number of some aspect of the figure, such as the total number of dots in the V-pattern or the total number of tiles in the Swimming Pool pattern. Other aspects of the pictorial growth pattern can be chosen for the dependent variable, such as the *number of border tiles* or the *number of pool tiles* in the Swimming Pool pattern.

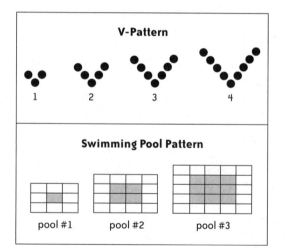

Fig. 20.1. Examples of pictorial growth patterns

Tools for Expressing Generalizations

Pictorial growth patterns are a rich context for exploring generalization, a major component of algebraic thinking (Kaput 1999). Teachers analyze, describe, and extend pictorial growth patterns with the ultimate goal of *generalizing* relationships in these patterns. Teachers can use many different tools to form generalizations, including the physical constructions of a pattern, algebraic symbols, and an explicit analysis of change.

Tool 1: The Physical Construction of a Pattern

A typical school approach for analyzing pictorial growth patterns is to translate a quantifiable aspect of the pictorial pattern into a number pattern and use the numerical data as a basis for analysis, thus adding an extra step of conversion into the process. By immediately translating the diagram to a numeric representation, one loses the opportunity to relate the numerical relationships directly to the context and to the physical construction of the pattern, and many crucial insights are lost (Orton, Orton, and Roper 1999). It stands to reason, then, that "a much more constructive approach [than immediate number conversion] is to ask students to build one element of the pattern physically and explain how it is put together, not in terms of number but in terms of its underlying physical structure" (Thornton 2001, p. 389). Students who analyze the physical structure or construction of a pictorial growth pattern often interpret the generalized relationship inherent in it. This focus on relationships among varying quantities can lead to a correct symbolic representation of the generalization (Orton, Orton, and Roper 1999; Thornton 2001).

The representation of a pictorial growth pattern is very useful in and of itself in promoting the analysis and generalization of relationships. I have introduced teachers to pictorial growth patterns using the Diamond-Dot task (Billings and Wells 2005) in figure 20.2, initially created for use in a teacher workshop exploring algebra concepts. This activity helps teachers to establish what constitutes a pictorial pattern and to intentionally use the physical construction of the pattern to analyze, extend, and generalize it. I discourage teachers from using numeric tables to analyze relationships between variables directly in pictorial growth patterns. After they can comfortably generalize a relationship directly from the physical construction of the pattern in a variety of contexts, we then explore and analyze the numeric representation of the pattern.

The first four questions of this activity encourage the teachers to directly examine the alignment of the dots in the pattern. By physically drawing the fourth diamond and by determining whether the figure in Question 2 fits into the pattern further in the sequence, the teachers need to analyze the diamond's dot construction. For example, some teachers claimed that the given diamond fit the pattern because "it has the correct number of dots for the sixth diamond" or "it fits because it is the sixth diamond rotated clockwise 90 degrees." Others suggested that it did not fit the pattern because "the extra dots aren't properly placed around the center square" but agreed that if they rotated the diamond so that the two extra dots stick out from the right and left of the square (rather than top and bottom), it would represent the

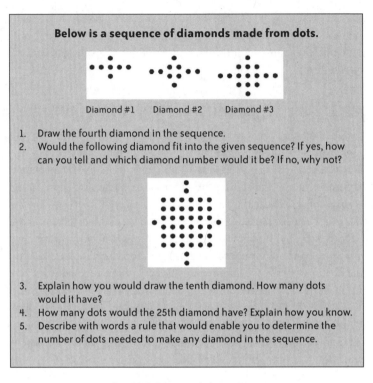

Below is a sequence of diamonds made from dots.

Diamond #1   Diamond #2   Diamond #3

1. Draw the fourth diamond in the sequence.
2. Would the following diamond fit into the given sequence? If yes, how can you tell and which diamond number would it be? If no, why not?

3. Explain how you would draw the tenth diamond. How many dots would it have?
4. How many dots would the 25th diamond have? Explain how you know.
5. Describe with words a rule that would enable you to determine the number of dots needed to make any diamond in the sequence.

Fig. 20.2. Diamond-dot pattern

sixth diamond. Although they initially disagreed, this type of discussion helped the teachers clarify what constitutes a pattern; the number as well as the direction and placement of the dots is crucial for continuing the pattern. By explaining *how* to draw the *n*th diamond in Question 3, teachers must extend the pattern and once again examine the physical construction of the figure. Thus, it is natural for teachers to continue using the physical construction of the pattern to predict that there are 631 dots in the 25th diamond (Question 4). One teacher explained:

> You make a 25 by 25 square of dots, which gives you 625 dots, and then add 6 to that to get 631 dots. The 6 comes from the 4 dots sticking out on the right and left of the square, two on each side, plus two more for the one dot on the top and one dot on the bottom of the square.

Through this extending process, the teachers shifted their focus to analyzing the relationship between the diamond number and the number of dots needed to make this diamond. Because they spent time analyzing the physical construction of the figures, they could identify the parts of the figure that stay the same from one diamond to the next (the six dots placed around the center square) and the parts of the diamond that change (the size of the center square made from an array of dots).

They then used this information to state a generalization for determining the number of dots in any diamond in the sequence.

Tool 2: Algebraic Symbols

Competence in algebra assumes facility with certain symbolic notation systems, including the use of symbols to record ideas and provide insights into mathematical situations. The use of algebraic symbols to represent and analyze mathematical situations is one of the four primary components of the Algebra Standard (NCTM 2000). Variables, expressions, and equations become shorthand tools for describing the relationships that emerge as teachers analyze, extend, and generalize pictorial growth patterns (Smith 2003).

Teachers should first verbalize generalizations, since representing a relationship with words is often easier than finding a symbolic generalization for this same relationship (English and Warren 1998). Articulating the generalization verbally builds a foundation for constructing a symbolic representation.

The pile growth pattern activity (fig. 20.3), adapted from materials developed through the Michigan Mathematics Middle School Reform project (Tucher et al. 2003) provides a context for using algebraic symbols as tools. In this activity, teachers are given a pattern that does not start with the first figure, and they need to determine what initial figures in this pattern look like. Next, they are asked to extend and analyze the pattern and then determine a general rule for describing the growth pattern, expressing this rule verbally and symbolically. As teachers find additional rules to describe the relationship and compare these rules, they build an informal understanding of the simplification and equivalence of expressions.

Asking "Backwards" Questions

Asking "backwards" questions provides opportunities for teachers to think more flexibly about ways to create, interpret, and represent generalizations. Backwards questions are questions that reverse the focus of the task; they may require the problem solver to begin analyzing a situation from a different starting point than the problem solver is used to or to make connections among representations or tools in different orders. Asking teachers backwards questions encourages them to continue to think about the patterns and generalizations inherent in these patterns from multiple perspectives. For example, the first question of the pile growth pattern is a backwards question. As well as analyzing how the piles continue to grow larger, teachers must also extend the pattern of piles in a backward direction to create smaller piles earlier in the sequence. This backwards question continues to challenge the teachers' understanding and facility to analyze a pictorial growth pattern using the physical construction of the figure.

To answer this backwards question, many teachers created the first pile (see fig. 20.4) by taking away tiles from pile 2 in the opposite manner in which they added

Examine the following pattern of "piles."

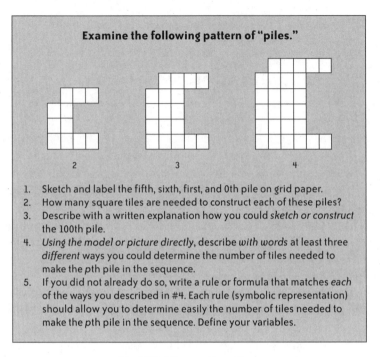

1. Sketch and label the fifth, sixth, first, and 0th pile on grid paper.
2. How many square tiles are needed to construct each of these piles?
3. Describe with a written explanation how you could *sketch or construct* the 100th pile.
4. *Using the model or picture directly*, describe *with words* at least three *different* ways you could determine the number of tiles needed to make the *p*th pile in the sequence.
5. If you did not already do so, write a rule or formula that matches *each* of the ways you described in #4. Each rule (symbolic representation) should allow you to determine easily the number of tiles needed to make the *p*th pile in the sequence. Define your variables.

Fig. 20.3. Pile growth pattern

tiles to pile 4 to build pile 5. However, they struggled to continue to reverse this mental process when removing tiles from pile 1 to create pile 0. Typically, teachers constructed pile 0 in one of the two ways found in figure 20.4. In both instances, the teachers used the physical construction of the pattern as a tool to create the 0th pile.

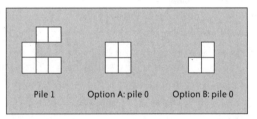

Fig. 20.4. Teachers' constructions of pile 1 and pile 0

Teachers who proposed option A often focused on the four tiles to the far right of each figure, identifying them as remaining constant. One teacher articulated, "There are always four extra tiles, so I kept the two on top and the two on bottom. To follow the pattern, there would be zero columns of tiles to the left of that." Teachers who proposed option B typically arrived at this visual representation by reasoning directly about the pattern instead of reversing their thinking; they extended the pattern to larger values for p (the pile number), found a generalization of the relationship based on the physical construction of the figures, and used this generalization to create the 0th pile. Since this was the strategy used by the majority of the teachers, we postponed our discussion of what the 0th pile looked like until after all teachers had ample opportunity to create their own generalizations. Teachers have occasionally suggested option B by reversing the construction process. For example, when analyzing consecutive terms in a backward direction, one teacher noted that the number of tiles in the leftmost column in the pile decreases by 1. She reasoned that since there are two tiles in the leftmost column of pile 1, there should be one tile in the leftmost column of the 0th pile. This teacher then observed that the number of columns in the piles also decreases by 1 between consecutive terms and reasoned that the 0th pile must have two columns of tiles. Likewise, the number of rows decreases by one, so the 0th pile must have two rows. Combining these observations, the teacher concluded that the pile would look like option B.

Using Algebraic Symbols as Tools to Represent a Generalization

As the teachers continued analyzing this pictorial growth pattern to answer questions 4 and 5, they partitioned the construction of a pile in different ways, which led to a variety of generalizations and rules. Figure 20.5 includes computer-generated versions illustrating the thinking behind six of the most common rules and sketches that emerged as teachers shared their rules in a large group discussion. Once again, the teachers needed time to explore *how* the pattern was physically constructed, observing how piles change and stay the same. As they extended the pattern and identified rules for predicting the total number of tiles needed for any pile, they naturally used symbols as a shorthand method for recording their generalizations.

As teachers shared their generalizations, we discussed how the generated symbolic rules recorded the *process* used to create the generalization. In order to establish an intentional record of how a generalization was derived, we did not simplify the rules. Often the rules were written in nonstandard forms. As each new rule and sketch was recorded on a whiteboard, we compared the process of partitioning the physical construction of the pile with the rule. For example, although all the expressions in figure 20.5 simplify to $p^2 + 2p + 3$, only one rule (b) illustrates how the pile may be visualized as a p by p square, with two rows of length p tiles and 3 "extra" tiles. As we discussed the many rules that emerged, teachers became more comfortable using variables and expressions to represent their generalizations. They could view the symbolic representation as a tool for recording a rule and the process used to construct it.

After establishing these different symbolic generalizations, teachers were encouraged to describe how they used their generalizations to create representations

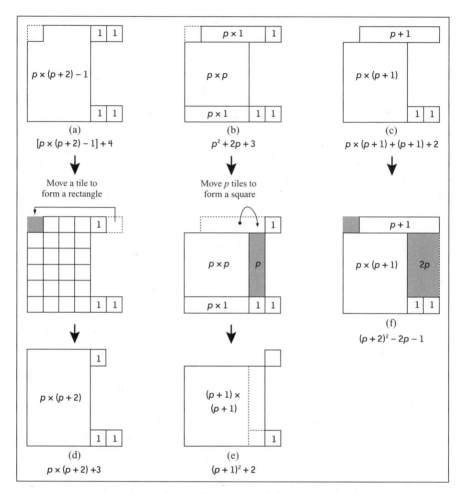

Fig. 20.5. Predicting the number of tiles in the pth pile

of the 0th pile. For example, one teacher explained why she thought the 0th pile looked like option B (see fig 20.4). "There is a 0 by 2 rectangle in the center but it has 0 tiles. I have three leftover tiles and put one on top, shifted over so it looks like the other piles, and the two below it." She viewed the construction of the pile as $3 + p \times (p + 2)$ (see fig. 20.5[d]). Another used the $p^2 + 2p + 3$ construction of the pile in figure 20.5(b) to justify why the 0th pile matches option B. He stated, "We have a 0 by 0 center square, a row of $0 + 1$ tiles on top of this square, and a row of $0 + 2$ tiles below it. Since there is no square, these two rows are squished together and we put the top row so that the upper left corner tile is missing." As we ended our discussion, the teachers ultimately concluded that option B (in fig. 20.4) was the most appropriate representation of the 0th pile because it matched the ways they had extended and generalized the relationship in this pattern.

Tool 3: An Explicit Analysis of Change

Analyzing change is a crucial aspect of thinking algebraically (NCTM 2000; Smith 2003) and is inherent to the process of analyzing, extending, and generalizing relationships found in pictorial growth patterns. However, teachers need an explicit awareness of how to identify and analyze change, and by isolating the analysis of change as a distinct tool, teachers are encouraged to intentionally reflect on change. They can then explicitly apply this knowledge as a tool for generalizing relationships.

Tasks like those found in figures 20.2 and 20.3 provide opportunities for teachers to analyze the change in a pattern by examining the physical construction of the figures; they analyze how the figures in the pattern physically change using two perspectives—how consecutive figures in a pictorial pattern change (a covariation analysis of change) and how aspects of the figure stay the same and change as the pattern continues. As teachers coordinate the figure number with the changing aspect of figure (a correspondence analysis of change), using the physical construction of the figures in the pattern to help guide this analysis, they are usually successful in generalizing the underlying relationship. In order to continue to extend teachers' abilities to analyze change, it is beneficial to ask teachers to engage in patterning tasks, such as the one found in figure 20.6, that encourage the creation of pictorial growth patterns. In Part 1 of this activity, only two figures of the pattern are given. As a result, there are numerous ways to extend the pattern. Item 1 encourages teachers to analyze change explicitly from a different perspective; they need to create their own pictorial growth pattern, using manipulative square tiles or grid paper, by systematically extending each term in the sequence.

Many teachers struggled as they extended the tile pattern. For example, some immediately began to construct tile #3 to "look like it will fit the pattern" *before* analyzing how the square tiles change between consecutive tile designs. However, since the teachers also needed to construct tiles #4 and #6, they typically reanalyzed their approaches, realizing the need to examine *how* and *if* the consecutive tile designs they created physically changed in predictable ways. Also, they began analyzing what stays the same and what changes between consecutive tile designs in their patterns. As teachers analyzed and constructed covariational and correspondence types of change, they could then construct a pictorial growth pattern.

Asking "Backwards" Questions to Develop Flexibility to Use Tools

Asking backwards questions, an idea described earlier in this article, challenges teachers to continue to grow in their abilities to use tools (physical constructions, algebraic symbols, and explicit analysis of change) flexibly to interpret and create generalizations. For example, Part I of the Make Your Own Tile activity (fig. 20. 6),

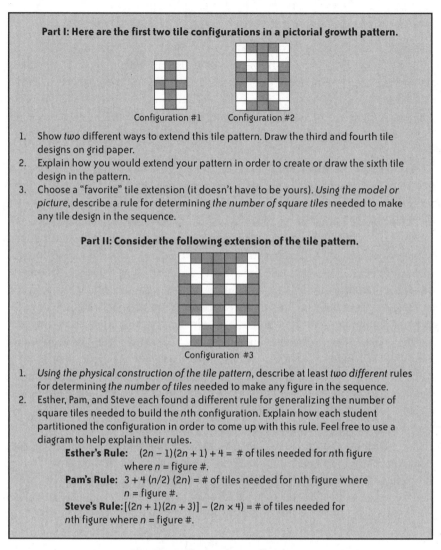

Part I: Here are the first two tile configurations in a pictorial growth pattern.

Configuration #1　　　　Configuration #2

1. Show *two* different ways to extend this tile pattern. Draw the third and fourth tile designs on grid paper.
2. Explain how you would extend your pattern in order to create or draw the sixth tile design in the pattern.
3. Choose a "favorite" tile extension (it doesn't have to be yours). *Using the model or picture*, describe a rule for determining *the number of square tiles* needed to make any tile design in the sequence.

Part II: Consider the following extension of the tile pattern.

Configuration #3

1. *Using the physical construction of the tile pattern*, describe at least *two different* rules for determining *the number of tiles* needed to make any figure in the sequence.
2. Esther, Pam, and Steve each found a different rule for generalizing the number of square tiles needed to build the nth configuration. Explain how each student partitioned the configuration in order to come up with this rule. Feel free to use a diagram to help explain their rules.

　　Esther's Rule:　$(2n - 1)(2n + 1) + 4 =$ # of tiles needed for nth figure where n = figure #.

　　Pam's Rule:　$3 + 4\,(n/2)\,(2n) =$ # of tiles needed for nth figure where n = figure #.

　　Steve's Rule:　$[(2n + 1)(2n + 3)] - (2n \times 4) =$ # of tiles needed for nth figure where n = figure #.

Fig. 20.6. Make your own tile pattern.

provides an opportunity for teachers to analyze change from a backwards perspective; instead of analyzing a given change, they *construct* change to extend a pattern systematically.

In Part II of this same tile activity, item 2 asks teachers to analyze the situation from a backwards perspective; start with the a symbolic rule and use this representation to design the physical construction that matches the rule. However, before the teachers are asked to make sense of given rules and connect these rules to the physical constructions of the patterns, they first need to create their own generalizations.

Teachers typically find generalizing the relationship in Part II, item 1 particularly challenging, since the figures grow in an "increasingly increasing" way. As teachers analyze change and use the physical construction of the figures to create generalizations, they can be encouraged to apply previously used strategies, like systematically rearranging the square tiles to create tile configurations that can be more easily generalized. Figure 20.7 illustrates how some teachers generalized the relationship between the tile number and the number of square tiles needed to construct the tile figure. As can be seen in figures 20.7a and 20.7b, teachers rearranged the tiles to create a square, ultimately leading to the generalization $(2n)^2 + 3$.

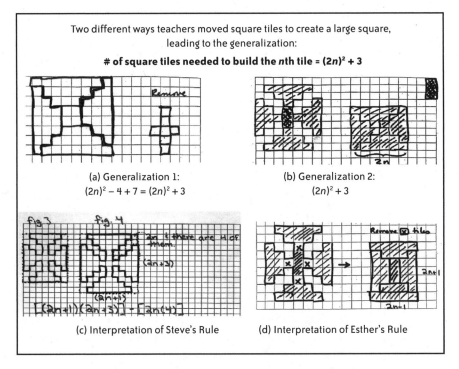

Two different ways teachers moved square tiles to create a large square, leading to the generalization:

# of square tiles needed to build the *n*th tile = $(2n)^2 + 3$

(a) Generalization 1:
$(2n)^2 - 4 + 7 = (2n)^2 + 3$

(b) Generalization 2:
$(2n)^2 + 3$

(c) Interpretation of Steve's Rule

(d) Interpretation of Esther's Rule

Fig. 20.7. Teachers' interpretation and creation of rules

One pair of teachers noticed that a "cross" made of seven tiles in the first figure is present in each of the subsequent figures in the pattern, and that identical arrangements of tiles can be found at the ends of each of the four "arms" of the cross. Since the cross remains fixed in each figure, they removed it and focused on the "changing aspect" of the figures, the configuration of the arms. They correctly observed that with each consecutive figure, an additional row of tiles, two tiles longer than the base row of the previous figure's arm, is added to the base of each arm. However, they could not coordinate the total number of tiles in the arm with the figure number. So, they color-coded each arm (to "see" that they had preserved the number of tiles in the figure) and rearranged the tiles to create a tile arrangement that can be indexed with the figure number and ultimately generalized. Eventually these two teachers found that by pushing the arms together, they could form a $2n \times 2n$ square that is missing four tiles in the center (see fig 20.7a). They then added seven tiles for the "cross" they had initially set aside, establishing the generalization of $(2n)^2 - 4 + 7$ tiles in the nth figure. Later they simplified the expression to $(2n)^2 + 3$.

Another pair of teachers also used a rearranging strategy to come up with this symbolic generalization. However, they partitioned the figure a bit differently. They separated each figure into a fixed center of three vertical tiles and four sets of "arms" (see. fig. 20.7b). After color-coding, they rearranged the arms to create a $2n \times 2n$ square. Essentially, this is the same square the first pair found, except that since each of these arms has a tip consisting of one tile, the four tips come together to fill in the interior of this $2n \times 2n$ square. Also, since they removed the center three tiles, they found the relationship $(2n)^2 + 3$ directly without needing to simplify their symbolic expression.

After creating their own generalizations, the teachers were ready (though reluctant) to answer item 2, a "backwards" question that reverses the order in which they must analyze the representations of the relationship in the pattern. Now, the starting points for analyses were the symbolic rules of Pam, Esther, and Steve. Teachers had to construct tile designs that would generate the students' rules. To solve the problems, the teachers often applied strategies they had previously found helpful for creating a generalization, such as the rearranging strategy that is useful for interpreting Pam's and Esther's rules. For example, in figure 20.7d, one teacher partitioned the figure into four arms in the same way as the teachers did for figure 20.7a, but kept three tiles fixed in the center and removed four tiles from the "cross." In order to construct Esther's rule, this teacher rearranged the four arms and center three tiles to form a $(2n + 1) \times (2n - 1)$ rectangle with four extra tiles.

However, a rearranging strategy does not always work, and interpreting Steve's rule encourages a different type of analysis of the physical construction of tile design. As the teachers analyzed this symbolic generalization, they typically separated the figure into two parts: $[(2n + 1) \times (2n + 3)]$ and $(2n \times 4)$. Some teachers focused their attention on the expression $(2n + 1) \times (2n + 3)$ and looked to see if a rectangle with these dimensions could be formed in the figure. Others focused on the expression $2n \times 4$ and determined if the quantity 4 is subtracted (or "left blank") $2n$ times or if the quantity $2n$ is subtracted four times some place in the figure. Regardless of where they began their analyses, these teachers eventually saw the tile figure encased within a larger rectangle in which four groups of $2n$ tiles have been removed (see fig. 20.7c).

Using Tools at a More Abstract Level

Teachers can extend their understanding of generalization to a more abstract level by exploring tasks such as the Undoing-Formulas task (see fig. 20.8). Once again, the typical order in which teachers make connections between the symbolic and pictorial representations is "backwards"; teachers start with a given symbolic representation of a relationship and then must physically construct a pictorial growth pattern that visually represents the rule. As part of this construction process, teachers must create and define variables and interpret how symbols can express a generalization of a relationship; they interpret change that is represented symbolically and then physically represent this change. It is imperative to encourage teachers to think of different ways to represent their rules pictorially so that the physical construction of the pattern clearly promotes the given symbolic rule. This approach of asking teachers backwards questions in which the teachers must engage in the construction process of creating a pictorial growth pattern not only deepens teachers' understanding of generalization and the flexible use of the tools but also encourages teachers to reanalyze the meanings of the operations and ways to represent them pictorially.

Here are four different "rules" for pictorial growth patterns.

Rule 1: $y = (3 \times n) + 2$

Rule 2: $y = [2 \times (n + 3)] - 1$

Rule 3: $y = [n \times (n + 1)] + (n - 1) + 2$

Rule 4: $y = (3 \times n) \times (n - 2)$

For each rule:

- Build at least three figures in a sequence that would lead to the rule. Make sure that the way the pattern is constructed lends itself to "seeing" this rule or generalization.

- Define or explain what n and y represent in your pattern.

- Write a description of the rule that would allow someone who has not seen your pattern or symbolic rule to re-create any figure in your pattern.

Fig. 20.8. Undoing-Formulas task

Initially, some teachers may tend to "plug in" values for n and draw that number of objects for each term in the sequence. Others strictly interpret the rules in terms of length, area, or volume and construct visual models accordingly. For example, in Rule 1, teachers may interpret $(3 \times n)$ as a rectangle with dimensions 3 by n, as 3 groups of n objects, or n groups of 3 objects (see fig. 20.9). Through an analysis of this rule, teachers can recognize that when a constant value is added or subtracted (in this instance, + 2), this part of the pattern should remain fixed from one figure to the next.

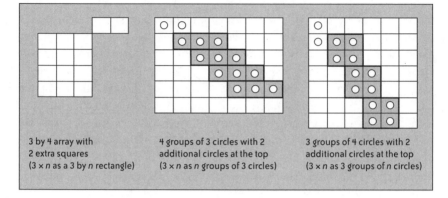

3 by 4 array with
2 extra squares
(3 × n as a 3 by n rectangle)

4 groups of 3 circles with 2
additional circles at the top
(3 × n as n groups of 3 circles)

3 groups of 4 circles with 2
additional circles at the top
(3 × n as 3 groups of n circles)

Fig. 20.9. Ways to represent y = (3 × n) + 2 pictorially when n = 4

Pulling It All Together: Teachers' Change in Thinking

As teachers study pictorial growth patterns, they should explicitly be asked to reflect on the mathematical concepts and tools they have learned in each activity and how they extend or connect to concepts previously studied. After repeated experiences and intentional reflection, teachers may grow to appreciate how these different types of tasks build up essential components of algebraic thinking. After reflecting on her experiences, one teacher wrote:

> At the beginning of the semester, the patterns were something that I had fun doing, but [I] didn't really see the importance [in] doing them to develop algebraic thinking. Algebra, to me, was something that I did in 8th grade, not in elementary school, where I first learned about the patterns. Slowly, I began to see how extending patterns can lead to an algebraic representation of the pattern in a way that even elementary students could understand when looking at a pictorial representation rather then a numeric representation. By looking at the pictorial representations of the pattern, extending, and generalizing it based on geometric representation, students can begin to actually see why the generalization of the pattern works.

Every time I explore pictorial growth patterns with teachers, I marvel that one setting can provide such a rich context for supporting algebraic thinking. The activities presented in this article are designed to deepen teachers' abilities to generalize as they explore relationships between two different variables in pictorial growth patterns. Using the physical construction of a pattern, analyzing how the terms in a sequence change, and using symbols to represent and communicate the generalization become useful tools for creating, interpreting, and representing generalizations. Answering "backwards questions" provides additional opportunities for teachers to develop facility using and making connections among these tools.

REFERENCES

Billings, Esther, and Pamela Wells. "Diamond-Dot Pattern." Task developed as part of a Building Mathematics Leaders, #050290-302, Title II Part A (3) Improving Teacher Quality Competitive Grant. Allendale, Mich.: Regional Math and Science Center, Grand Valley State University, 2004–05.

English, Lyn D., and Elizabeth A. Warren. "Introducing the Variable through Pattern Exploration." *Mathematics Teacher* 91 (February 1998): 166–70.

Ferrini-Mundy, Joan, Glenda Lappan, and Elizabeth Phillips. "Experiences with Patterning." *Teaching Children Mathematics* 3 (February 1997): 282–89.

Kaput, James J. "Teaching and Learning a New Algebra." In *Mathematics Classrooms That Promote Understanding,* edited by Elizabeth Fennema and Thomas A. Romberg, pp. 133–56. Mahwah, N.J.: Lawrence Erlbaum Associates, 1999.

National Center for Research in Mathematical Sciences and Freudenthal Institute. *Mathematics in Context: Patterns and Figures.* "V- and W- Formations," pp. 6–9. Chicago: Encyclopaedia Britannica Educational Corp., 1998.

National Council of Teachers of Mathematics (NCTM). *Principles and Standards for School Mathematics.* Reston, Va.: NCTM, 2000.

Orton, Anthony, Jean Orton, and Tom Roper. "Pictorial and Practical Contexts and the Perception of Pattern." In *Pattern in the Teaching and Learning of Mathematics,* edited by Anthony Orton, pp. 120–36. London: Cassell, 1999.

Smith, Eric. "Stasis and Change: Integrating Patterns, Functions, and Algebra throughout the K–12 Curriculum." In *A Research Companion to "Principles and Standards for School Mathematics,"* edited by Jeremy Kilpatrick, W. Gary Martin, and Deborah Schifter, pp. 136–50. Reston, Va.: National Council of Teachers of Mathematics, 2003.

Thornton, Stephen. "New Approaches to Algebra: Have We Missed the Point?" *Mathematics Teaching in the Middle School* 6 (March 2001): 388–92.

Tucher, Phil, Ruth Tsu, Barbara Shreve, and Carlos Cabana. "Pile Pattern Group Challenge." Activity from Michigan Middle School Mathematics Reform Project (National Science Foundation Grant No. ESI-9819466). Western Michigan University, 2003.

21

Analyzing Students' Work: A Context for Connecting and Extending Algebraic Knowledge for Teaching

Beth Herbel-Eisenmann
Elizabeth D. Phillips

The quality of mathematics teaching and learning depends on what teachers do with their students —and what teachers can do depends on their knowledge of mathematics.

—*Deborah Loewenberg Ball*

THE ACTIVITY described in this article highlights one way to develop teachers' pedagogical content knowledge (PCK). A major component of PCK is the ability (1) to anticipate and analyze what students understand or misunderstand in a particular content area (e.g., algebra) and (2) to have strategies available for addressing those talents and needs (Schoenfeld 2006). If teachers have a profound understanding of patterns of change between quantities, of multiple representations, and of how these ideas develop and connect to one another, it increases "the potential of making the process of learning algebra meaningful and effective" for students (Friedlander and Tabach 2001, p. 173).

A promising form of professional development (PD) for developing PCK is one that encourages groups of teachers to examine samples of students' work resulting from rich problem settings. This kind of PD has the potential to enhance teachers' mathematical and pedagogical understandings (Crockett 2001; Crespo 2000; Wilcox and Lanier 2000). Through examining students' work, teachers generate evidence for claims related to what they think students know. In the process they often find opportunities to reexamine their own knowledge. Such assessment can also allow for well-informed planning so that teachers can better assist students in developing their mathematical understandings.

In this article, we offer an example of a PD activity that includes analyzing a set of students' work on an eighth-grade algebra problem. First, we introduce the focus problem and briefly describe activities for teachers that can increase their awareness of students' algebraic understandings of patterns of change. Second, we offer a summary of teachers' insights about the students' solutions from our work with this activity in preservice and in-service teacher education. We contend that the mathematical content and processes teachers discuss allow them to deepen their understanding of both algebra and students' thinking. Third, we address how these insights provide opportunities for teachers to connect and extend their own algebraic knowledge for teaching and to explore some algebraic ideas in ways they had not considered previously. We conclude with implications of these insights for teachers' instructional decisions.

The Creating Patterns Problem

The problem and students' work originate from the PD project, the Michigan Algebra Initiative (MAI), funded from 1996 through 1998 by Michigan's Eisenhower Higher Education division. The learning activities that compose the PD materials were designed to help teachers think deeply about algebra and about students' algebraic reasoning. The activities were organized around the following four mathematical and pedagogical ideas: (1) patterns of change between two variables and their use as an organizing theme in the study of algebra; (2) the role of multiple representations in algebraic reasoning; (3) making instructional decisions by drawing on these algebraic ideas; and (4) the significance of using mathematical problems to develop students' conceptual knowledge of algebra. Several of the learning activities in the PD materials drew on sixteen algebra problems that were developed by MAI and field-tested with grade 8 students enrolled in several Michigan schools using the Connected Mathematics curriculum materials (CMP) (Lappan et al. 1998) and from several non-CMP grade 8 algebra classes.

We selected Creating Patterns (see fig. 21.1) for this article because it is a rich problem with interesting work by students. It offers teachers an opportunity to explore linear, exponential, and quadratic patterns of change. The focus on patterns of change associated with specific functions and the multiple representations associated with the patterns of change are crucial ideas in understanding functions. They also furnish a coherent way to think about algebra. The teachers with whom we have worked have found this problem both different from their prior algebraic experiences and somewhat challenging, especially the exponential and quadratic relationships. For a related PD experience from the MAI work that focuses on linear relationships, see Herbel-Eisenmann and Phillips (2005).

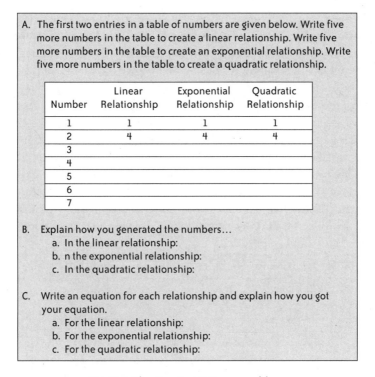

A. The first two entries in a table of numbers are given below. Write five more numbers in the table to create a linear relationship. Write five more numbers in the table to create an exponential relationship. Write five more numbers in the table to create a quadratic relationship.

Number	Linear Relationship	Exponential Relationship	Quadratic Relationship
1	1	1	1
2	4	4	4
3			
4			
5			
6			
7			

B. Explain how you generated the numbers...
  a. In the linear relationship:
  b. n the exponential relationship:
  c. In the quadratic relationship:

C. Write an equation for each relationship and explain how you got your equation.
  a. For the linear relationship:
  b. For the exponential relationship:
  c. For the quadratic relationship:

Fig. 21.1. The Creating Patterns problem

Getting Started: Solving the Problem

Like others who have developed materials to be used with teachers (Stein et al. 2000; Wilcox and Lanier 2000; Barnett and Ramirez 1996), we have found it important for teachers to solve the problem themselves before they examine students' work. Many teachers' experiences and perceptions of algebra involved a symbolic view of algebra that focused on solving equations and combining and simplifying expressions. Recognizing, representing, and reasoning about patterns of change associated with particular functions from a context, table, graph, or equation was new to some teachers. Thus many teachers needed time to make sense of the ideas and representations required to solve the problem. Some teachers struggled to generate a table of values, especially for the exponential and quadratic relationships. Working on the problem helped the teachers engage in the mathematical ideas and better prepared them to examine the students' work more carefully.

The teachers typically worked alone or in small groups first and then shared their strategies and reasoning with the entire group. Some teachers drew on information about linear, exponential, and quadratic functions to generate their tables. For example, they applied their knowledge of how two points on a line can be used to write a linear equation. Several used trial and error. Some anticipated that their students would approach the problems in ways similar to their own. If the teachers had prior experiences with patterns of change and multiple representations, they sometimes anticipated that their students might solve the problem in ways similar to those illustrated in the set of students' work we shared with them.

Each of these types of functions has a unique pattern of change. By "pattern of change" we mean that when the x-value in the table increases by 1 each time, the y-value increases or decreases by a unique pattern. For the linear function, the pattern of change is constant and additive. For the exponential, it is constant and multiplicative. The quadratic pattern of change can be characterized by constant successive second differences between y-values. For example, figure 21.2 shows the patterns of change for the Creating Patterns problem: the linear pattern of change is $+3$, the exponential pattern of change is $\times 4$, and the second difference of the quadratic relationship is $+2$.

Number	Linear Relationship		Exponential Relationship		Quadratic Relationship	First Difference	Second Difference
1	1		1		1		
		> +3		> ×4		> +3	> +2
2	4		4		4		
		> +3		> ×4		> +5	> +2
3	7		16		9		
		> +3		> ×4		> +7	> +2
4	10		64		16		
				> ×4		> +9	> +2
5	13		256		25		
				> ×4		> +11	> +2
6	16		1024		36		
				> ×4		> +13	
7	19		4096		49		
...	...		...		...		
Possible equation	$y = 3x - 2$		$y = 0.25(4^x)$		$y = x^2$		

Fig. 21.2. Patterns in linear, exponential, and quadratic functions

We used the following questions to guide the teachers' analysis of students' work:

- What are some mathematical goal(s) for the problem?
- How do students analyze the relationships?
- What understandings do students exhibit about patterns of change associated with different functions?
- What strategies do they use to identify a particular function, generate a table, or write an equation?
- What language do they use to refer to the mathematical objects and processes?
- What representations do the students use?
- How do they use the representations to solve the problem?

- What information about the context can be interpreted from a table, graph, or equation?

- What are the advantages and disadvantages of each representation?

- How thorough or clear are the responses?

- What other questions would I want to ask the student?

Learning by Looking Closely at Students' Work

After teachers had a chance to solve the problem and to share their insights, they examined the students' work carefully and articulated what they thought each student understood about the mathematics in the problem. By doing this, the teachers came to understand the mathematics and the students' thinking in more nuanced ways.

In the next few sections, we summarize the discussions we have had with teachers related to each part of the problem. Although the MAI materials include seven students' solutions to this problem, we focus on the three that tend to be most central to the teachers' discussions: Lucy, Marty, and Nancy (figs. 21.3, 21.4, and 21.5, respectively).

Most of Lucy's work was fairly typical in the sense that she solved the problem in ways similar to the other students whose work we do not discuss here. Her explanation of how she found the linear equation using linear patterns of change, however, attracted teachers' attention because typically they had not seen students reason this way. Marty's solution tended to become a focus because he was the only one to generate a different quadratic function pattern. Most students used a $y = x^2$ pattern to generate the quadratic table. Nancy's work was the most complete and articulate of the set of students' solutions. This may be the reason teachers tended to discuss her work in more detail than some of the other students. (More detail is given about teachers' discussions of the students' work in the following sections.)

Part A: Filling in the Tables

The teachers were surprised to see how students used ideas about patterns of change that were unique to each relationship to generate the patterns. Few teachers reported seeing their own students use first and second differences to find values in linear and quadratic tables. Some teachers who were not familiar with using patterns of change to analyze functions needed time to learn about patterns of change that characterize each function and how these changes are represented in tables, graphs, and equations. They learned that for linear functions, as the x-values increase by a constant amount, the first difference of successive y-values is constant. They pointed out that most students used the first difference, 3, to generate a table for the linear relationship. Likewise, they observed that for exponential functions, as the x-values increase by a constant amount, there is a constant ratio between

Number	Linear Relationship	Exponential Relationship	Quadratic Relationship
1	1	1	1
2	4	4	4
3	7	16	6
4	10	64	7
5	13	256	6
6	16	1024	4
7	19	4096	1

B. Explain how you generated the numbers

In the linear relationship:

1-4 is a difference of 3... go up by three.

In the quadratic relationship:

Climbs by 3, 2, 1 ... Drops by 1, 2...

SYMMETRICAL above and below 7

Creating Patterns

C. Write an equation for each relationship and explain how you got your equation.

For the linear relationship

$$Y = 1 + 3(X-1)$$

The table starts at 1, and goes up by 3 each time.

I tried 1+3X, but realized the X place was one too high, so I put X-1 instead of X to make it work.

For the exponential relationship

$$Y = 4(X-1)$$ Tried 4^X, for 1*4*4... but also needed X-1

Far as I got - 5/26/98

Fig. 21.3. Lucy's solution to the Creating Patterns problem

Number	Linear Relationship	Exponential Relationship	Quadratic Relationship
1	1	1	1
2	4	4	4
3	7	16	6
4	10	64	7
5	13	256	7
6	16	1024	6
7	19	4096	4
8	23	16384	1

B. Explain how you generated the numbers

In the linear relationship:

The linear relationship goes up by 3 each time the number Colume goes up one.

In the quadratic relationship:

you add three to the first number two to the second number 1 to the four and when you get to zero you start the opposite way

In the exponential relationship:

In exponential relationship you time the number by four to get the next number and then times that number by four So on.

C. Write an equation for each relationship and explain how you got your equation.

For the linear relationship

$3x - 2 + 3$ X = the number Column

3 = How much you add to get the next number

-2 = to get 1 on the number column the same as the table shown

For the exponential relationship

$4^x \times .25$ 4^x = the rate of change in the exponential colo.

.25 = 0 on the number Column

Fig. 21.4. Marty's solution to the Creating Patterns problem

A. The first two entries in a table of numbers are given below. Write five more numbers in the table to create a linear relationship. Write five more numbers in the table to create an exponential relationship. Write five more numbers in the table to create a quadratic relationship.

Number	Linear Relationship	Exponential Relationship	Quadratic Relationship
1	1	1	1
2	4	4	4
3	7	16	9
4	10	64	16
5	13	256	25
6	16	1024	36
7	19	4096	49

B. Explain how you generated the numbers

In the linear relationship:

Linear means there is a constant rate in the table, so since it went up by 3 from 1 to 4 (or x: 1 to 2), I made my slope 3. (See table)

In the exponential relationship:

There was a growth factor of 4 between 1 and 4, so I went from 4 to 16 (4^2) and 16 to 64 (4^3) (see table)

In the quadratic relationship: I made a 2nd difference of 2. (See table)

C. Write an equation for each relationship and explain how you got your equation.

For the linear relationship

$$y = 3x + {}^-2$$

Slope going up by 3 each time (See table)

y intercept at -2 (starting point)

(I took 3 the slope away from 1 to get the y-intercept) See Table

For the exponential relationship

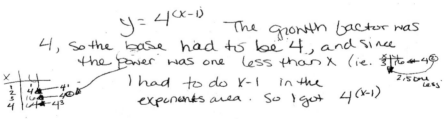

$$y = 4^{(x-1)}$$

The growth factor was 4, so the base had to be 4, and since the power was one less than x (ie. 3 to 4 2 is one less) I had to do x-1 in the exponents area. So I got $4^{(x-1)}$

For the quadratic relationship

$$y = x^2$$

Fig. 21.5. Nancy's solution to the Creating Patterns problem

successive values of y. Therefore, many students used a multiplicative factor of 4 to generate the table. The teachers noticed that the linear and exponential tables seemed relatively easy for students.

The teachers observed that the students' responses to the quadratic relationship were quite varied. They noticed that some students, like Nancy, recognized that the numbers could be perfect squares ($y = x^2$). They also pointed out that other students, like Marty, tried to use a pattern of change for quadratic functions; that is, they created a table in which the second differences were constant. Initially, all the teachers thought Marty's table for a quadratic relationship was incorrect. They thought this because most students used the commonly known pattern of perfect squares and the other two relationships had only one solution. So, they assumed that there was only one correct pattern for this relationship. In their exploration of Marty's solution, however, they found that his second differences were constant. This meant that Marty's solution was also correct.

Teachers observed that regardless of their correctness, many of the students' solutions for the quadratic pattern drew on the symmetric property for quadratic functions. For example, Lucy's incorrect response *increased* by 3, 2, 1, and then *decreased* by 1, 2, and 3. At first some teachers thought that Lucy was correct. It was not until the group looked at the first and second differences that they were convinced that Lucy's pattern was not quadratic. Some teachers did not know about the symmetric property, which prompted an extended discussion about symmetry. Other teachers illustrated the graph of the quadratic function to show it was symmetric around a line of reflection (or line of symmetry), that the line was perpendicular to the x-axis, and that it passed through a maximum or minimum point. Each point on the graph is symmetric to another point on the graph with respect to the line of symmetry: that is, $(x_1, a) < —— > (x_2, a)$, and this symmetry is reflected in the corresponding table of values. Although the particular student's increases or decreases were not all correct, the teachers thought that the students' work indicated a holistic sense of how the table should look with respect to the symmetric property.

Part B: Explaining How They Generated the Tables

The teachers noted that all the students provided correct explanations for the linear tables they generated. They also noted that the language students used in their explanations varied and that their language choices provided information about their understanding of tables. For example, some students recognized the constant additive relationship and described the table using recursive language, as in the following: "add the same number each time," "goes up at a constant rate," and "up by 3." Marty understood the constant additive relationship but went a step further to coordinate the x- and y-values in a functional manner by saying, "It goes up by 3 each time [the] number column goes up one" (see fig. 21.4). Nancy used the term *slope* when she described the table (see fig. 21.5). Some teachers observed that the students' language could offer valuable insights into their algebraic understanding. For example, they wondered if Nancy connected the rate of change she gave in the table to the slope of a line that would represent the data on a coordinate graph.

Teachers and students tend to use a range of language for mathematical ideas when they work with multiple representations. Students' choice of language can provide teachers with important insights into the layers of meaning students have constructed for ideas like slope and y-intercept (Herbel-Eisenmann 2002). Some groups of teachers discussed whether it was important for students to use complete sentences in their explanations (something that Lucy did not do) or whether the work should be judged by how well the students could communicate their thinking.

The teachers continued to see similar reasoning in how students created the table for exponential patterns. Most students saw the multiplicative relationship and described it as "multiply by the same number" or "times 4." Nancy was the only student to include the term *growth factor,* which was the term used in the curriculum materials (see fig. 21.5). The teachers also noticed that there was less consistency across the descriptions of the quadratic table. Some teachers observed that four of the students (including Lucy and Marty) may have tried to connect their responses to their perception of what the graph was supposed to look like. This holistic view of the graph, however, did not always translate into tables that reflected correct symmetry. The exception to this was Marty's work. The teachers assumed that Marty used the symmetry property to generate his unique correct table. However, they did note that he did not use symmetry or second differences in his explanation. Again, teachers identified a range of strategies in the students' explanations. Some students used first or second differences, whereas others explicitly described the pattern of perfect squares (e.g., "continued the pattern of x^2").

Part C: Writing Equations and Explaining Them

The teachers were intrigued by the reasoning that students brought to bear to the writing of equivalent equations for the linear relationship. As illustrated in figures 21.3–5, students wrote three different linear equations. The one that teachers seemed to be most interested in was Lucy's equation because the form she used does not usually arise in teachers' solutions. For the linear relationship, most students (and teachers) used the slope-intercept form of a linear equation, $y = mx + b$. They worked backward in the table to find the y-intercept $(0, b)$, which is $(0, -2)$. They recognized that the constant rate of change is the slope or the coefficient m of x in the equation. They used the y-intercept of -2 and the slope of 3 to write $y = -2 + 3x$. Some teachers had never been exposed to the process of using the rate of change to work backward in a table to find the y-intercept for an equation. In some situations this prompted a discussion of the relative merits of representing and connecting information in a situation to a table, equation, or graph.

By contrast, Lucy began with 1, the first x-value in the table, and noticed that the y-value "goes up by 3 each time." She used this information to write the expression $1 + 3x$ for y. When she checked her work, she observed that the values in the x column were shifted "one too high." She adjusted the equation to $y = 1 + 3(x - 1)$, which made "it work." Other students, like Marty, had the correct y-intercept for the linear relationship, but their explanations for getting the y-intercept were not clear.

Teachers made similar observations about students' equations for the exponential relationship. Some students wrote the correct equations, $y = 4^{x-1}$ or $y = 0.25 (4^x)$. To create the latter equation, teachers conjectured that students used the growth factor of 4 to work backward from the point $(1, 1)$, dividing 1 by 4 to get the y-intercept of $(0, 0.25)$. Some students wrote incorrect equations, the most popular being $y = 1(4^x)$. The teachers assumed this error was the result of those students thinking that 1 was the y-intercept, since it was the first entry in the table. One teacher did not know how to check to see if $y = 4^{x-1}$ and $y = (0.25)4^x$ were equivalent. Another teacher used the rules of exponents to convince herself that $(0.25)4^x = (1/4)4^x = (4^{-1})4^x = 4^{x-1}$.

For the quadratic equations, Marty was the only student to identify a correct pattern that was different from the function $y = x^2$. However, he did not write an equation. We reminded the teachers that the assessment was done under time constraints, so perhaps Marty ran out of time. The teachers pointed out that they did not have a complete picture of what he understood about the equation for this quadratic relationship. Most teachers were compelled to figure out the equation for Marty's data. Some teachers entered the table values into a graphing calculator and got the equation $y = -0.5x^2 + 4.5x + -3$ using quadratic regression. Another teacher entered the equation into her graphing calculator to see if the table was an exact match to Marty's. The issue of whether regression formulas generated by a graphing calculator gave a precise equation or not was not raised. One teacher who was involved in the MAI project reported that her students analyzed patterns in the table to find an equation. She reported that her students drew on a previous observation—that the constant rate of change was one-half the value of the coefficient of x^2 in the general quadratic equation, $y = ax^2 + bx + c$. They reasoned backward from the table to find the y-intercept c. Finally they found b by substituting values of one point into the equation and solving for b. As shown in figure 21.6, the teacher described how her students' process worked with Marty's table.

By examining the students' work, teachers became more aware of the mathematics embedded in the problem and the diversity of students' algebraic reasoning. Some teachers—particularly those who did not have strong mathematics backgrounds—did not know how the quadratic pattern of change was related to its equation. Some did not remember how to generate a quadratic equation given three points on the graph. Through their explorations and their solving of algebraic problems, teachers learned more mathematics. We observed that the teachers began to ask themselves questions like these:

| Marty's Quadratic Relationship | | | | Finding the Equation $y = ax^2 + bx + c$ |

x	y		
0	-3		
		> +4	> -1
1	1		
		> +3	> -1
2	4		
		> +2	> -1
3	6		
		> +1	> -1
4	7		
		> +0	> -1
5	7		
		> -1	> -1
6	6		
		> -2	> -1
7	4		
		> -3	
8	1		

a is half the finite difference

$a = -0.5$

$(0, -3)$ is the *y*-intercept

$c = -3$

$y = -0.5x^2 + bx - 3$

Substitute a point, say, $(1, 1)$ into the equation and solve for *b*.

$1 = -0.5(1) + b(1) - 3$

$b = 4.5$

$y = -0.5x^2 + 4.5x - 3$

Fig. 21.6. Solving for *a*, *b*, and *c*

- What are the variables in the problem and how are they related?
- Is the relationship linear? Exponential? Quadratic?
- What patterns in the problem suggest that it is linear? Nonlinear?
- How can I recognize the pattern if it is represented in a contextual problem, a table, a graph, or with an equation?
- How can tables, graphs, and equations of the relationships be used to pose and answer given questions?
- What information does an equivalent form of the equation provide?
- How can I use this information to solve the problem?

In the next section, we share more about the mathematical explorations in which the teachers engaged.

Pushing beyond the Students' Solutions: Teachers' Extended Mathematical Explorations

Many of the discussions of the students' solutions veered off into productive mathematical explorations where the teachers found themselves justifying, extending, and connecting their understandings of the mathematics in the problem. Some of these explorations were prompted by teachers' curiosity and some by the facilitator. For example, one group wanted to know more about the patterns of change for quadratic equations. After looking at several tables for quadratic relationships, the teachers—like the students in the MAI teacher's classroom mentioned in the previous section—observed that the coefficient for x^2 was one-half the value of the second difference. Some teachers wondered if this observation was true for all quadratic relationships. After exploring this idea, one group of teachers proposed an explanation. As shown in figure 21.7, they used the successive values x, $x + 1$, and $x + 2$ for x in the general quadratic expression, $ax^2 + bx + c$, and then proceeded to find the first and second differences for the quadratic expressions. The second difference was $2a$. Teachers who had a strong mathematics background found the connection to calculus interesting: the constant second difference is the second derivative of the quadratic function.

Value of x	Value of $ax^2 + bx + c$	First difference	Second difference
x_1	$ax_1^2 + bx_1 + c$		
		$a(2x+1)+b$	
$x_1 + 1$	$a(x_1+1)^2 + b(x_1+1) + c$		$2a$
		$a(2x+3)+b$	
$x_1 + 2$	$a(x_1+2)^2 + b(x_1+2) + c$		

Fig. 21.7. Showing that the second difference is 2a

Typically after a discussion like this, we raised a related question: Do other polynomial functions have unique patterns of change, or are they unique to linear and quadratic relationships? To answer this question, teachers started with the simplest first-, second-, third-, and fourth-degree polynomial functions, $y = x$, $y = x^2$, $y = x^3$, and $y = x^4$. They concluded that as the x-values increase by 1, in a cubic (third-degree polynomial function) the third differences of successive values of y were constant; in a fourth-degree polynomial function, the fourth differences of successive values of y were constant; and so on. All polynomial functions can be characterized by finite differences. In many of our discussions with teachers, we found that the use of finite differences to analyze patterns of change for polynomial functions was new to them.

In some of the discussions, teachers raised questions about how the patterns of change in the tables were represented in the graphs of the functions. They quickly saw how the changes in the x- and y-values in the table for linear and exponential functions were reflected in the ratios of the corresponding horizontal and vertical distances between two points on the graph. They found that for linear functions, this ratio was the slope; for exponential functions, it was the growth factor. The quadratic changes were more thought provoking. One group of teachers decided to start with a set of simple linear, exponential, and quadratic functions (like those shown in fig. 21.8) to explore how patterns of change are reflected in graphs.

These teachers observed that for quadratic functions, the ratio is equal to

$$\frac{y_2 - y_1}{1},$$

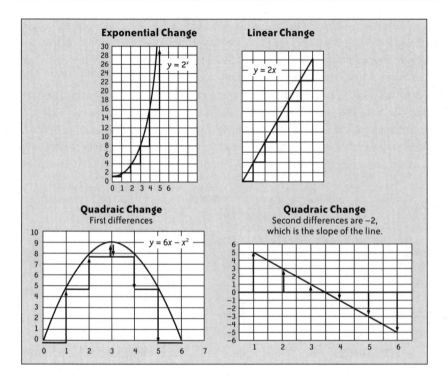

Fig. 21.8. Graphical representations of patterns of change

which is the first difference. These differences are represented by the vertical differences between two consecutive points. Furthermore, the differences between successive vertical differences can be arranged to form a line whose slope is equal to the second difference. Some teachers commented that the graphs provided a visual image of the patterns of change for each function. For example, for quadratic functions, the ratio increased and then decreased symmetrically or vice versa.

In one PD session a group of teachers became curious about the connections between this problem and calculus. The group diverged into a brief discussion of this topic. They learned how the ratio,

$$\frac{y_b - y_a}{x_b - x_a},$$

between any two points (x_b, y_b) and (x_a, y_a) on a graph of a function is called the average rate of change over the interval x_a to x_b. They talked about the limit of the ratio as the distance between x_a and x_b approaches zero, which is called the instantaneous rate of change at point x_a or the slope of the tangent line at x_a. In general, teachers were learning about the first derivative of the function at x_a. In a "time, distance, and rate" context, this ratio is also the instantaneous velocity at point x_a.

In another discussion, one teacher noted that all the equations for the linear relationship and for the exponential relationship were equivalent. She also thought there were more equations for the quadratic pattern than the two that appeared in the students' work. After a brief discussion, the teachers recalled that two points uniquely determine a line and hence its equation. They then drew a similar conclusion about the exponential pattern because two points uniquely determine the growth factor, or the b in the equation $y = a(b^x)$. Once the growth factor (or b) is determined, the value for a can be found by substituting one of the given points into the equation.

After some discussion, the teachers decided that two points are not sufficient to determine a unique quadratic pattern. The third point in the table is arbitrary. Once the third point is selected, then the second difference is determined and the succeeding values in the table can be found. Teachers concluded that three points are needed to find the constant second difference and the values of a, b, and c in $y = ax^2 + bx + c$. We have found that for many teachers, this problem is one of the first they encounter that focuses their attention on the fact that three points are needed to determine a unique quadratic relationship.

Teachers who examined this set of students' work suggested a range of potential follow-up activities, including ways to help students better understand (a) the connection between the symmetry of the graph of a quadratic function and the corresponding table and (b) why quadratic functions have symmetry. Teachers also suggested questions they would ask students in order to probe their understanding.

Following the discussion of the students' work, the teachers generated a list of related mathematical ideas they wanted to explore:

- Compare the characteristics of linear functions to nonlinear functions.

- Explore patterns of change for polynomial and nonpolynomial functions.

- Represent patterns of change in a table, graph, and as an equation.

- Examine critical features of a function (x- and y-intercepts, patterns of change, symmetry, maximum and minimum points) and how they appear in a table, graph, and equation of the function.

- Change a parameter in an equation and explore how this affects the graph and table of the equation (e.g., changing only the b in $y = mx + b$ would result in a set of parallel lines on the graph that all have the same additive pattern of change in the y-values of the tables).

- Connect the patterns of change to fundamental ideas in calculus.

- Discuss the role of patterns of change as a unifying idea for an algebra curriculum.

Teachers discussed instructional strategies that might help students connect their knowledge of tables to graphs and equations (and vice versa). The teachers came to learn how important it is to pay close attention to the representations and language that students use and that by better understanding their students' thinking, they can make more informed decisions about what to teach next.

Conclusion

We have worked with teachers to help them develop a coherent vision of algebra and deepen their understanding of it. We have offered throughout the year one-day workshops, one-to-two-week workshops, and four-to-six-day workshops. We have also used similar activities in preservice and graduate courses. Over time, through similar experiences around a set of coherent problems and the corresponding work by students on these problems, we saw changes in how teachers thought about algebraic content and viewed the teaching and learning of algebra. In follow-up sessions we saw changes in teachers' insights into the ways they analyzed students' thinking. They became more reflective about focusing on what the work showed about students' understanding, what the appropriate evidence was for the claims, and what they might do in their classes to address the issues that were raised by the students' work. Teachers also began to look for additional rich problems and ways to adapt their own curriculum materials to encourage deeper student reasoning and understanding.

The PD explanations described here deepened teachers' algebraic understandings by helping them (*a*) develop a broader view of algebra; (*b*) understand and use patterns of change to study a range of functions; (*c*) create and interpret representations to gain information and make predictions about a relationship or context; (*d*) make connections between patterns of change and how they affect multiple representations of linear, exponential, and quadratic functions; and (*e*) develop an appreciation for equivalent expressions and the role they play in representing equivalent ways to think about a situation.

Teachers saw that it is important to plan a coherent mathematical experience for their students because "having a deep understanding requires that learners connect pieces of knowledge, and that connection in turn is a key factor in whether they can use what they know productively in solving problems" (Kilpatrick, Swafford, and Findell 2001, p. 118).

REFERENCES

Barnett, Carne, and Alma Ramirez. "Fostering Critical Analysis and Reflection through Mathematics Case Discussions." In *The Case for Education: Contemporary Approaches Using Case Methods,* edited by Joel A. Colbert, Peter Desberg, and Kimberly Trimble, pp. 1–13. Boston: Allyn & Bacon, 1996.

Crespo, Sandra. "Seeing More than Right and Wrong Answers: Prospective Teachers' Interpretations of Students' Mathematical Work." *Journal of Mathematics Teacher Education* 3 (2000): 155–81.

Crockett, Michele D. "Inquiry as Professional Development: Creating Dilemmas through Teachers' Work." *Teaching and Teacher Education* 18 (2001): 609–24.

Friedlander, Alex, and Michal Tabach. "Promoting Multiple Representations in Algebra." In *The Roles of Representation in School Mathematics,* 2001 Yearbook of the National Council of Teachers of Mathematics (NCTM), edited by Albert A. Cuoco, pp. 173–85. Reston, Va.: NCTM, 2001.

Herbel-Eisenmann, Beth A. "Using Student Contributions and Multiple Representations to Develop Mathematical Language." *Mathematics Teaching in the Middle School* 8 (October 2002): 100–105.

Herbel-Eisenmann, Beth A., and Elizabeth D. Phillips. "Using Student Work to Develop Teachers' Understanding of Algebra." *Mathematics Teaching in the Middle School* 11 (September 2005): 62–66.

Kilpatrick, Jeremy, Jane Swafford, and Bradford Findell, eds. *Adding It Up: Helping Children Learn Mathematics.* Washington, D.C.: National Academy Press, 2001.

Lappan, Glenda, Jim Fey, William Fitzgerald, Susan Friel, and Elizabeth Phillips. *The Connected Mathematics Project.* Palo Alto, Calif.: Dale Seymour Publications, 1998.

Schoenfeld, Alan H. "Mathematics Teaching and Learning." In *Handbook of Educational Psychology,* 2nd ed., edited by Patricia A. Alexander and Philip H. Winne, pp. 479–510. Hillsdale, N.J.: Lawrence Erlbaum Associates, 2006.

Stein, Mary K., Margaret S. Smith, Marjorie Henningsen, and Edward Silver. *Implementing Standards-Based Mathematics Instruction: A Casebook for Professional Development.* New York: Teachers College Press, 2000.

Wilcox, Sandra, and Perry E. Lanier, eds. *Using Assessment to Reshape Mathematics Teaching: A Casebook for Teachers and Teacher Educators, Curriculum and Staff Development Specialists.* Mahwah, N.J.: Lawrence Erlbaum Associates, 2000.